CHAPTER
1
Sort and Classify
HARCOURT
Math
9780153527111
AF600851

Circle the objects that look like the object in the middle.

Grateful acknowledgment is made to HarperCollins Publishers for permission to reprint the cover photograph from *Exactly the Opposite* by Tana Hoban. Copyright © 1990 by Tana Hoban.

Printed in the United States of America

Photography Credits:

All photography by Harcourt photographers listed, © Harcourt: Weronica Ankarorn, Victoria Bowen, Ken Kinzie, Sheri O'Neal, Quebecor Imaging, and Terry Sinclair.

Illustration Credits:

Linda Bild: Storybook; **Michelle Noiset:** 1, 2; **Richard Holding:** 5, 6, 7; **Susan Hall:** 8, 9, 13, 14; **Jane Yamada:** 10, 19, 20, 21, 22; **Daniel DelValle:** 11, 12; **Nancy Freeman:** 17; **Mary Thelen:** 23.

15 16 17 18 19 20 1678 16 15 14 13 12 11
4500311726

SCHOOL HOME CONNECTION

Dear Family,

Today we started Chapter 1, Sort and Classify. We will learn about positions, such as over and under and left and right. We will also learn to sort objects that are alike in some way.

Love,

____

left

right

sort (to put into groups) These shapes can be sorted by their color.

group (a set or a collection) These shapes are all alike in color. They make a group.

Visit *The Learning Site* for additional ideas and activities. www.harcourtschool.com

ACTIVITY

- Invite your child to help you sort the laundry. Ask your child to tell how the clothes in each pile are alike. (*They are all white towels.*) Then ask what word(s) can be used to name each pile (*dark clothes, jeans*).

BOOKS TO SHARE

To read about sorting and classifying with your child, look for these books at your local library.

Exactly the Opposite, by Tana Hoban. Morrow, 1997.

How Many Snails? by Paul Giganti, Jr. Morrow, 1994.

Is It Red? Is It Yellow? Is It Blue? by Tana Hoban. Morrow, 1987.

MATERIALS: a different kind of small object, such as buttons, pennies, or paper clips, for each player

DIRECTIONS: Play with a partner and decide who goes first. Each player takes a turn placing one object in a space. To win, a player must have three of his or her objects going across, down, or diagonally and say in what way they are alike.

Name ______________________________

Top, Middle, Bottom

Circle the top block.
Circle the bottom clown.
Circle the middle hat as you go from top to bottom.

Use red to color the flowerpot in the top window. Use yellow to color the flowerpot in the middle window. Use blue to color the flowerpot in the bottom window.

HOME ACTIVITY • Ask your child to show you the *top, middle,* and *bottom* shelves of a bookcase, closet, or cabinet.

Name ___________________________

In, Out

- Circle the bird that is in the cage.
- Circle the fish that is out of the bowl.
- Circle the car that is out of the box.
- Circle the bear that is in the balloon.

Draw a car in the sandbox. Draw a truck out of the sandbox.

HOME ACTIVITY • Lay a piece of yarn in a circle on the floor. Have your child tell you when he or she is in the circle or out of the circle.

Name ___________________________

Above, Below, Over, Under

Circle the rabbit that is above the table. Mark an X on the rabbit that is below the table.

Circle the object that is over the boat. Mark an X on the object that is under the boat.

Circle the bird that is over the sand castle. Circle the crab that is under the sand castle. Circle the shell that is below the bridge.

HOME ACTIVITY • Have your child point to objects that are *above, below, over*, and *under* things in your home.

Name ______________________________

Left, Right

Draw green apples on the tree on the left.
Draw red apples on the tree on the right.

Left

Right

Use red to circle the car on the right.
Use green to circle the building on the left.
Use red to circle the tree on the right.

HOME ACTIVITY • Have your child describe the pictures, using the words *left* and *right*.

Name ______________________________

Problem Solving Skill
Use a Picture

Circle the butterfly that is over the clown suit. Circle the pair of shoes on the left. Look at the shelf with hats. Circle the hat in the middle.

Color the top balloon. Color the bird that is below the other bird. Color the gift that is on the right. Color the clown that is out of the hoop.

HOME ACTIVITY • Have your child draw an outline of a house. Tell him or her to add a chimney on top, windows in the middle, and a tree to the left of the house.

Name ____

Review

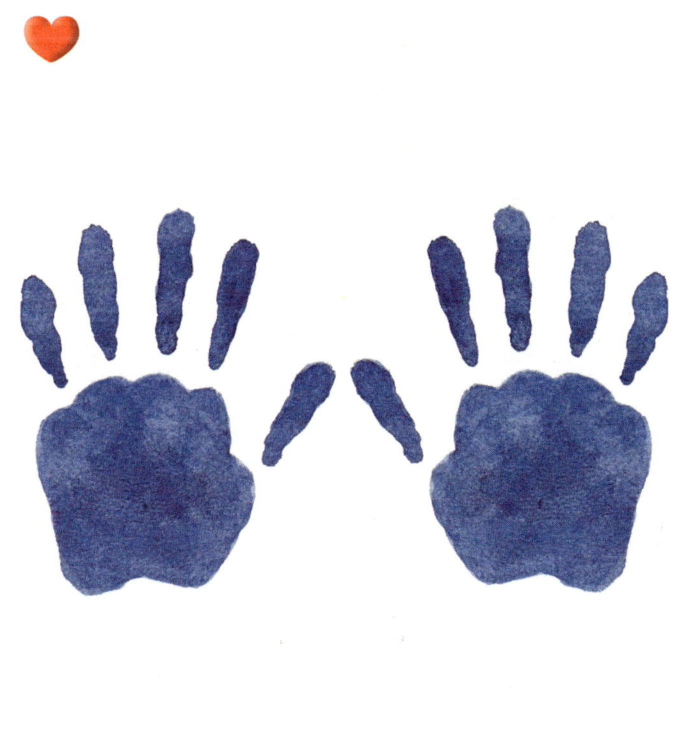

Circle the top block and mark an X on the bottom block.
Circle the fish that is in the fishbowl.
Circle the bird that is over the tree.
Circle the right hand and mark an X on the left hand.

Cumulative Review

Color the top clown red. Color the middle clown blue.
Color the bottom clown yellow.
Circle the bird that is out of the bird cage.
Circle the butterfly that is above the table.
Mark an X on the butterfly that is below the table.
Color the tree on the left green. Color the tree on the right red.

Name ____________________

Algebra: **Sort by Color or Shape**

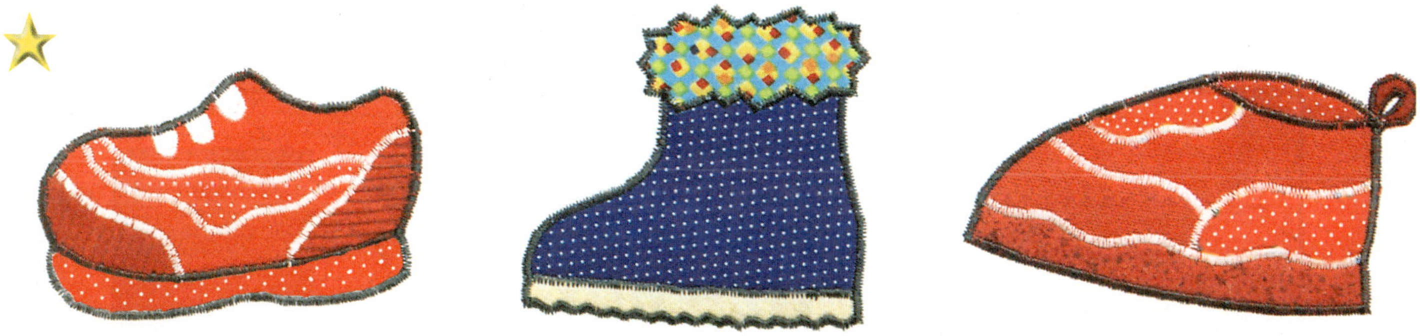

Sort the shoes by color. Mark an X on the one that is not like the others.

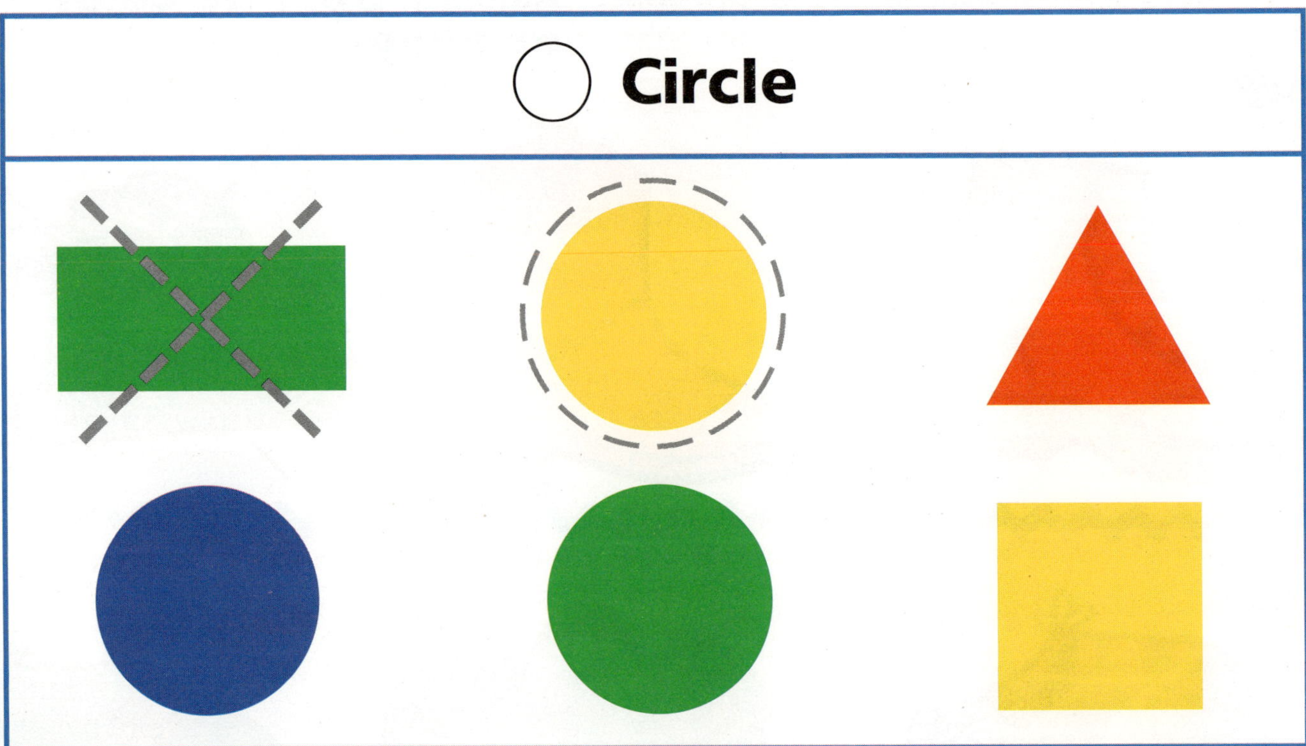

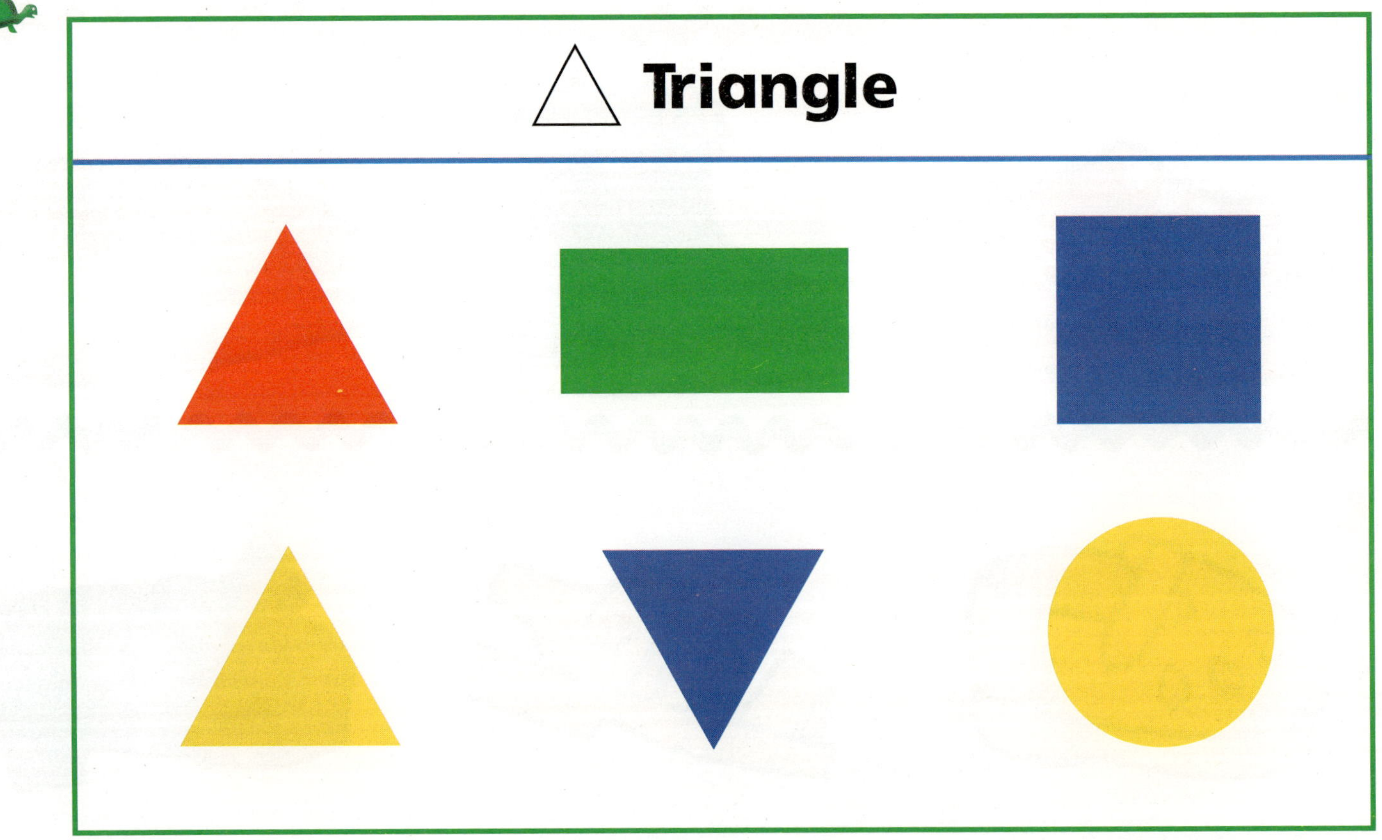

Circle the shapes that belong in the group. Mark an X on the shapes that do not belong.

HOME ACTIVITY • Mix up three pairs of socks of different solid colors. Ask your child to sort the socks by color.

Name ______________________________

Algebra: **Sort by Size or Kind**

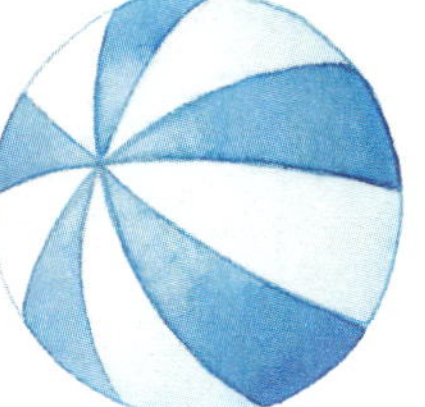

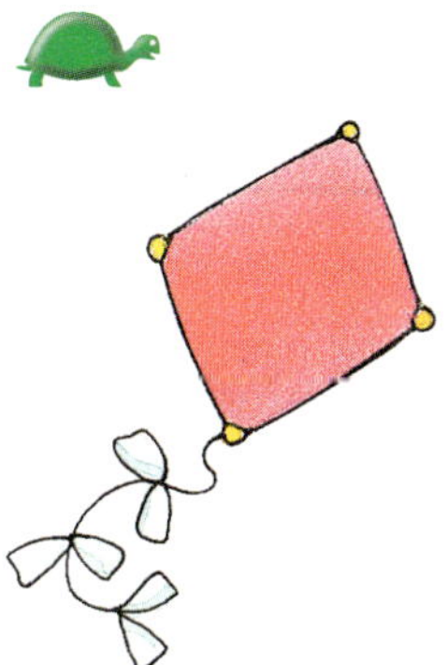

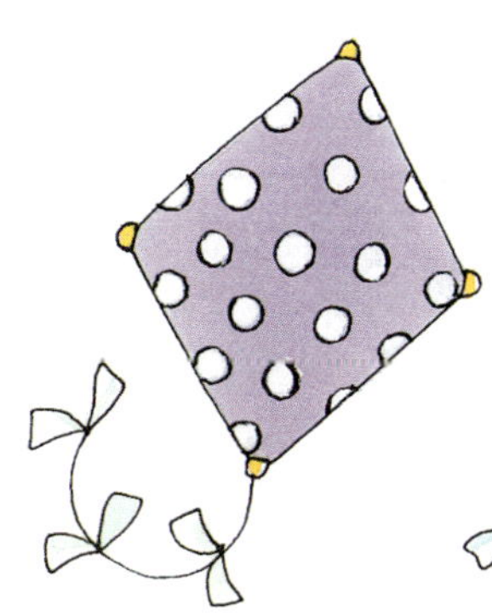

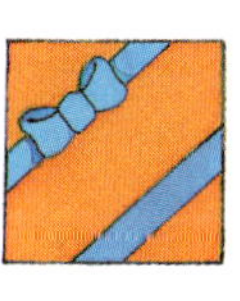
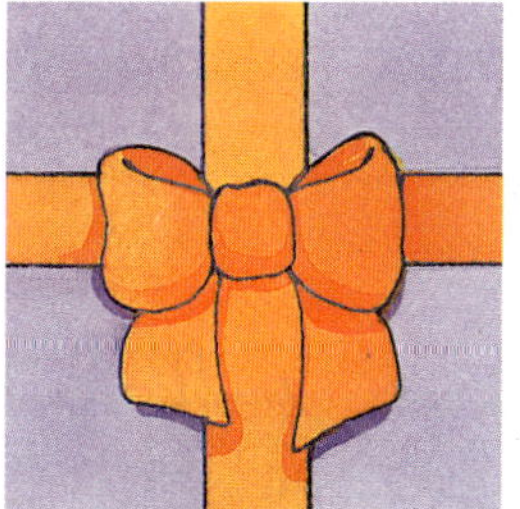

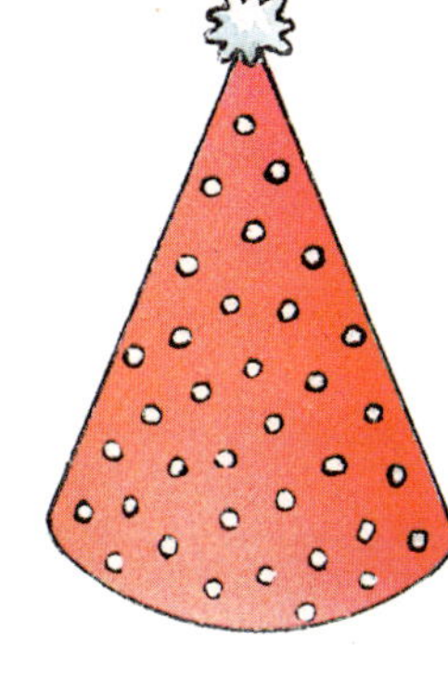

Look at the ball at the beginning of the row. Circle the balls that are the same size.
Look at the kite at the beginning of the row. Circle the kites that are the same size.
Look at the gift at the beginning of the row. Circle the gifts that are the same size.
Look at the hat at the beginning of the row. Circle the hats that are the same size.

Sort the shirts by kind.
Draw each shirt on the clothesline that has shirts of the same kind.

HOME ACTIVITY • Help your child sort his or her shirts by kind.

Name ___________________________

Make a Concrete Graph

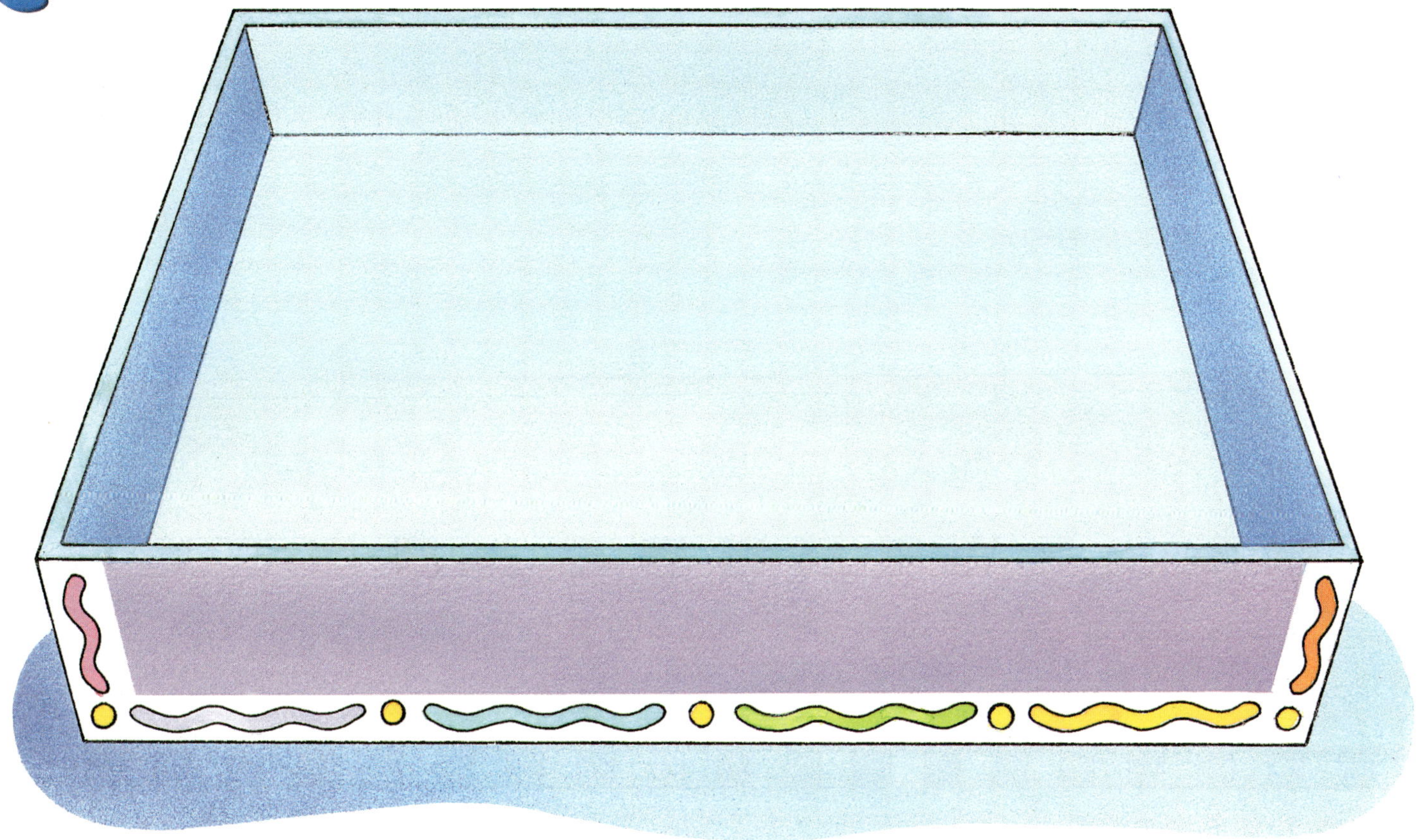

Red and Blue Cubes

Red				
Blue				

Place a handful of connecting cubes in the box. Sort your cubes by color.

Move your red cubes to the top row on the graph. Move your blue cubes to the bottom row on the graph. What does this graph tell you about the cubes?

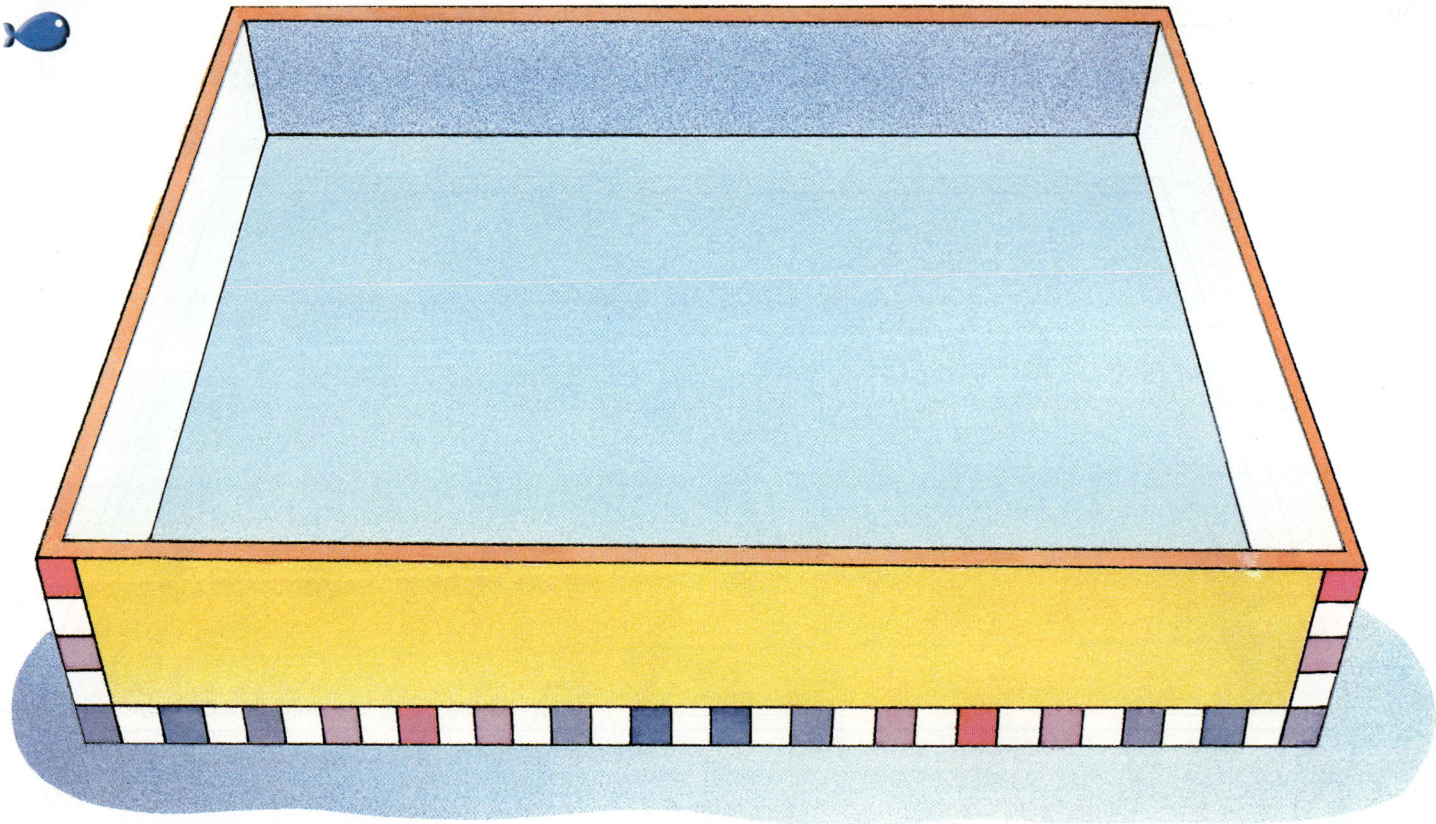

Large and Small Bears

Place a handful of bear counters in the box. Sort your bear counters by size.

Move your large bear counters to the top row on the graph. Move your small bear counters to the bottom row on the graph. What does this graph tell you about the bear counters?

HOME ACTIVITY • Ask your child to tell you what he or she learned from making this bear graph.

Name ____________________________________

Problem Solving Strategy
Use Logical Reasoning

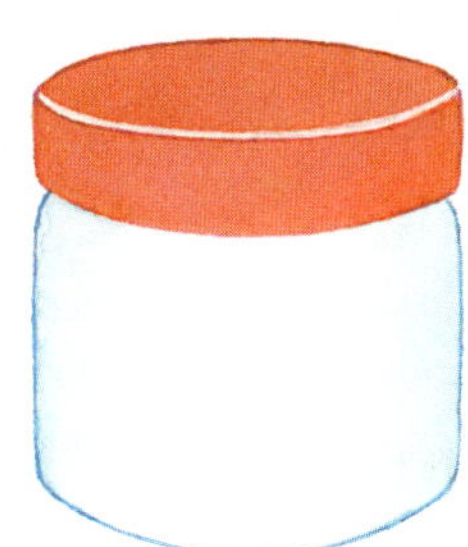
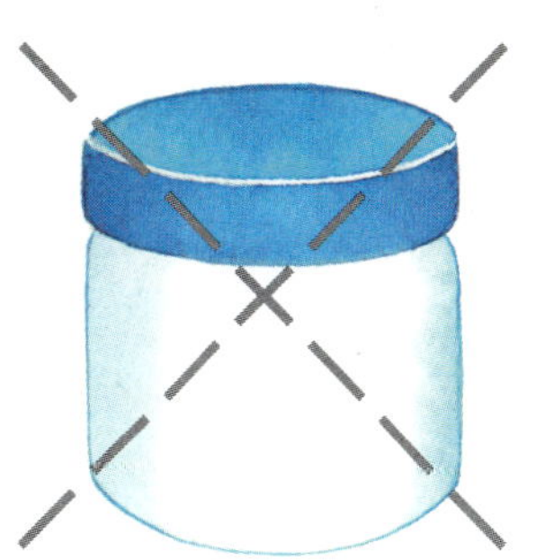
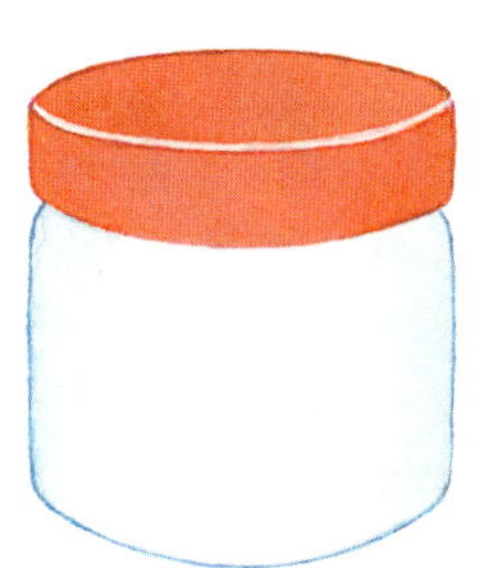

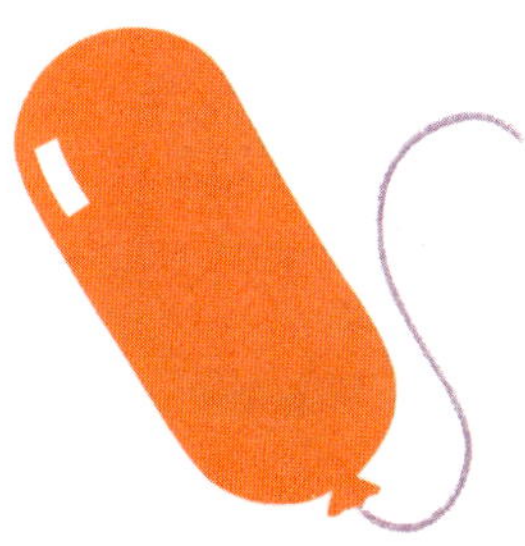

Three of the objects are alike. Which object does not belong with the others? Mark an X on it, and tell why.

   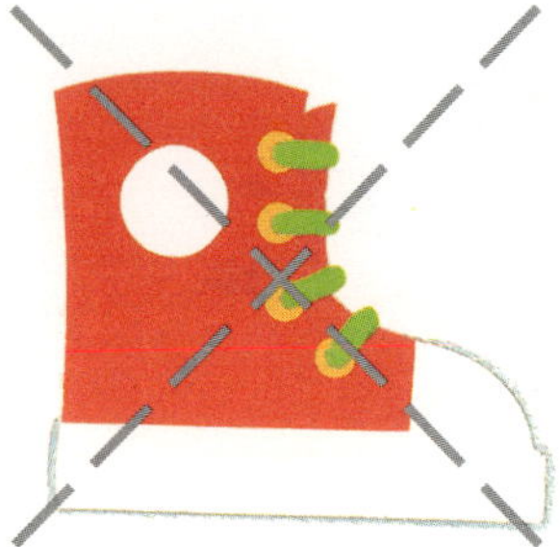

Three of the objects are alike. Which object does not belong with the others? Mark an X on it, and tell why.

HOME ACTIVITY • Help your child sort his or her toys by shape. Ask why certain toys do not belong in each group.

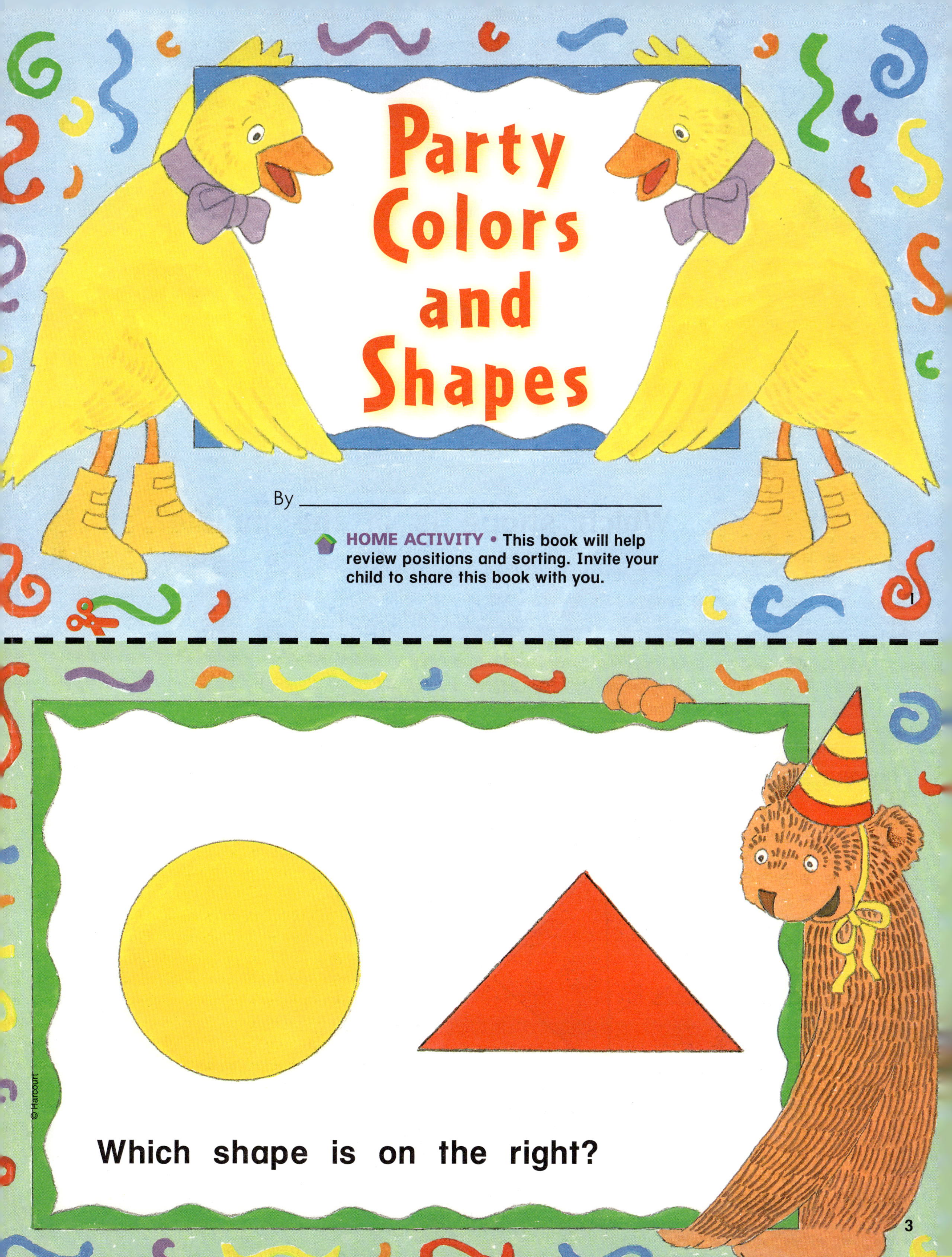
Party Colors and Shapes
By ______________________
HOME ACTIVITY • This book will help review positions and sorting. Invite your child to share this book with you.
1
© Harcourt
Which shape is on the right?
3

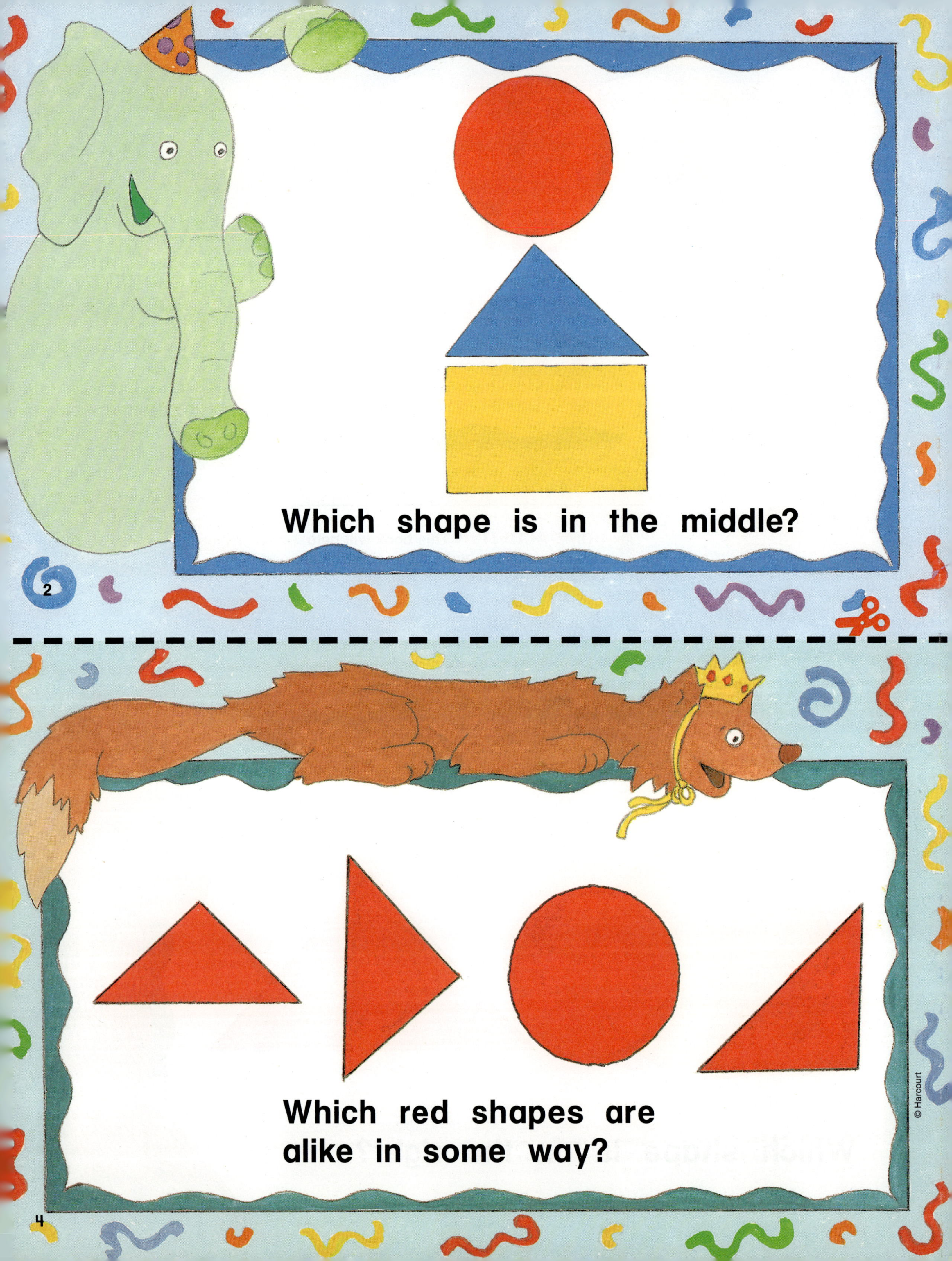
Which shape is in the middle?
2
Which red shapes are
alike in some way?
© Harcourt
4

Which present does not belong?

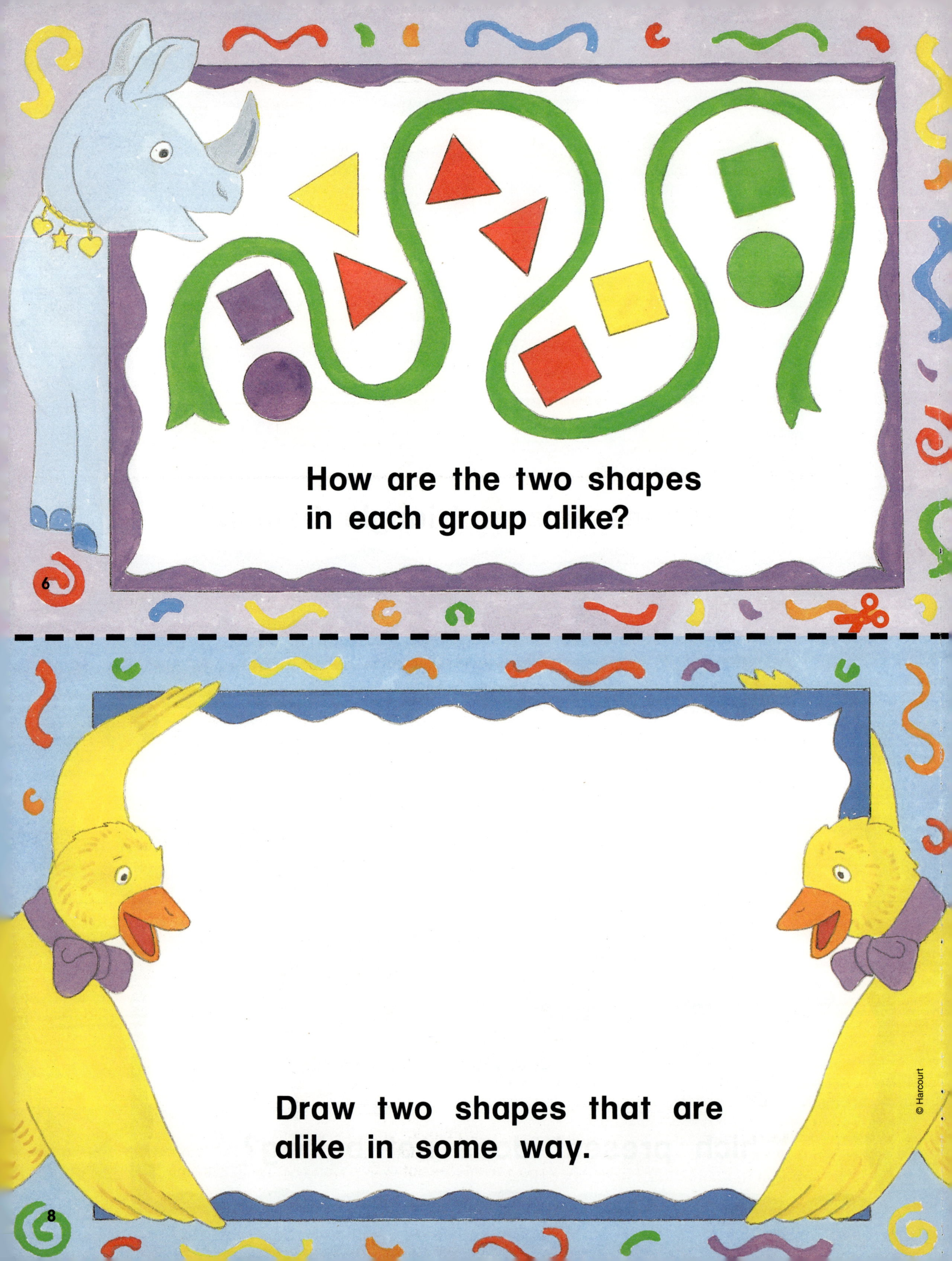

How are the two shapes in each group alike?

Draw two shapes that are alike in some way.

Name ____________________

Review

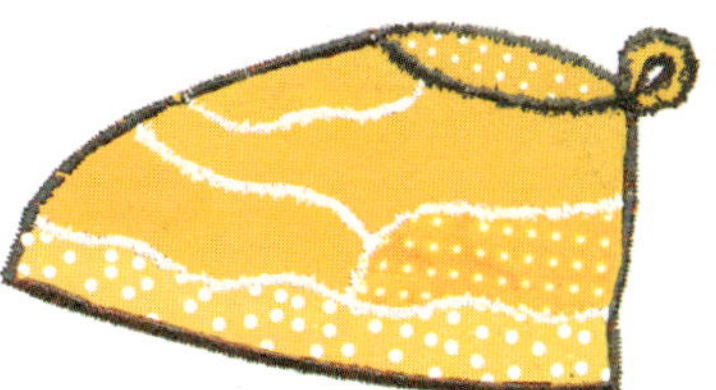

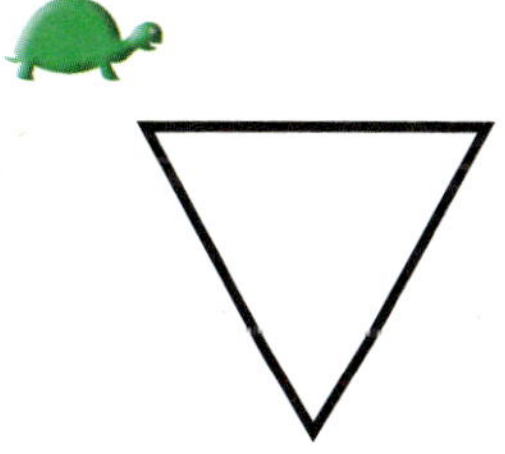

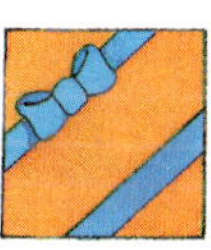

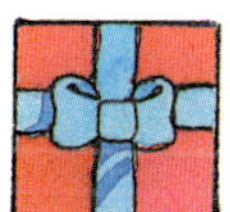

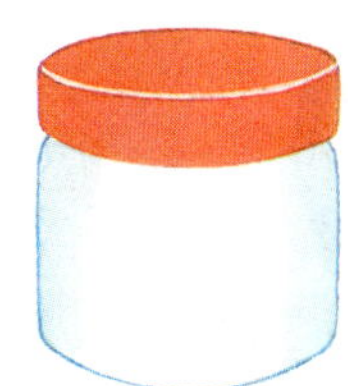
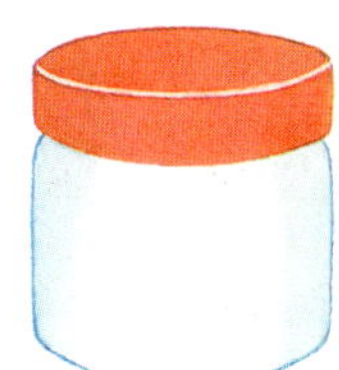
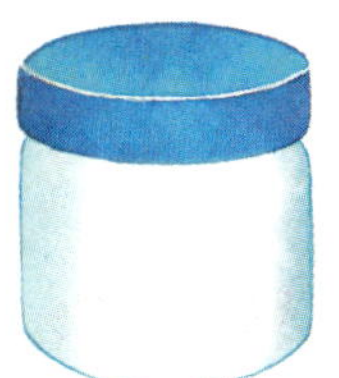

Sort the shoes by color. Mark an X on the shoe that is not like the others.
Look at the shape at the beginning of the row. Circle the shapes that are the same. Mark an X on the shapes that do not belong.
Look at the gift at the beginning of the row. Circle the gifts that are the same size.
Look at the flower at the beginning of the row. Circle the flowers that are the same kind.
Mark an X on the object that does not belong.

Cumulative Review

Circle the middle hat as you go from top to bottom.
Circle the dog that is out of the doghouse.
Circle the gift on the left and mark an X on the gift on the right.
Look at the shape at the beginning of the row. Circle the shapes that are the same. Mark an X on the shapes that do not belong.

Name ____________________

Test

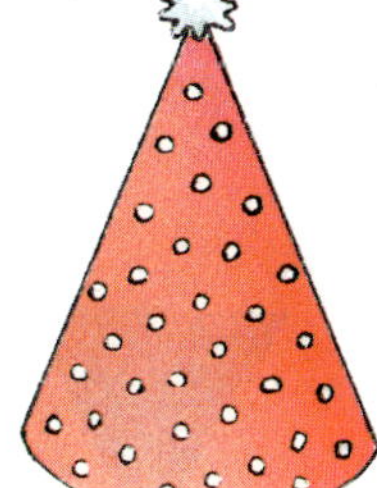

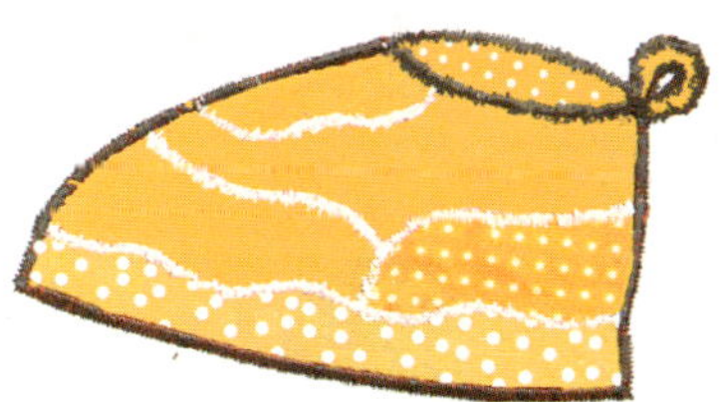

Circle the object below the bridge.
Circle the hand on the right.
Look at the hat at the beginning of the row. Circle the hats that are the same size.
Sort the shoes by color. Mark an X on the shoe that is not like the others.
Mark an X on the object that does not belong.

CHALLENGE

Alike in Color and Shape

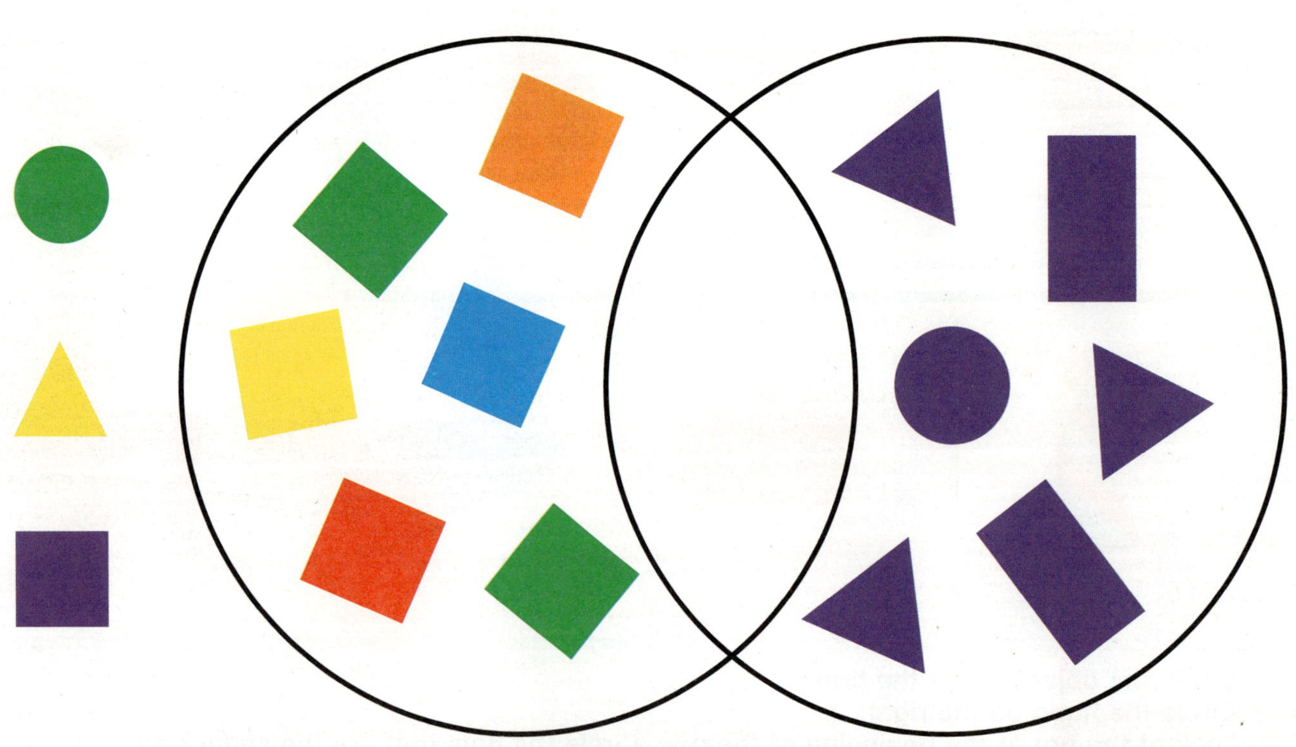

Draw the shape that belongs in both groups. Tell why.

CHAPTER 2 Patterns

HARCOURT Math

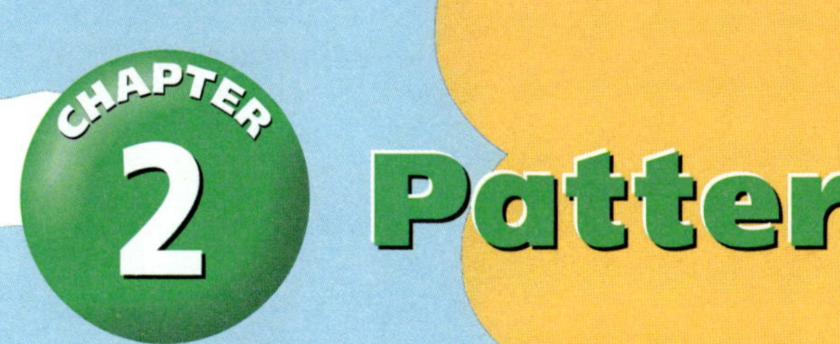

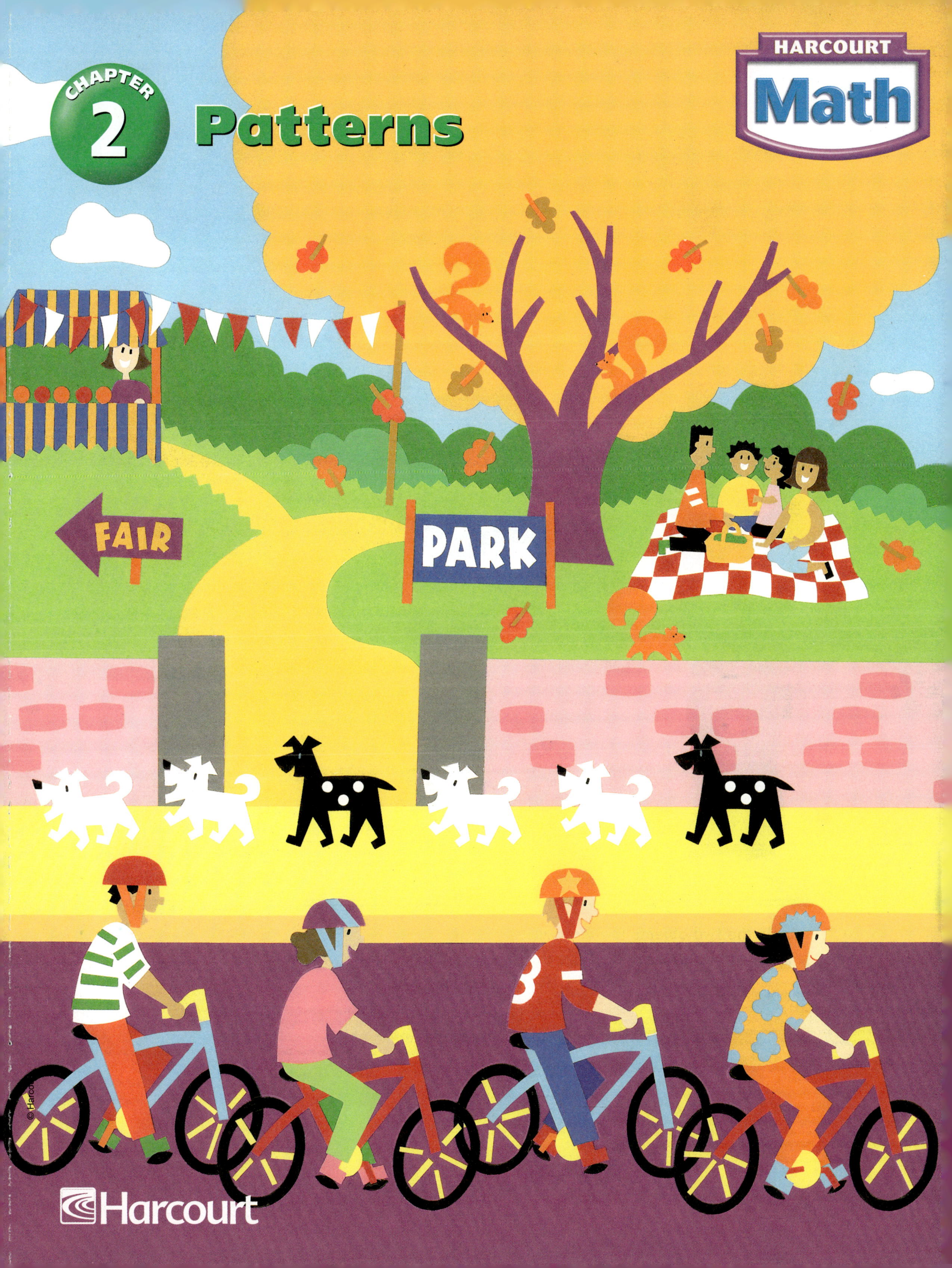

Harcourt

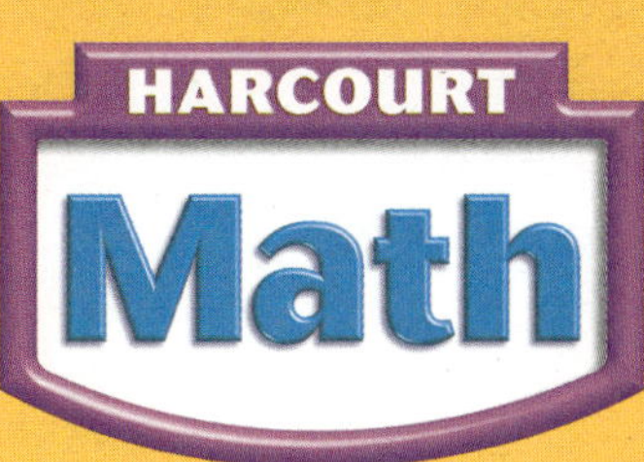

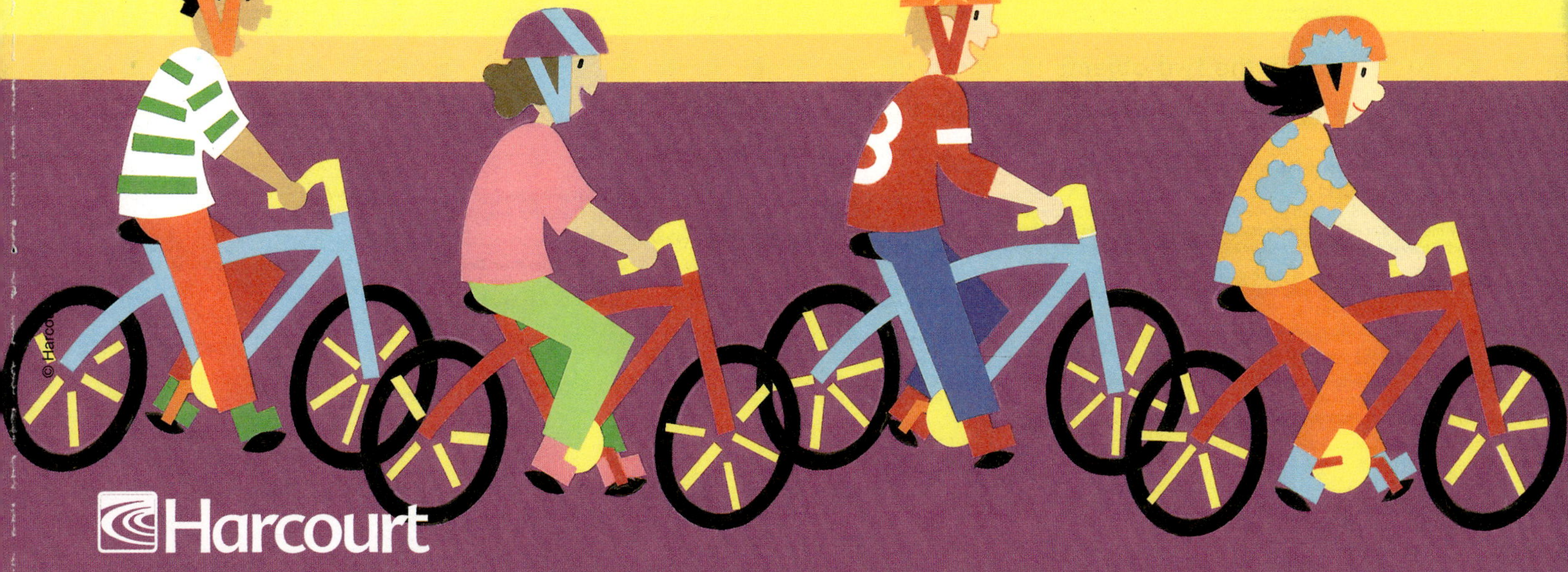

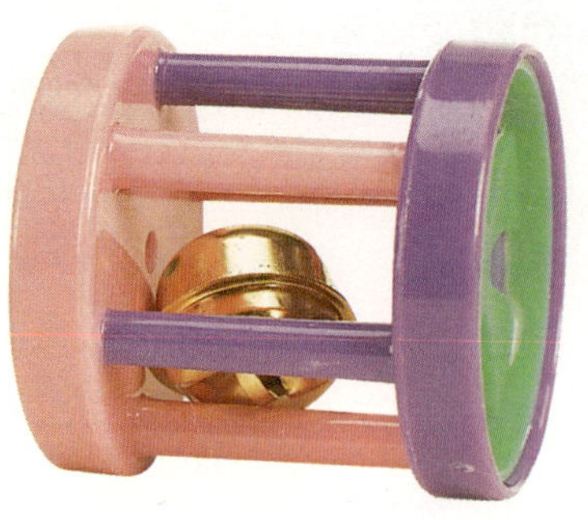

Circle the two objects that are alike.

Grateful acknowledgment is made to Childrens Press, a Scholastic Library Publishing imprint, for permission to reprint the cover illustration from *Math Counts: Pattern* by Henry Pluckrose. © 1994 by Watts Books. Published by Childrens Press®, 1995.

Printed in the United States of America

Photography Credits:

All photography by Harcourt photographers listed, © Harcourt: Veronica Ankarorn, Victoria Bowen, Ken Kinzie, Sheri O'Neal, Quebecor Imaging, and Terry Sinclair.

Illustration Credits:

Joe Boddy: 51, 52 storybook; **Deborah Borgo:** 31, 41, 42; **Shelley Dieterichs:** 33, 34, 43; **Nancy Freeman:** 44; **Patrick Girouard:** 32; **Heidi King:** 52; **Dan McGeehan:** 47, 48; **Jill Meyerhoff:** 39, 40, 45, 46; **Mary Thelen:** cover.

15 16 17 18 19 20   1678   16 15 14 13 12 11
4500311726

SCHOOL HOME CONNECTION

Dear Family,

Today we started a new chapter, Patterns. We will copy patterns, show what comes next in patterns, and make new ones. We will also find the part of a pattern that repeats again and again.

Love,

____

patterns

- Help your child discover patterns in wallpaper, clothing, or dishes. Look for patterns outdoors together as well.

BOOKS TO SHARE

To read about patterns with your child, look for these books in your local library.

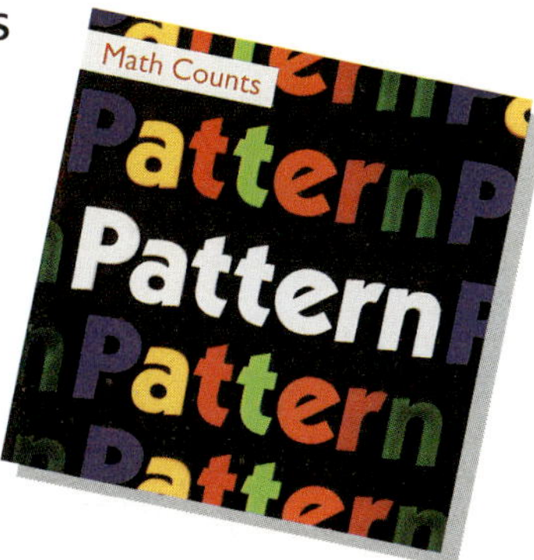

Math Counts: Pattern, by Henry Pluckrose. Children's Press, 1995.

One, Two, Three, Jump! by Penelope Lively. Simon and Schuster, 1999.

Visit *The Learning Site* for additional ideas and activities. www.harcourtschool.com

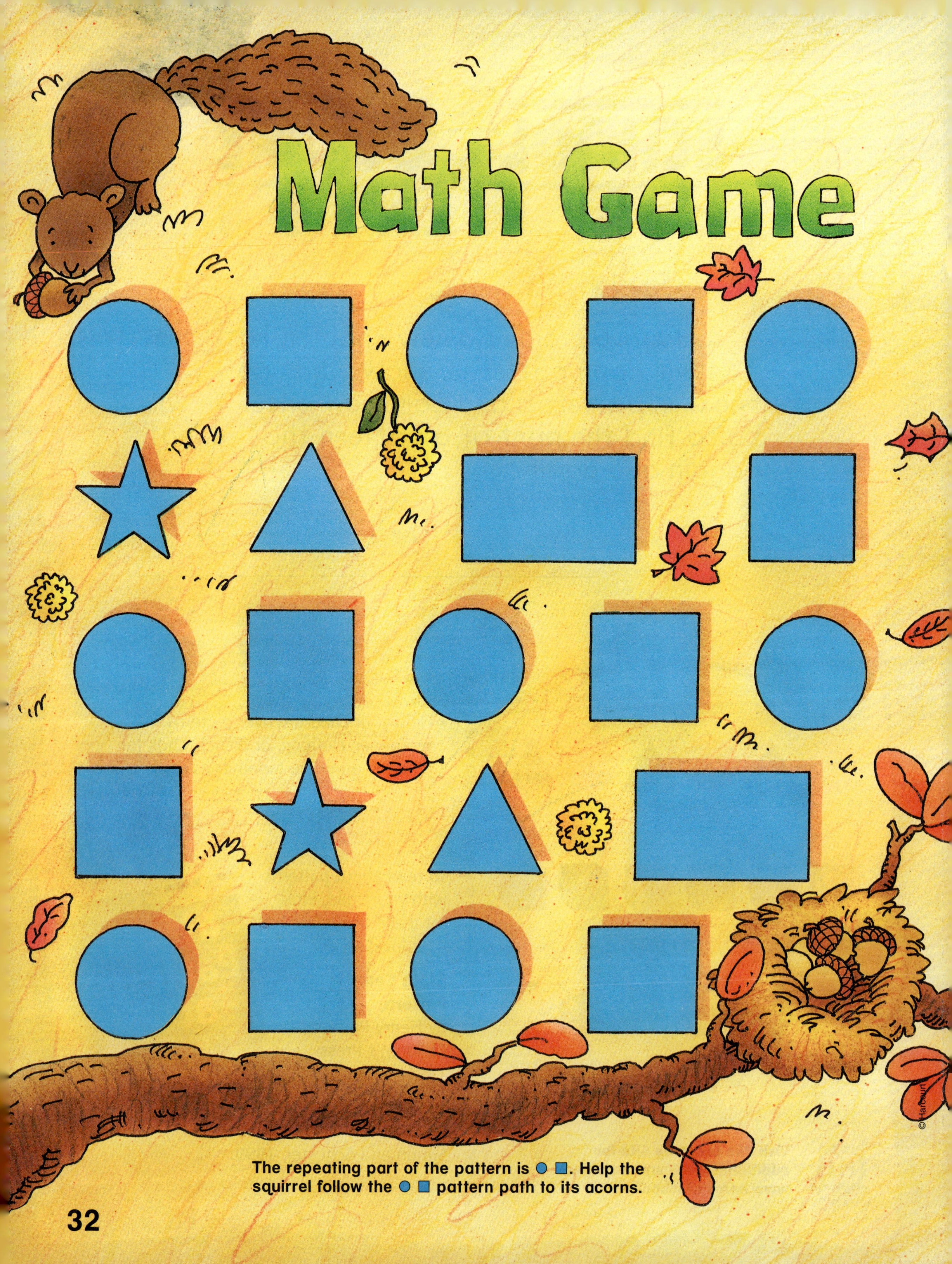
Math Game
The repeating part of the pattern is ● ■. Help the squirrel follow the ● ■ pattern path to its acorns.
© Harcourt

Name ______________________________

Algebra: Movement Patterns

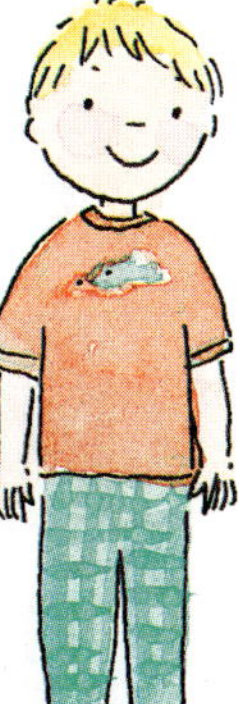

Act out the pattern. Say the pattern as you act out each part. Circle what you would most likely do next.

Act out the pattern. Say the pattern as you act out each part. Circle what you would most likely do next.

HOME ACTIVITY • Invite your child to show you a sound or action pattern. Copy your child's pattern.

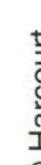

Name ___________________________

Algebra: Read and Copy Simple Patterns

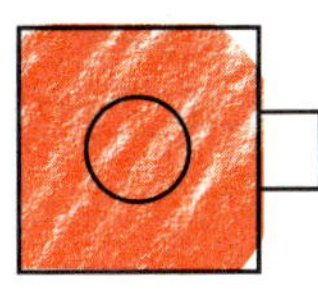 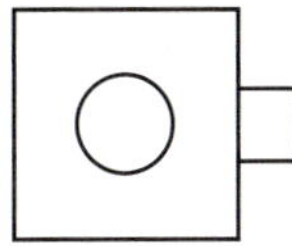 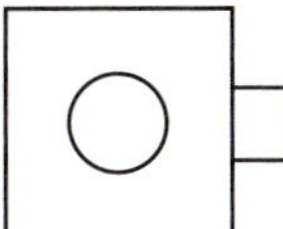 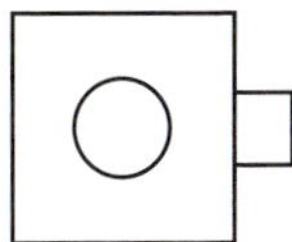 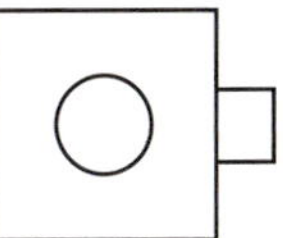 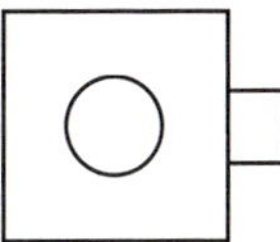

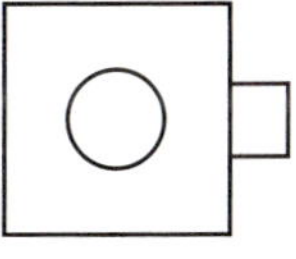 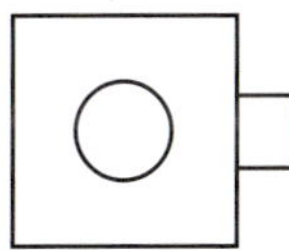 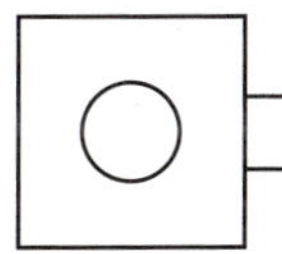 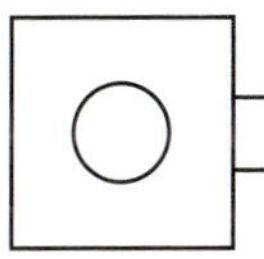 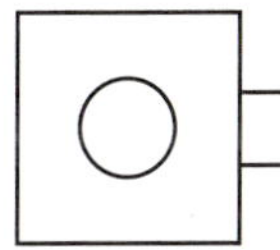 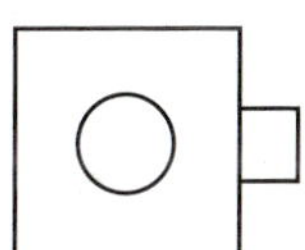

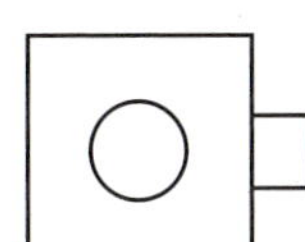  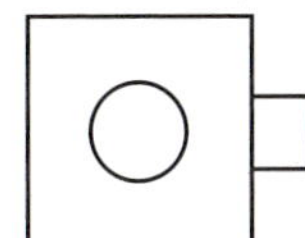 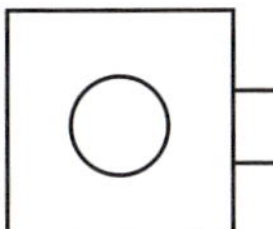 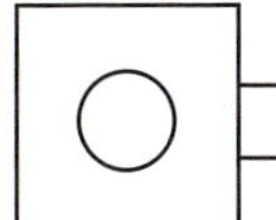 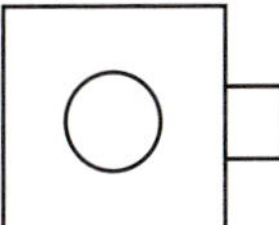 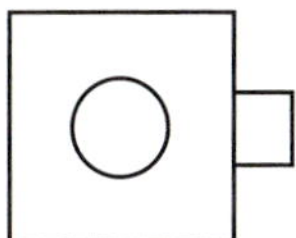

Put cubes on the pattern. Read the pattern. Color the cubes to copy the pattern.

Read the pattern. Color the bear counters to copy the pattern.

HOME ACTIVITY • Help your child find patterns in buildings, wallpaper, or fabrics. Have your child draw the patterns he or she finds.

Name ___________________________

Algebra: Copy and Extend Patterns

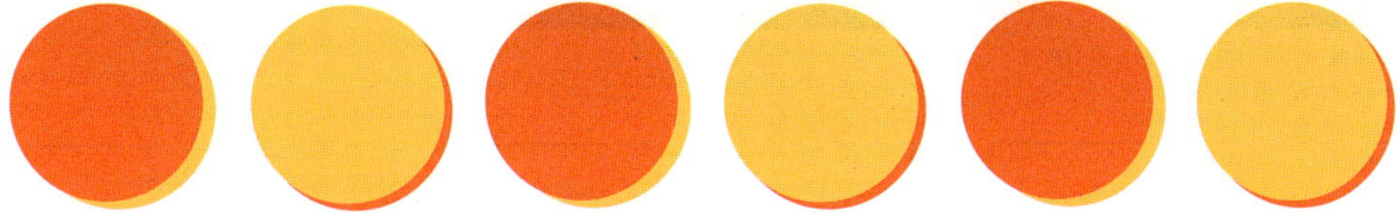

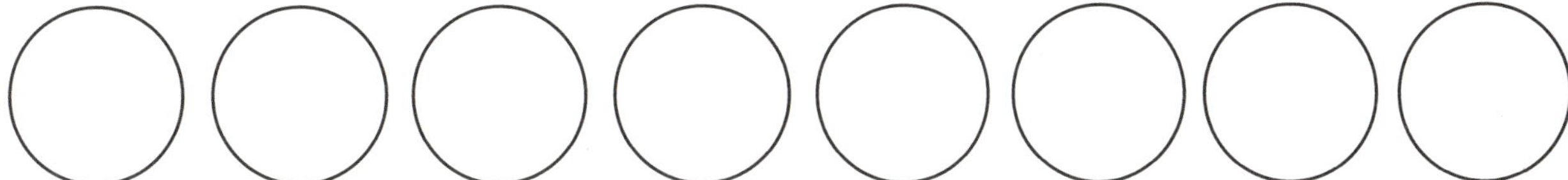

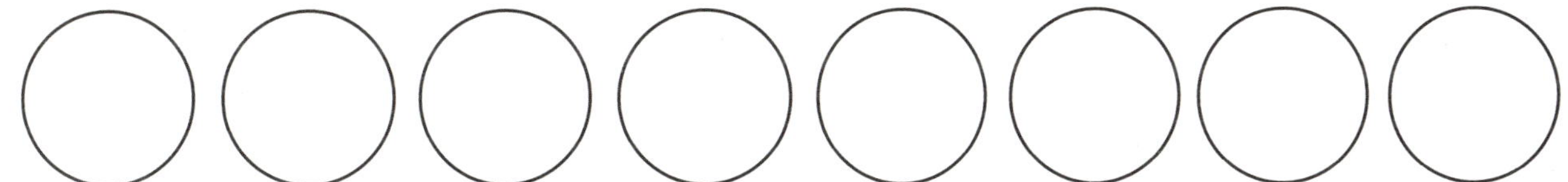

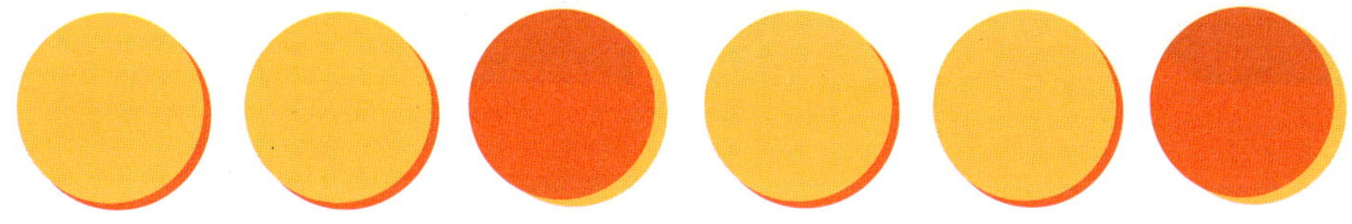

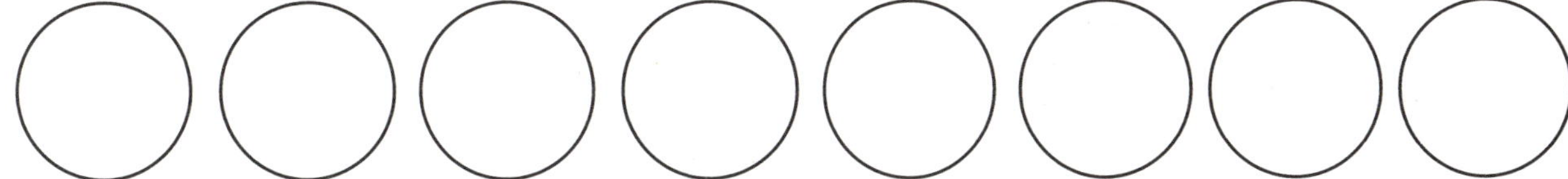

Color the counters to copy the pattern and show what most likely comes next.

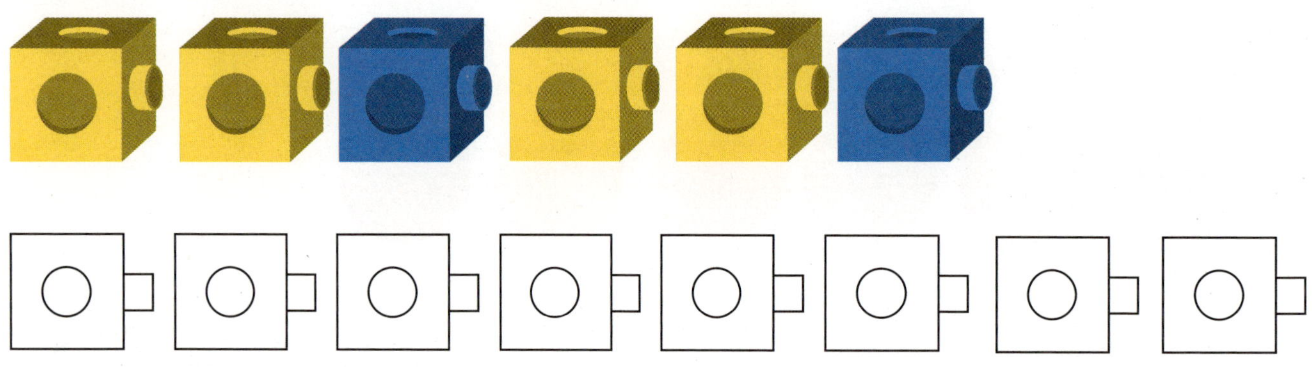

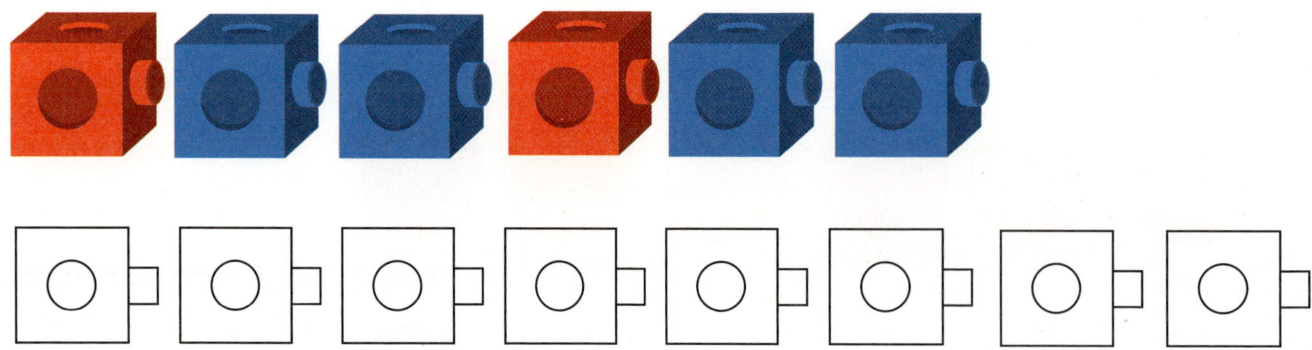

Color the cubes to copy the pattern and show what most likely comes next.

HOME ACTIVITY • Have your child sort pasta pieces by color and/or shape, arrange them in a pattern, and then string them to make a necklace.

Name ________________________________

Algebra: **Predict and Extend Patterns**

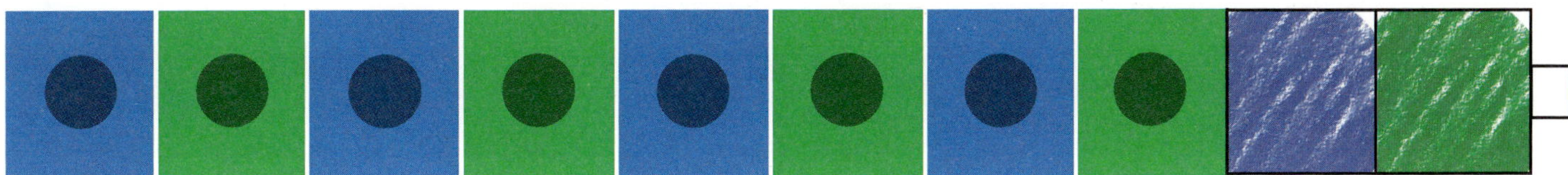

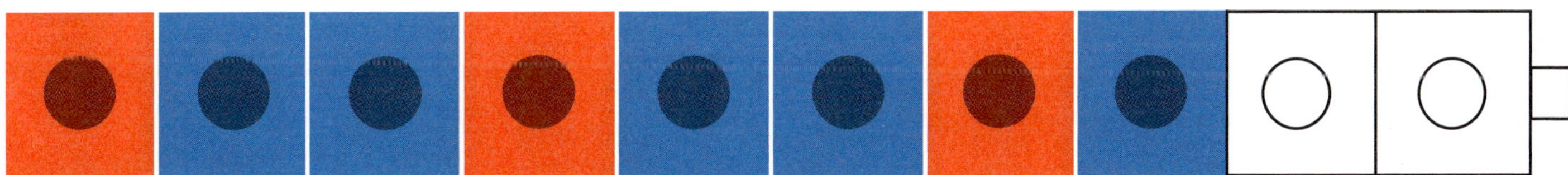

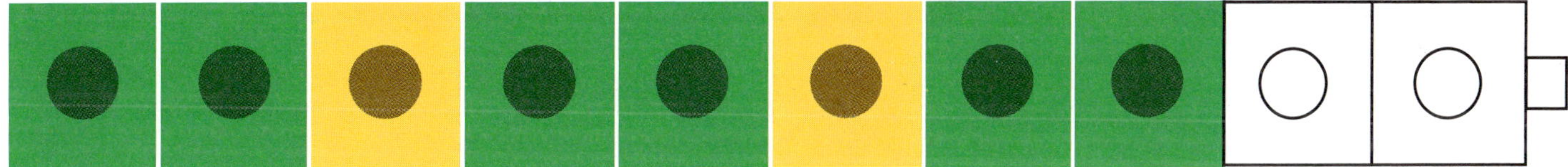

What color cubes do you think come next? Color the cubes to show what most likely comes next.

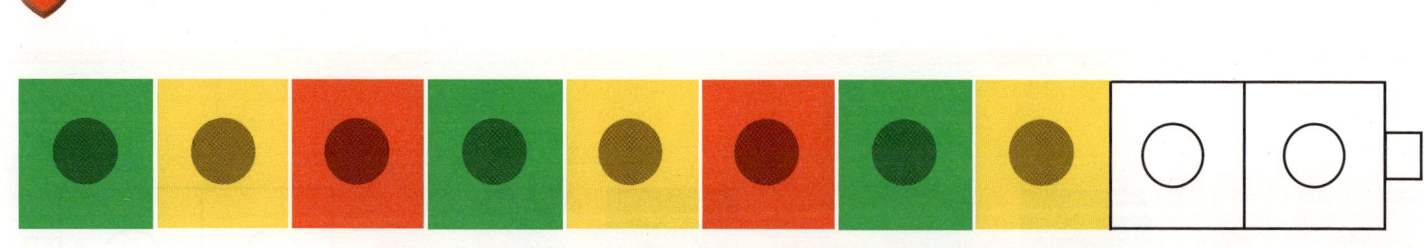

What color counters do you think come next? Color to show what most likely comes next.
What color cubes do you think come next? Color to show what most likely comes next.

HOME ACTIVITY • Help your child use simple objects to make a pattern.

Name ______________________

Problem Solving Skill
Transfer a Pattern

Use bear counters or act out to show the same pattern. Draw the pattern.

PROBLEM SOLVING

Use counters or act out to show the same pattern. Draw the pattern.

HOME ACTIVITY • Have your child use different objects to show one of the patterns on this page.

Name ______________________________

✓ Review

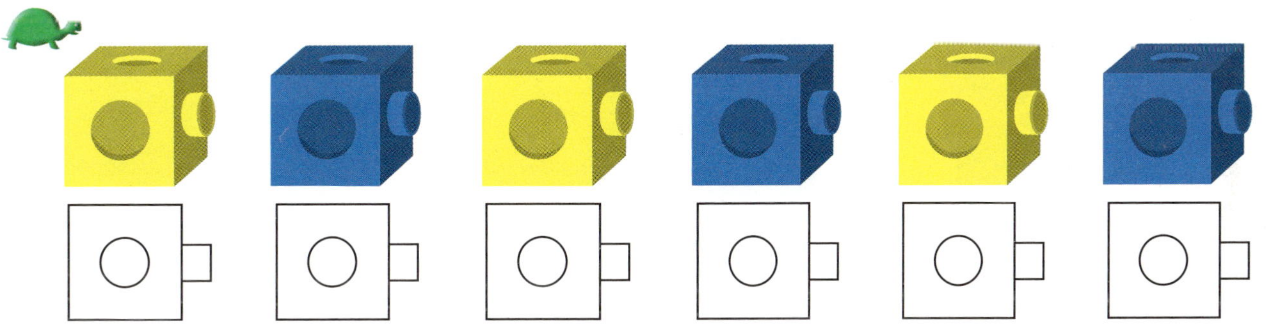

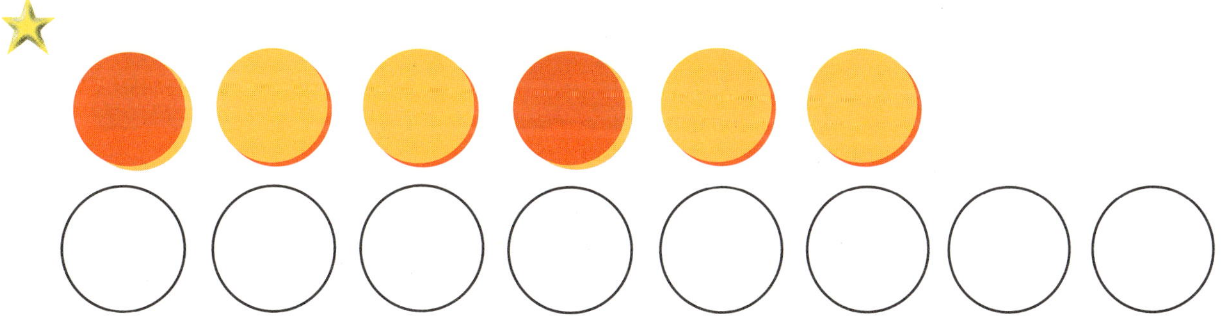

Circle what you would most likely do next.
Color the cubes to copy the pattern.
Color the counters to copy the pattern and show what most likely comes next.
Color to show what most likely comes next.

Cumulative Review

Circle the tree on the right.
Sort the shoes by color. Mark an X on the shoe that is not like the others.
Color the bears to copy the pattern.
Color to show what most likely comes next.

Name ________________________________

Algebra:
Understand a Pattern

Read the pattern. Circle the part that repeats again and again.

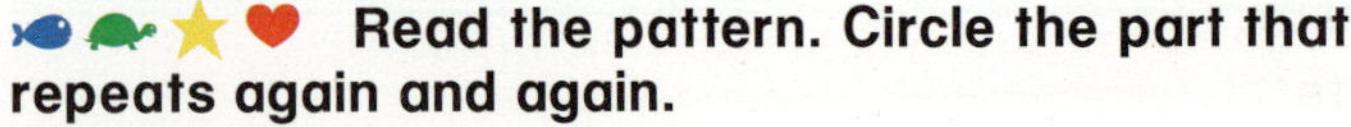

Read the pattern. Circle the part that repeats again and again.

HOME ACTIVITY • Make a simple pattern. Invite your child to read it and tell which part repeats again and again.

Name ________________________________

Algebra: Create a Pattern

Use counters to make your own pattern. Draw your pattern.

Use large and small bear counters to make your own pattern. Draw your pattern.

Use pattern blocks to make your own pattern. Draw your pattern.
Use crayons to make your own pattern. Draw your pattern.

HOME ACTIVITY • Have your child create a pattern with his or her toys. Ask your child to tell which part repeats again and again.

Name ______________________________

Problem Solving Skill
Use a Pattern

Read the pattern. Tell what part repeats again and again. Draw and color the missing shape in the pattern.

PROBLEM SOLVING

Read the pattern. Tell what part repeats again and again. Draw and color the missing shape in the pattern.

HOME ACTIVITY • Arrange objects in a pattern. Remove one object from the pattern. Have your child tell you the missing object and place it to complete the pattern.

By ______________________

HOME ACTIVITY • This book will help review patterns. Invite your child to share this book with you.

What pattern do you see?
Color to copy the pattern.

What pattern do you see?
Talk about it.

What pattern do you see?
Color the apples to copy
the pattern. Then show what
most likely comes next.

What pattern do you see?
Draw dots to show what
most likely comes next.

What pattern do you see?
Draw pumpkins to show
what most likely comes next.

What pattern do you see? Use counters or act out to show the same pattern.

Draw flowers to make your own pattern. What pattern do you see?

What pattern do you see?
Draw and color the
missing shape.

What pattern do you see?
Read the pattern and tell
a friend.

Make and draw your own pattern. What pattern do you see?

What patterns do you see?

Name ____

Review

- Circle the part of the pattern that repeats again and again.
- Use bear counters or act out to show the same pattern. Draw the pattern.
- Use connecting cubes to make your own pattern. Draw your pattern.

Cumulative Review

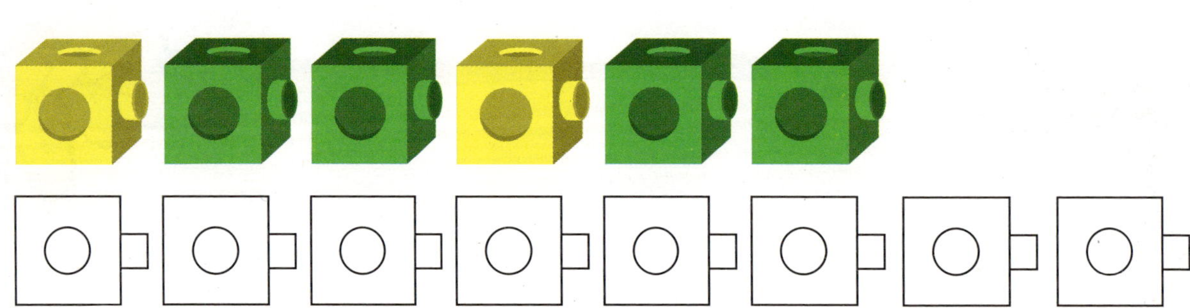

Look at the shape at the beginning of the row. Circle the shapes that are the same. Mark an X on the shapes that do not belong.
Look at the flower at the beginning of the row. Circle the flowers that are the same kind.
Color the cubes to copy the pattern and show what most likely comes next.
Circle the part that repeats again and again.

Name ____________________

Test

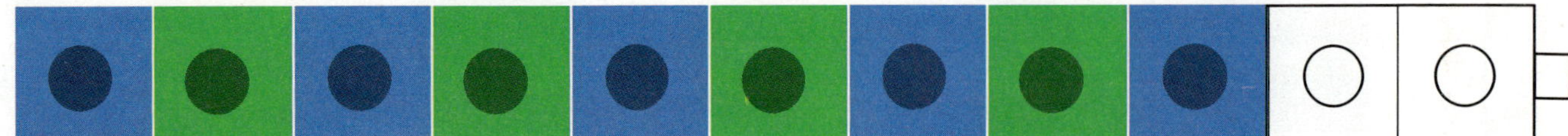

- Color the bears to copy the pattern.
- Color the cubes to show what most likely comes next.
- Use bear counters to show the same pattern. Draw the pattern.
- Use cubes to make your own pattern. Draw your pattern.

CHALLENGE

Follow the Pattern

Follow the ■ ● pattern to help the puppy find his home.
Draw a line to follow the pattern.

HARCOURT
Math
CHAPTER
3
Numbers 0 to 5
© Harcourt
Harcourt

Color to copy the pattern and show what most likely comes next.

Grateful acknowledgment is made to Greenwillow Books, a division of William Morrow & Company, Inc. for permission to reprint the cover illustration by Jose Aruego and Ariane Dewey from *One Duck, Another Duck* by Charlotte Pomerantz. Illustration copyright © 1984 by Jose Aruego and Ariane Dewey.

Printed in the United States of America

Photography Credits:

All photography by Harcourt photographers listed, © Harcourt: Weronica Ankarorn, Victoria Bowen, Ken Kinzie, Sheri O'Neal, Quebecor Imaging, and Terry Sinclair.

Illustration Credits:

Ken Bowser: 62; **Sarah Dillard:** 71, 72; **Rusty Fletcher:** 77, 78; **Liisa Chauncy Guida:** 57; **Jennifer Beck Harris:** 69, 70; **Obadinah Heavner:** 65, 66; **Reggie Holliday:** 56; **Phyliss Horning:** cover; **Dave Klug:** 63, 64; **Benton Mahan:** 62, 75, 76; **Dan McGeehan:** 73, 74; **David Slonim:** storybook; **Steve Sullivan:** 62; **Deborah Tilley:** 61, 64; **Pamela Thomson:** 58; **Stan Tusan:** 59, 60.

15 16 17 18 19 20 1678 16 15 14 13 12 11
4500311726

SCHOOL HOME CONNECTION

Dear Family,

Today we started a new chapter, Numbers 0 to 5. We will learn how to match groups of objects. We will also learn to count objects, making sure that we have counted each one. We will study the numbers 0, 1, 2, 3, 4, and 5.

Love,

____

Vocabulary Power

more **fewer**

There are more flowers than butterflies.
There are fewer butterflies than flowers.

same as **How many?**

The number of frogs is the same as the number of lily pads.
How many frogs do I see? I see three.

Visit *The Learning Site* for additional ideas and activities. www.harcourtschool.com

ACTIVITY

- Invite your child to count with you.
- As you set the table, have your child match groups of items, such as forks and spoons, to see which groups have more, the same, or fewer.

BOOKS TO SHARE

To read books about counting with your child, look for these books in your local library.

One Duck, Another Duck, by Charlotte Pomerantz. Greenwillow, 1984.

Just Enough Carrots, by Stuart J. Murphy. HarperCollins, 1997.

Ten Black Dots, by Donald Crews. HarperCollins, 1986.

MATERIALS: small bag with 5 small objects (beans, buttons), a set of game markers (pennies, paper clips) for each partner

DIRECTIONS: Play with a partner and decide who goes first. Starting at zero, choose a path. Each player takes a turn grabbing a handful of items from the bag. The player counts the items, finds the matching number on his or her path, and places a marker on the number. The first player to have a marker on all of his or her lily pads wins.

Name ______________________________

Algebra: **Equal Groups**

Color one box for each animal.

Draw a ball of yarn for each cat.
Draw a stand for each bird.

HOME ACTIVITY • Set out a small group of items. Have your child make a group of items to match the number of items in your group.

Name ______________________________ **Algebra: More**

Draw lines to match the objects in the two groups. Compare the groups. Circle the group that has more.

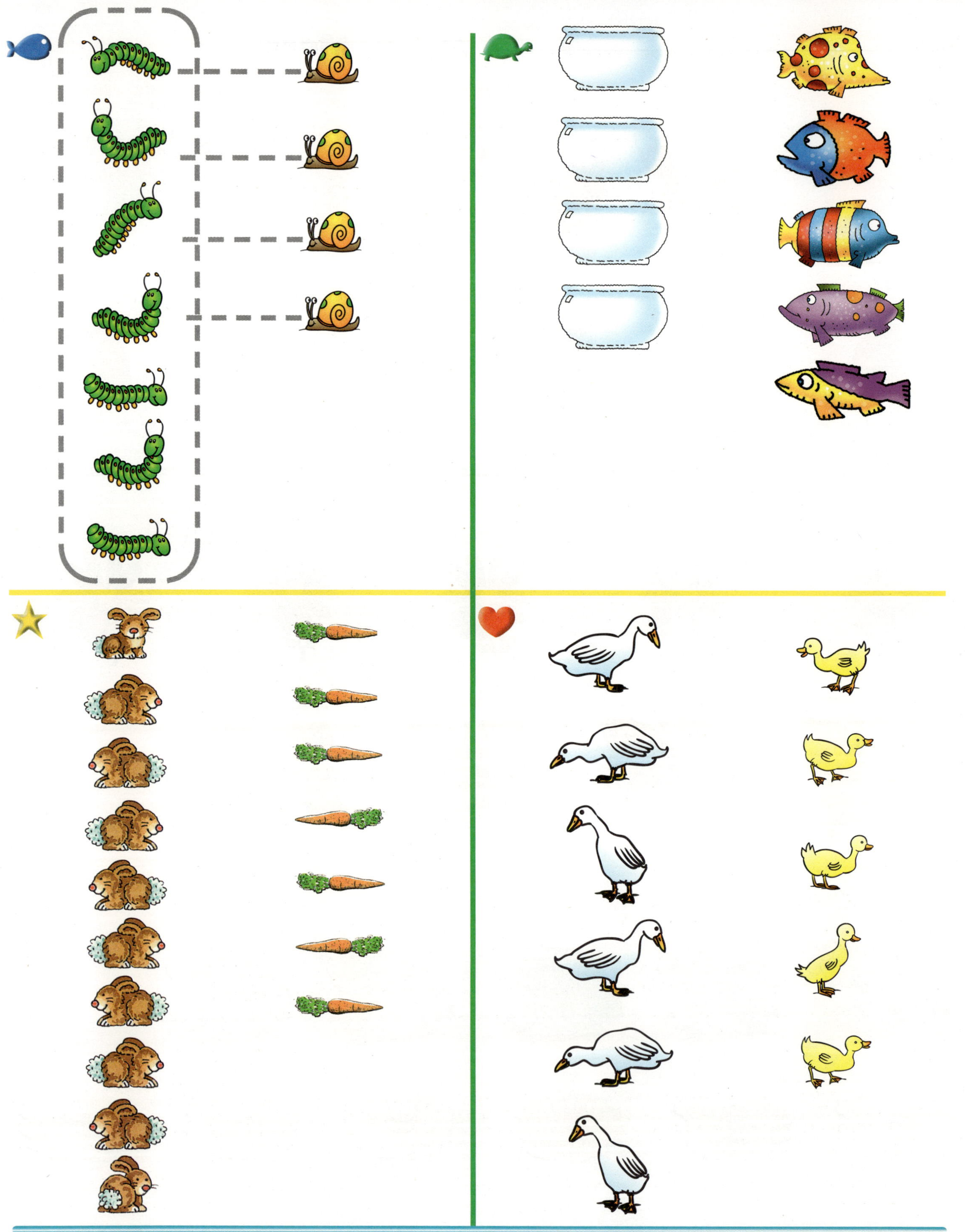

Draw lines to match the objects in the two groups. Compare the groups. Circle the group that has more.

HOME ACTIVITY • Ask your child to match the objects in two groups to find out which group has more.

Name ____________________

Algebra: **Fewer**

Draw lines to match the animals in the two groups. Compare the groups. Circle the group that has fewer.

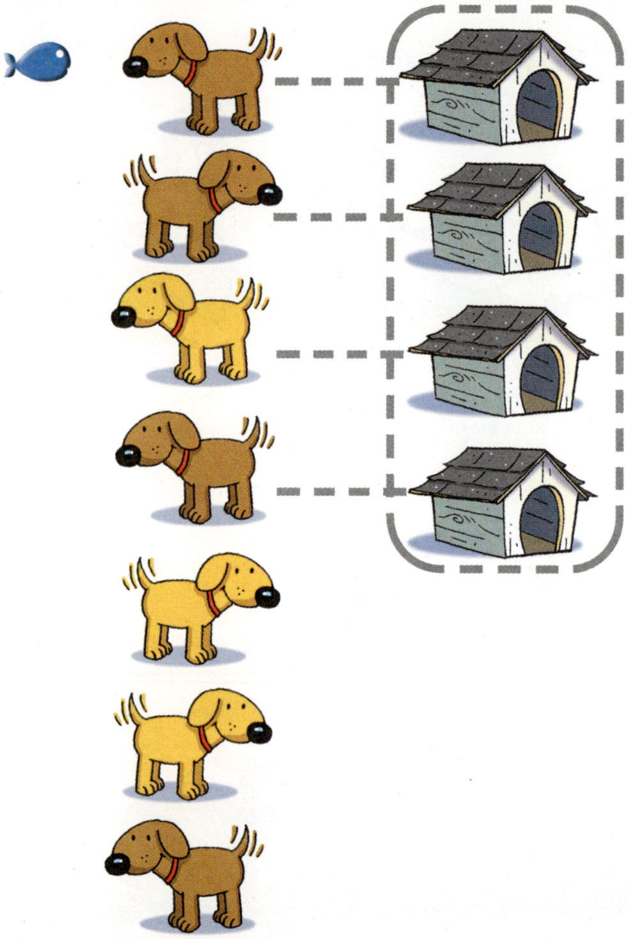

Draw lines to match the objects in the two groups. Compare the groups. Circle the group that has fewer.

HOME ACTIVITY • Have your child match the objects in two groups to find out which group has fewer.

Name ____________________

Problem Solving Strategy
Make a Graph

Put a handful of counters on the sunflower. Are there more red counters or yellow counters? Move the counters to the graph. Circle the group with more counters.

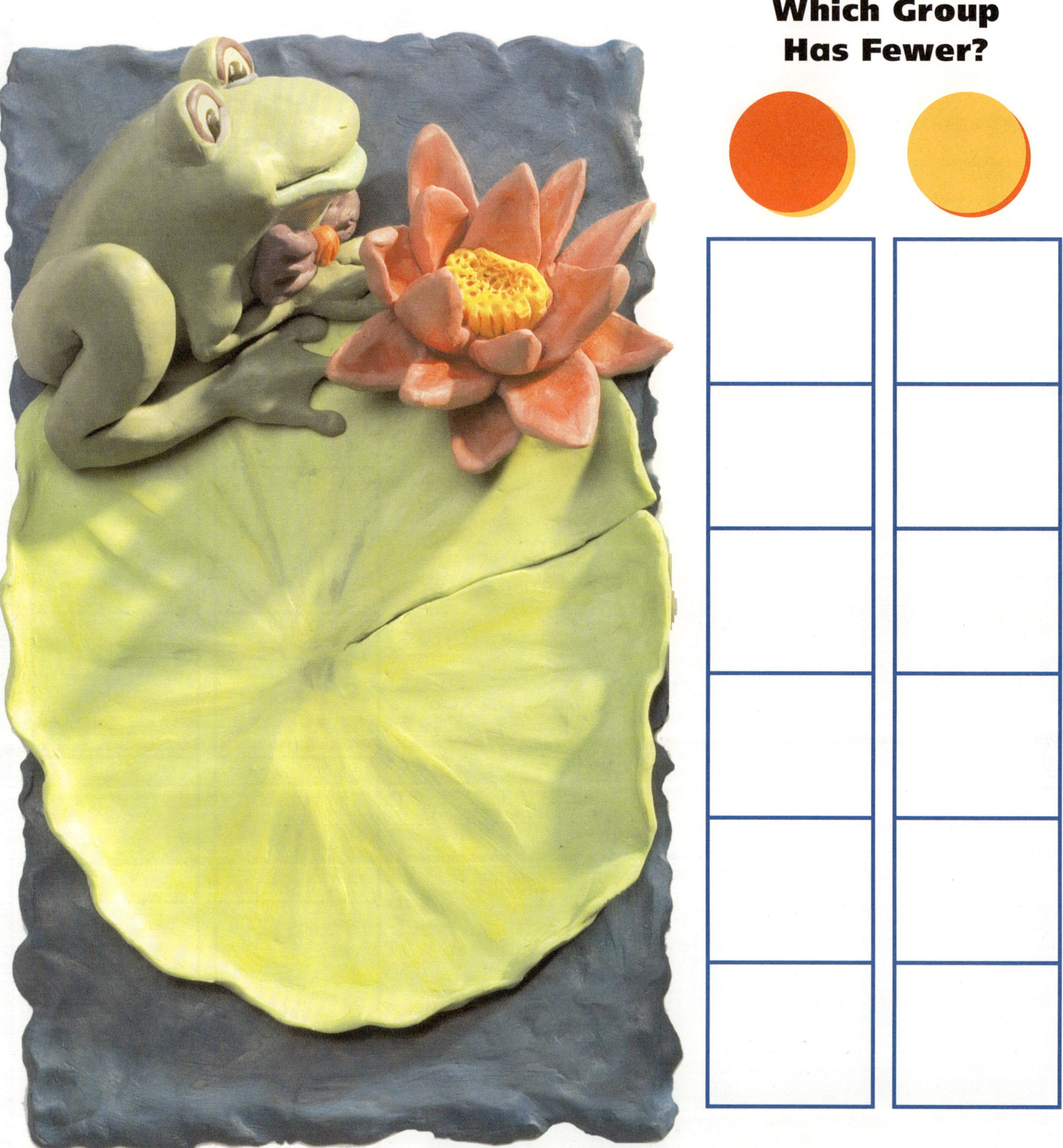

Which Group Has Fewer?

Put a handful of counters on the lily pad. Are there fewer red counters or yellow counters? Move the counters to the graph. Circle the group with fewer counters.

HOME ACTIVITY • Show your child a pile of two kinds of toys, such as blocks and balls. Have him or her make a graph by first lining up the blocks and then lining up the balls next to them. Ask your child which group has more.

Name ____________________

Review

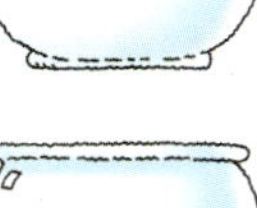
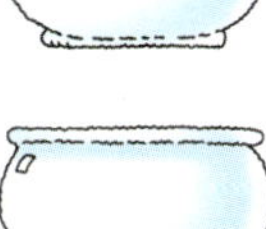

Draw a ball for each glove.
Draw lines to match the objects in the two groups. Compare the groups. Circle the group that has more.
Draw lines to match the objects in the two groups. Compare the groups. Circle the group that has fewer.
Circle the row on the graph with more shapes.

Cumulative Review

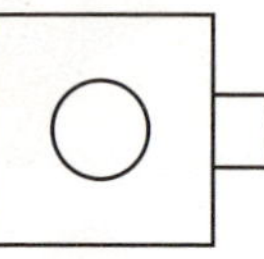
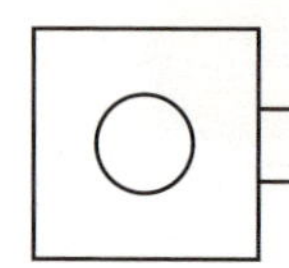
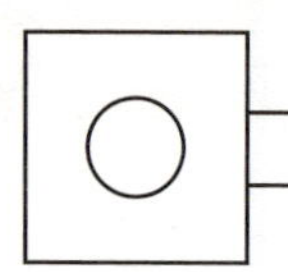
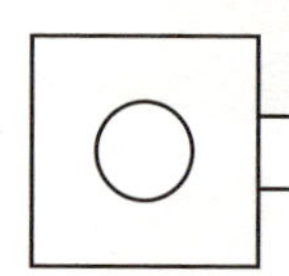
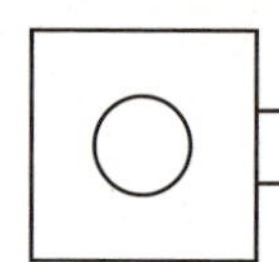
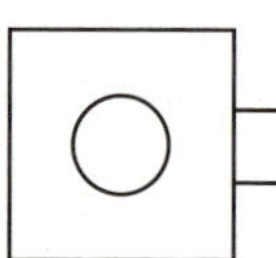

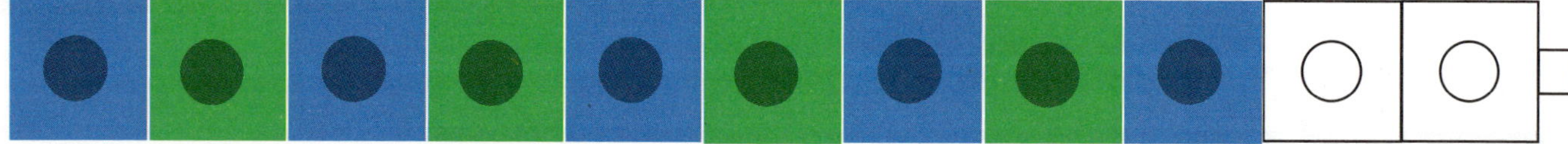

Circle the kites that are the same size.
Read the pattern. Color the cubes to copy the pattern.
Color the cubes to show what most likely comes next.
Circle the group that has more.

Name ______________________________

One, Two, Three, Four

Look at the big picture. Use connecting cubes to show how many. Draw the cubes. Trace the number.

Count the animals in the group. Write the number.

HOME ACTIVITY • Draw two unequal groups of objects. Have your child match one penny to each object in each group. Which group has more? Which group has less?

Name ______________________

Five

5

five

Count the pinecones. Trace the number 5.
Circle the groups that have 5 pinecones.

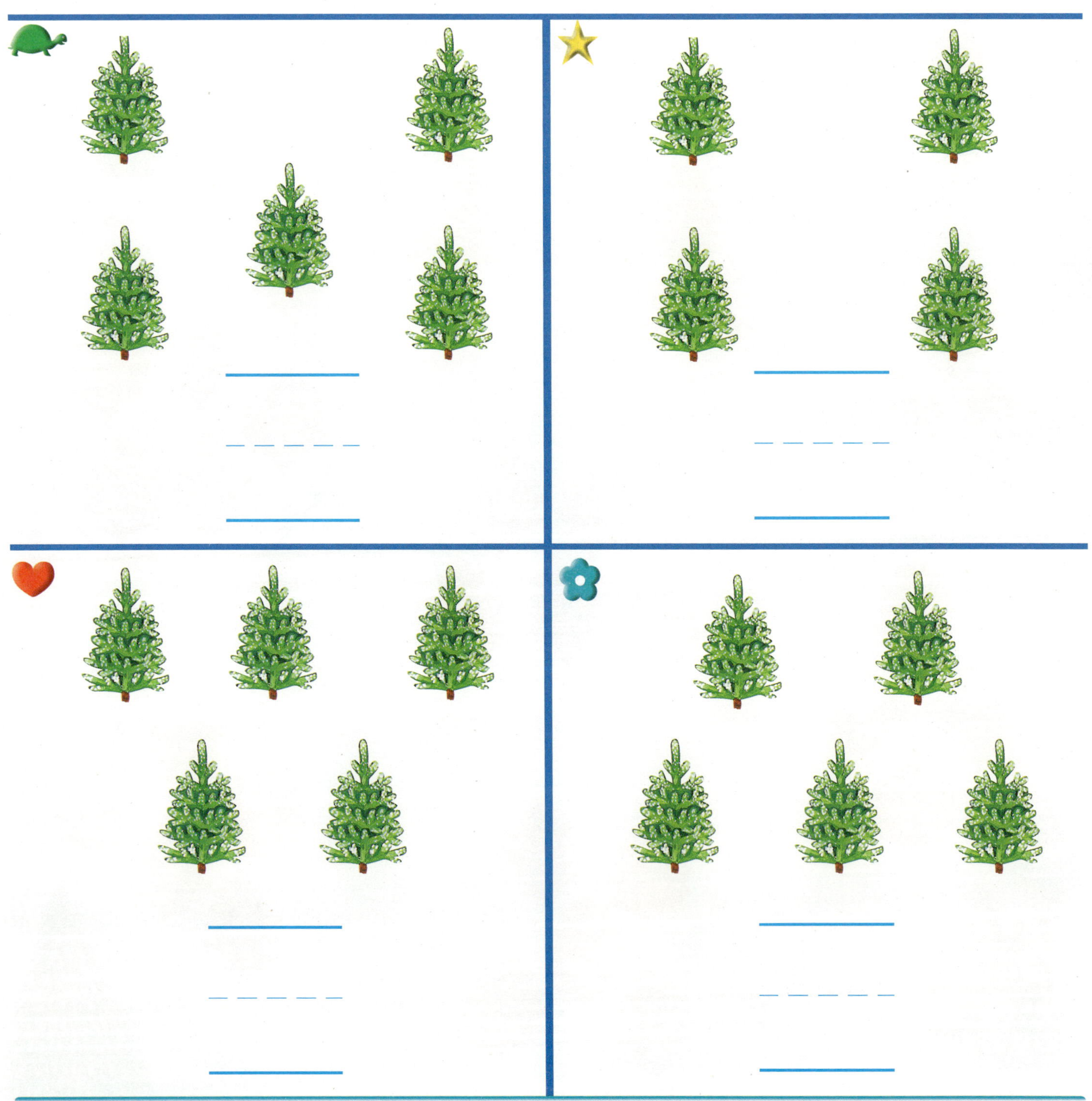

Trace the number 5.

Count the trees. Write the number that tells how many.

HOME ACTIVITY • Have your child find groups of 5 objects at home, in stores, and around the neighborhood.

Name ________________________

Zero

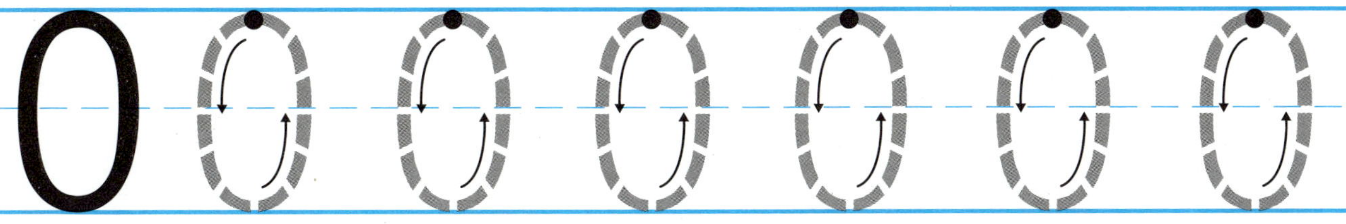

zero

Trace the number 0.

Count the penguins. Write the number that tells how many.

How many ?

0 (2)

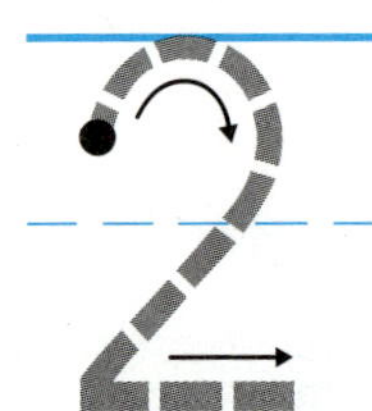

How many ?

0 4

How many ?

0 3

How many ?

0 5

Count the puffins. Circle the number that tells how many. Then write the number.

HOME ACTIVITY • Hide 0, 1, and 2 buttons under three cups. Move the cups around and ask your child to find the one that has 0 buttons under it.

Name ______________________

Before and After on a Number Line

0 1 2 3 4 5

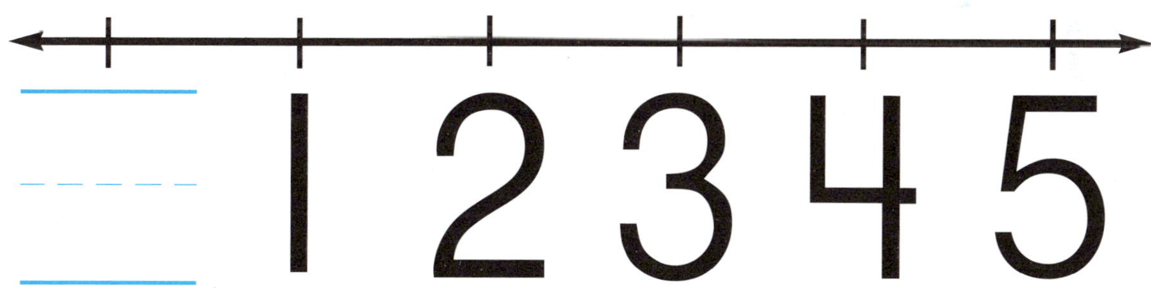

0 1 2 3 4 ___

___ 1 2 3 4 5

Write the number that is after 2.
Write the number that is after 4.
Write the number that is before 1.

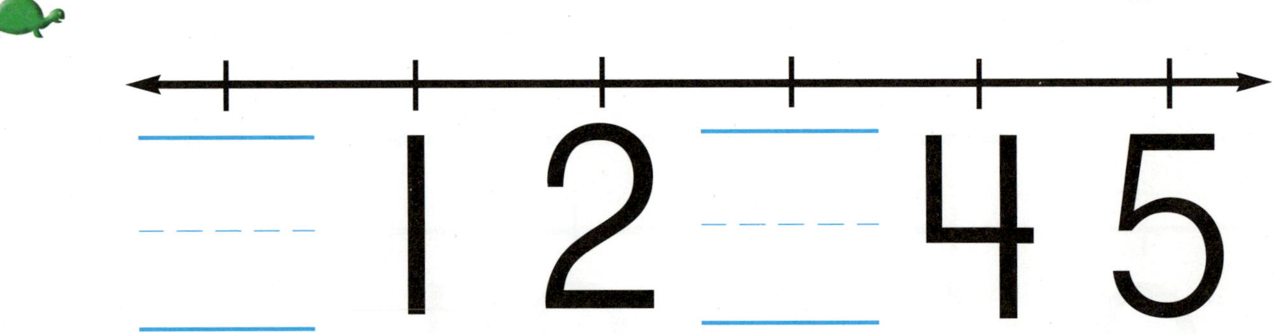

Write the number that is before 2.
Write the number that is after 3.
Write the number that is before 1.
Write the number that is after 2.
Write the number that is before 3.
Write the number that is after 4.

HOME ACTIVITY • Ask your child to use the words *before* and *after* to describe numbers on a number line (for example, *4 is before 5,* and *5 is after 4*).

Name ______________________________

Problem Solving Skill
Use Estimation

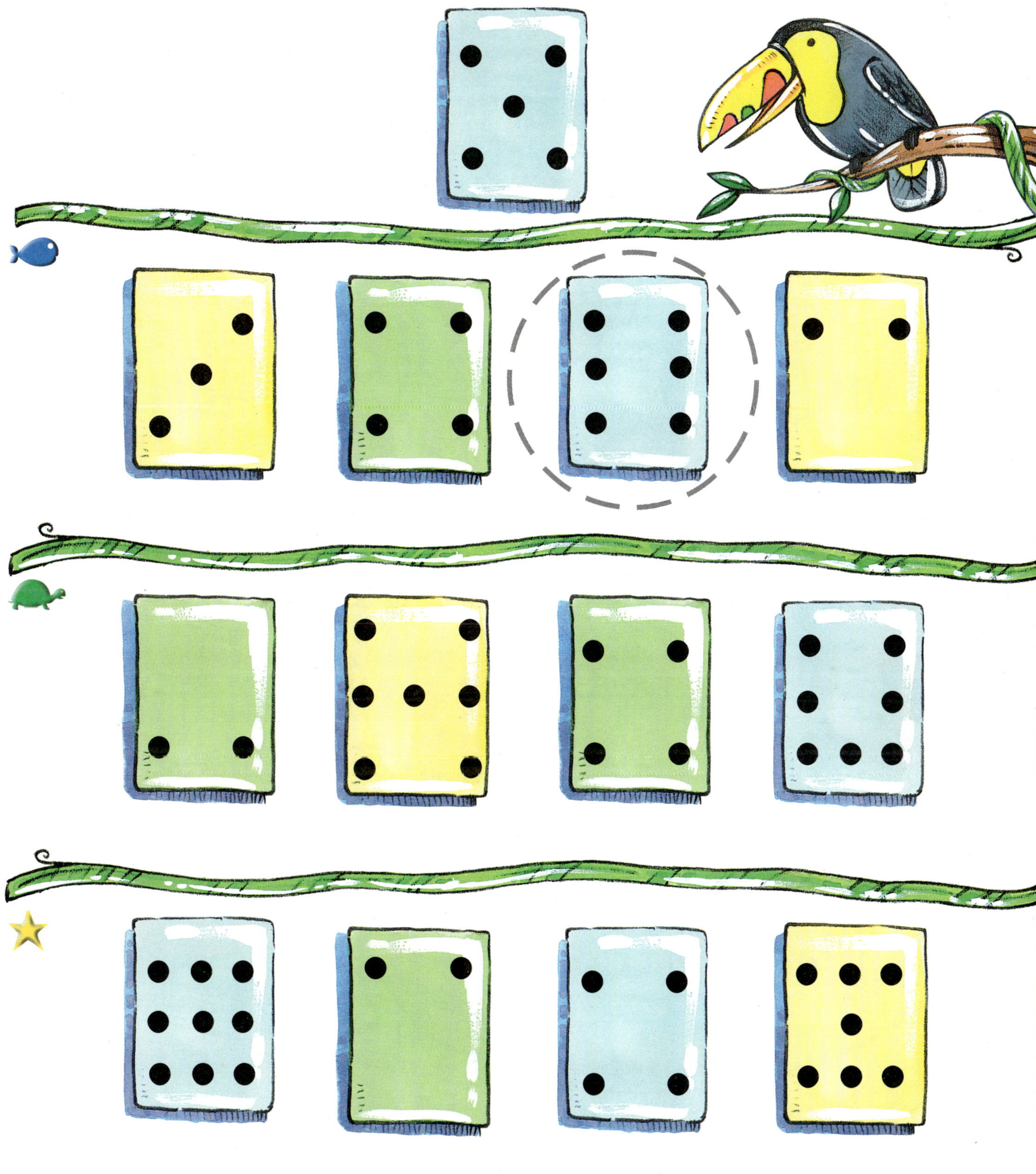

Look at the card at the top of the page. It has 5 dots. Without counting, find cards with more than 5 dots. Circle the cards with more than 5 dots.

PROBLEM SOLVING

Look at the ladybug at the top of the page. It has 5 dots. Without counting, find ladybugs with fewer than 5 dots. Circle the ladybugs with fewer than 5 dots.

HOME ACTIVITY • Have your child place 5 dried beans in one jar and an unknown number in a matching jar for you to estimate how many. Then count together to find the exact number.

By ______________________________

HOME ACTIVITY • This book will help review the numbers 0 to 5. Invite your child to share this book with you.

I can circle the group with more birds.

I can draw 1 bird in each nest.

I can circle the group with fewer birds.

I can circle the group with 4 birds.

I can draw birds on each branch to show the number.

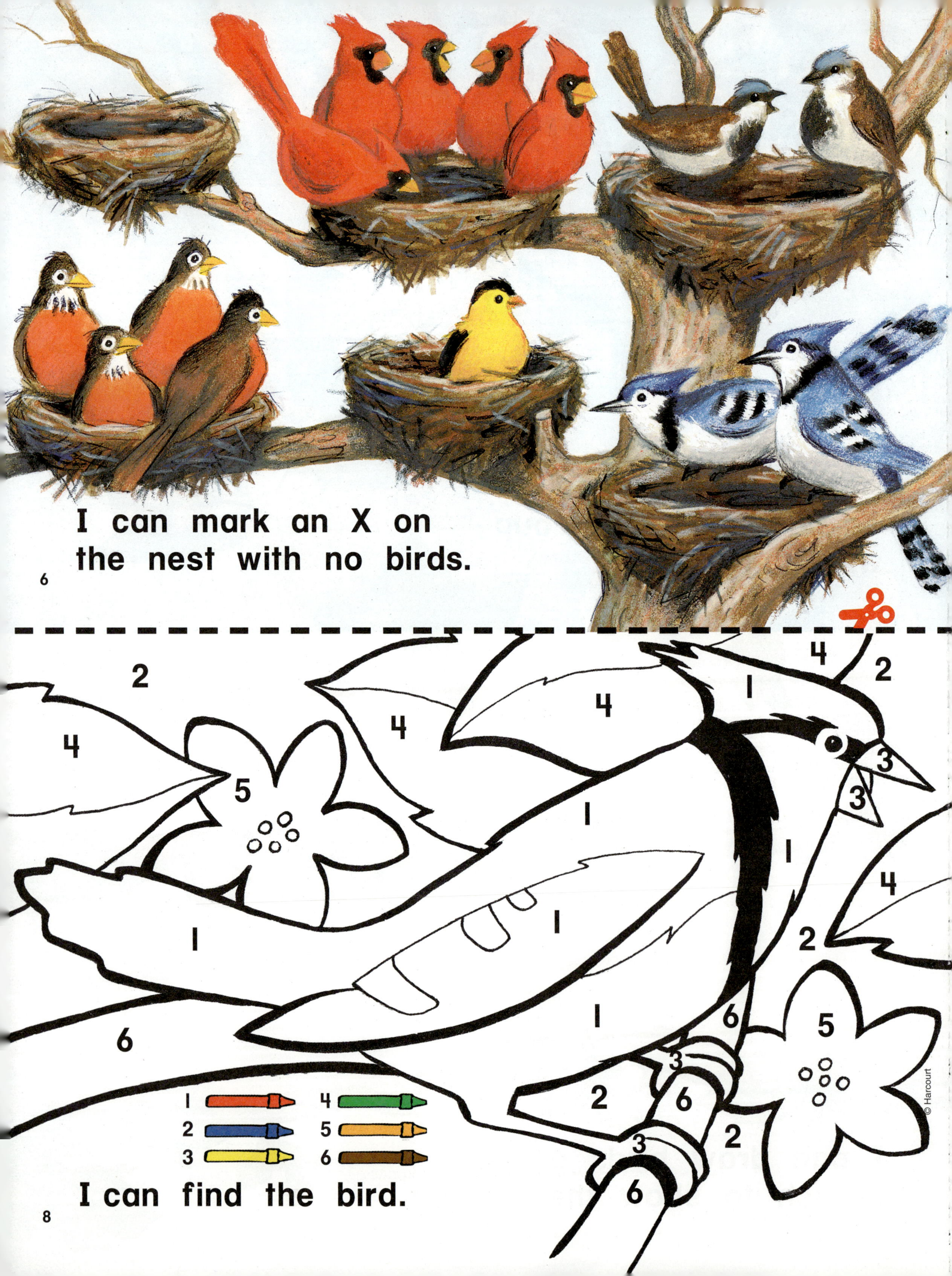

I can mark an X on the nest with no birds.

I can find the bird.

Name ______________________________

Review

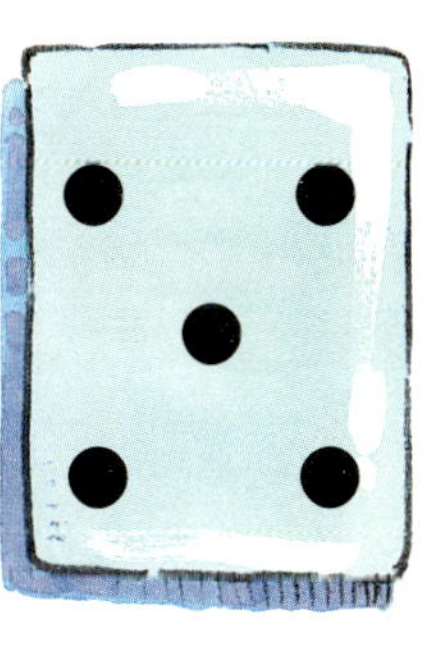

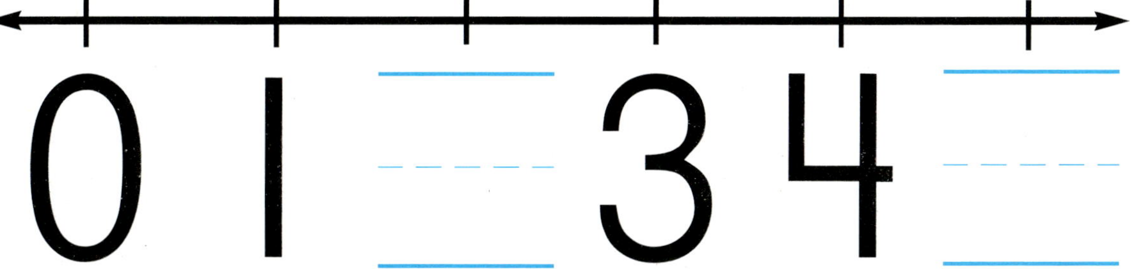

0 1 ___ 3 4 ___

Count the objects in the group. Write the number.

Look at the card with 5 dots. Without counting, circle the card with fewer than 5 dots.

Write the number that is before 3. Write the number that is after 4.

CHAPTER 3 • REVIEW

Cumulative Review

Mark an X on the object that does not belong.
Color to show what most likely comes next.
Use counters to show the same pattern. Draw the pattern.
Count the shapes. Circle the number that tells how many.

Name ________________________________

Test

0 ___ 2 3 ___ 5

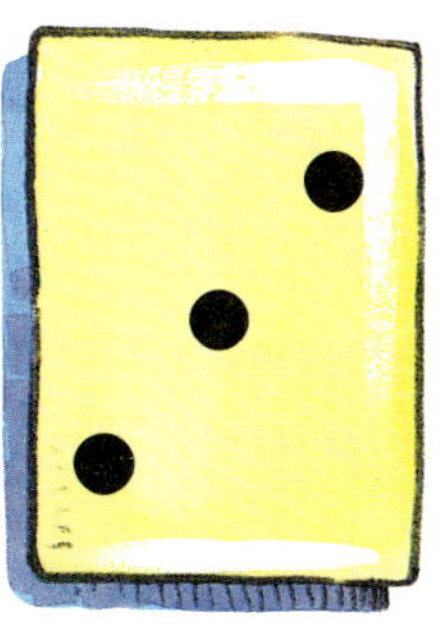

Circle the group that has more.
Circle the group that has 5 pine cones.
Write the number that is before 2. Write the number that is after 3.
Look at the card with 5 dots. Without counting, circle the card with fewer than 5 dots.

CHAPTER 3 • TEST

CHALLENGE

Number Patterns

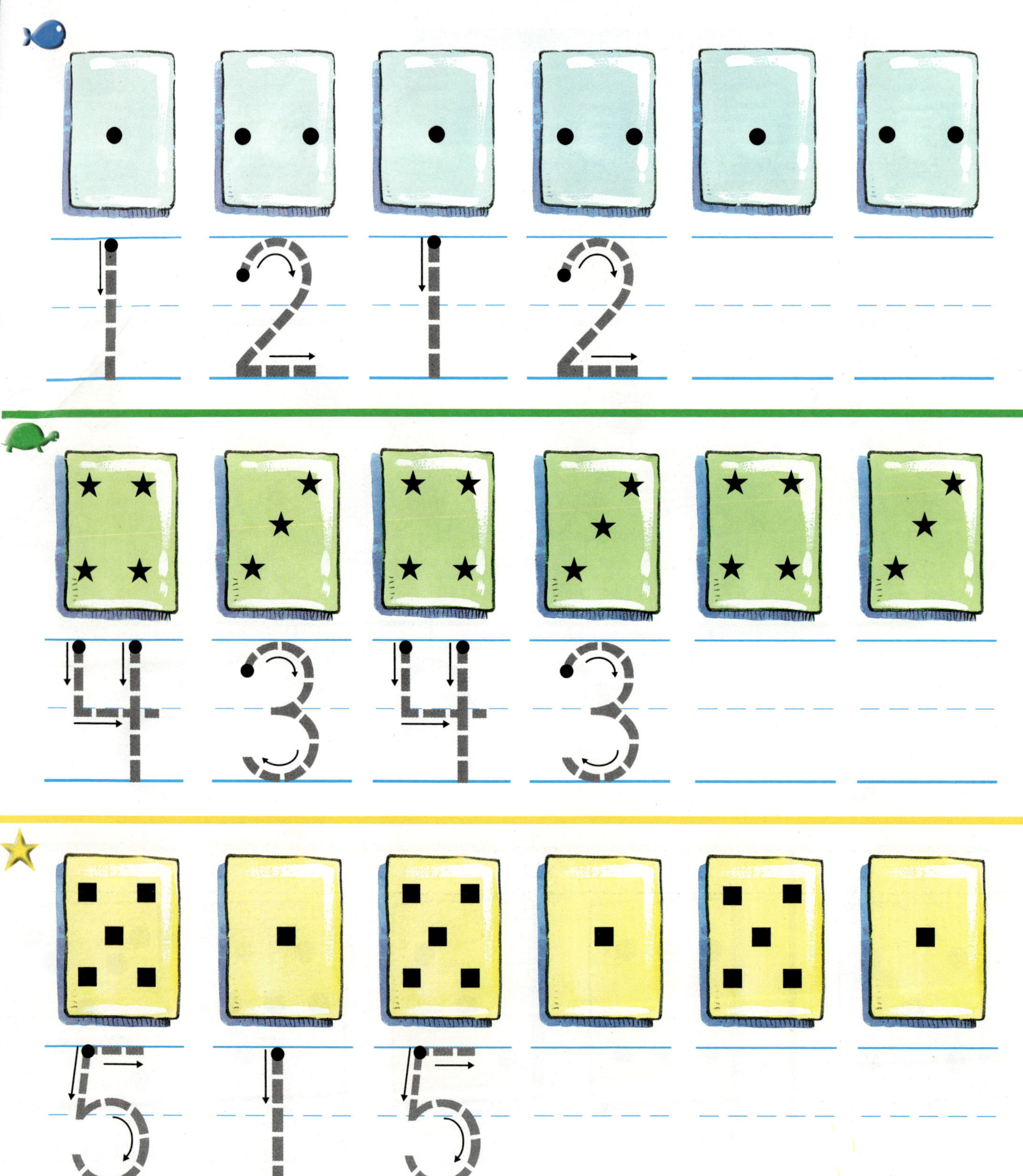

Look at the pattern.
Write the numbers that come next.

CHAPTER 3 • CHALLENGE

CHAPTER
4
Numbers 6 to 10
HARCOURT
Math
© Harcourt
Harcourt

Count the ants in each group.
Circle the groups that have the same number of ants.

Grateful acknowledgment is made to HarperCollins Publishers for permission to reprint the cover illustration by Felicia Bond from *The Right Number of Elephants* by Jeff Sheppard. Illustration copyright © 1990 by Felicia Bond.

Printed in the United States of America

Photography Credits:

All photography by Harcourt photographers listed, © Harcourt: Weronica Ankarorn, Victoria Bowen, Ken Kinzie, Sheri O'Neal, Quebecor Imaging, and Terry Sinclair.

Illustration Credits:

Ken Bowser: 91, 92; **Shirley Beckes:** 91, 92; **Roberta Collier-Morales:** 87, 89, 90; **Daniel DelValle:** 86; **Ben Mahan:** storybook; **John Nez:** 103, 104; **Rosiland Soloman:** cover, 83; **Ken Spengler:** 84; **Joe Veno:** 93, 94; **Jane Yamada:** 99, 100.

15 16 17 18 19 20 1678 16 15 14 13 12 11
4500311726

SCHOOL HOME CONNECTION

Dear Family,

Today we started a new chapter, Numbers 6 to 10. We will match these numbers to groups of objects and learn which group has more than or less than another.

Love,

____

6 six

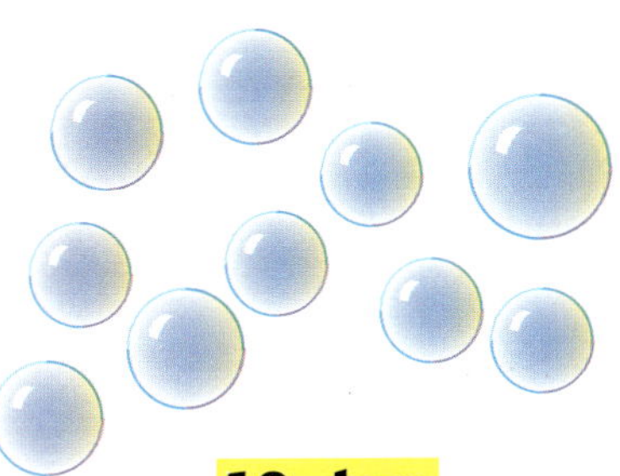

10 ten

ACTIVITY

- Have your child count groups of six, seven, eight, nine, and ten objects.
- Have your child compare two groups of objects. Ask him or her which group has more.

BOOKS TO SHARE

To read about numbers with your child, look for these books at your local library.

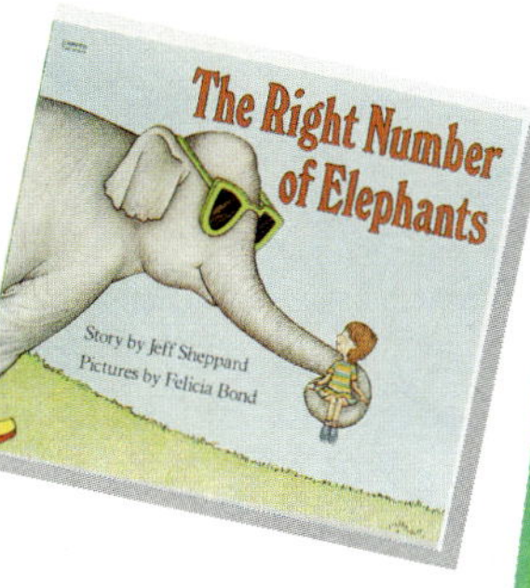

The Right Number of Elephants, by Jeff Sheppard. HarperCollins, 1990.

Who's Counting? by Nancy Tafuri. Greenwillow, 1986.

Barn Cat, by Carol P. Saul. Little Brown, 1998.

Visit *The Learning Site* for additional ideas and activities. www.harcourtschool.com

Math Game

MATERIALS: number cube (6–10), paper clips, buttons

DIRECTIONS: Play with a partner and decide who goes first. Each player chooses either paper clips or buttons as game markers. One player tosses the number cube, reads the number, and counts out that many of his or her game markers onto one of the spaces for that number on the game board. Players take turns until the game board is filled. The player who has filled more spaces on the game board wins.

Name ______________________________

Six and Seven

Place counters in the nests to show how many. Draw the counters in the nests. Trace the numbers.

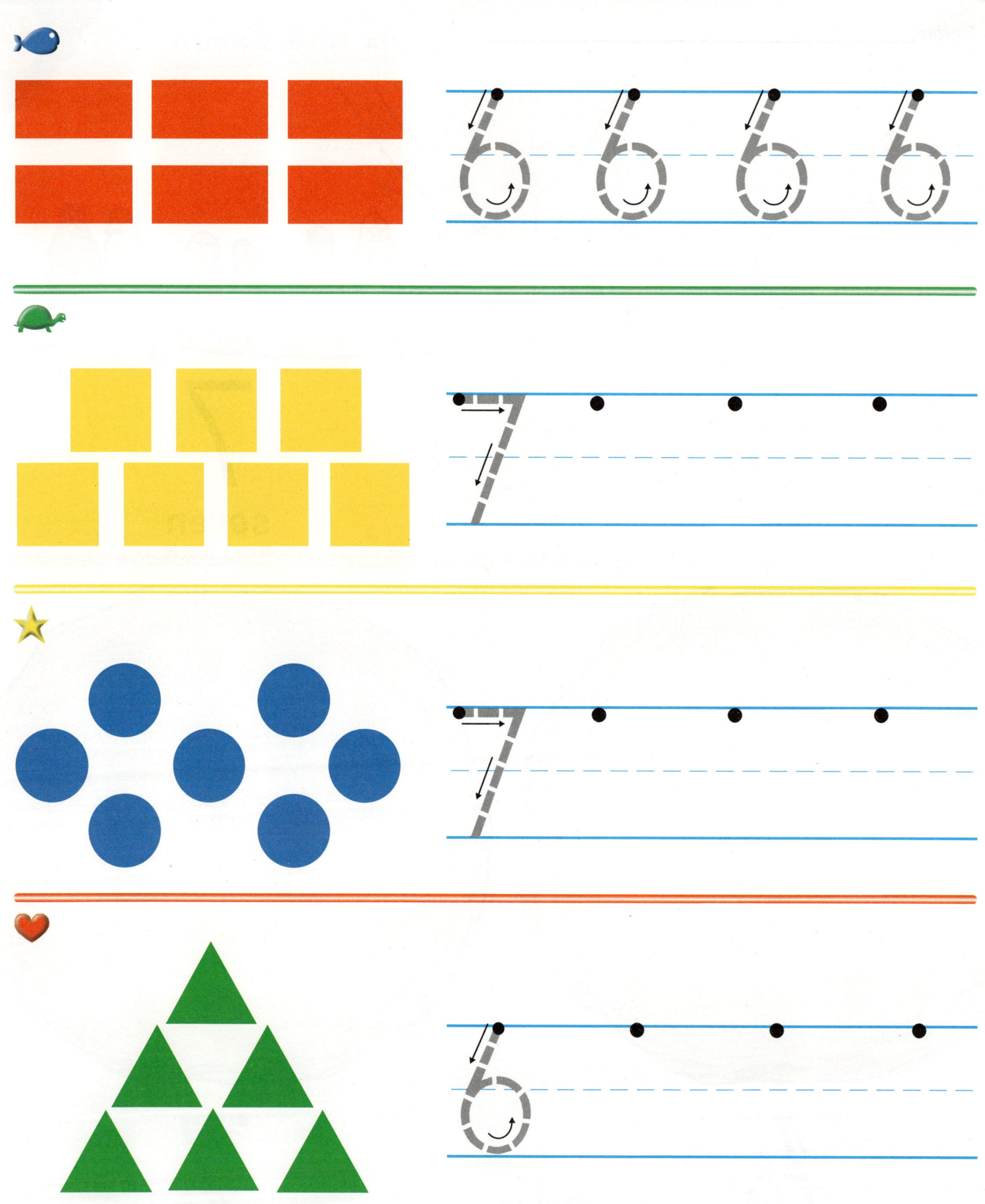

Count the shapes in the group. Write the number.

HOME ACTIVITY • Remind your child that there are seven days in the week. Say the days together. Have your child raise one finger for each day and then count the raised fingers.

Name ______________________________

Eight and Nine

eight 8

nine 9

Count the dots in the group. Trace and write the number.
How many are in the picture? Count. Write the number.

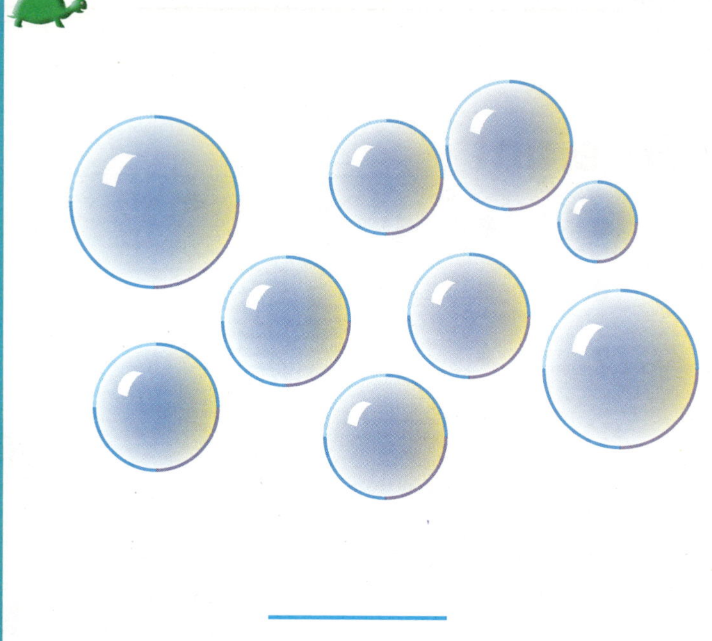

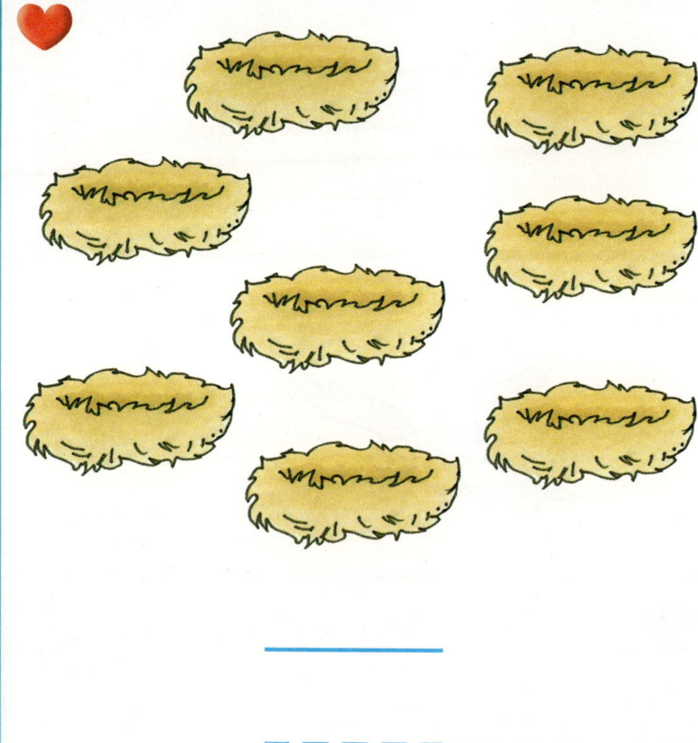

Count. Write the number that tells how many.

HOME ACTIVITY • Challenge your child to arrange 9 pennies in different ways, such as in a row, column, or square.

Name ______________________

Ten

ten

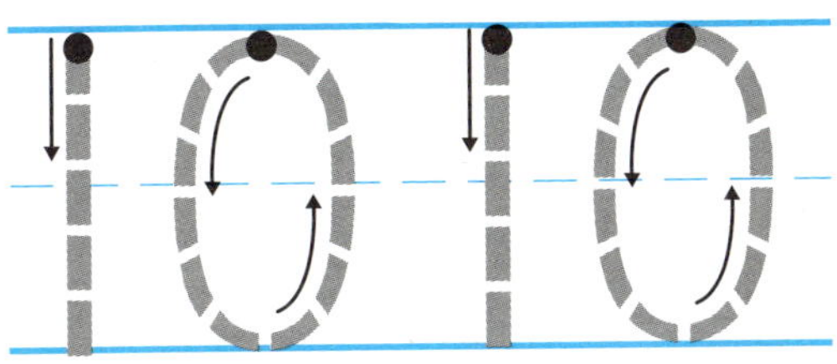

Count the bees. Trace the number.

Draw more bees to make a group of 10.

10

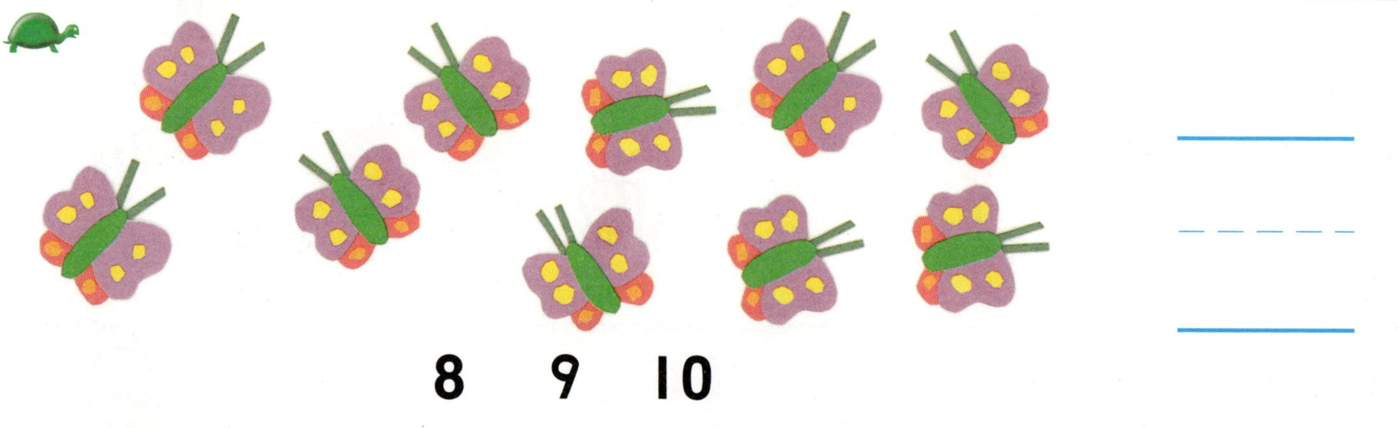

8 9 10

6 7 8

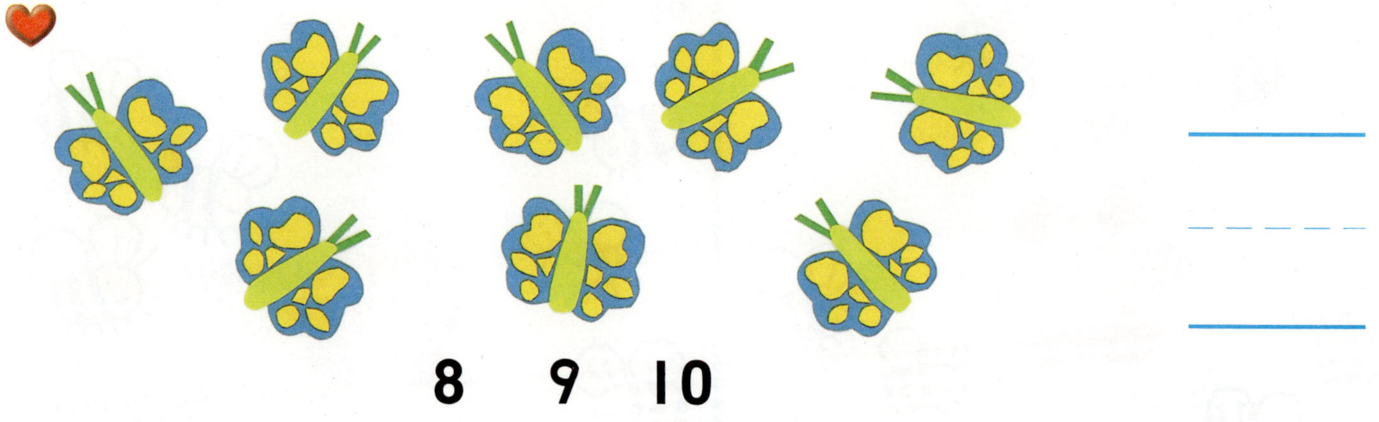

8 9 10

Write the number 10.
Count the butterflies. Circle the number that tells how many. Write the number.

HOME ACTIVITY • Have your child count his or her toes and write the number that tells how many.

Name ________________________

Problem Solving Strategy
Make a Model

Connect 10 cubes. Then make one break to get two groups—one with more cubes than the other. Put the groups on the work space. For each group, draw the cubes and write the number. Circle the number that is greater. Use different numbers to make 10 each time.

Connect 10 cubes. Then make one break to get two groups—one with more cubes than the other. Put the groups on the work space. For each group, draw the cubes and write the number. Circle the number that is less. Use different numbers to make 10 each time.

HOME ACTIVITY • Have your child use pennies to show the number of people in your home at two different times of the day. Have him or her write the numbers. Ask if one number is more or if they are the same.

Name ______________________________

Review

6 7 8

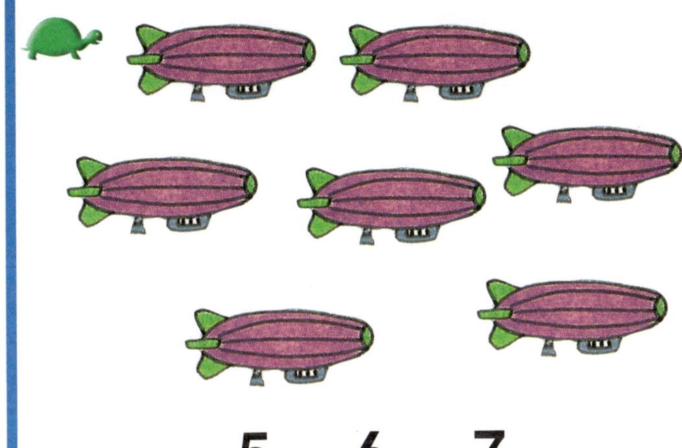

5 6 7

7 8 9

8 9 10

Count the objects in the groups. Circle the number that tells how many.

Count the cubes in each group and write the numbers. Circle the number that is greater.

Cumulative Review

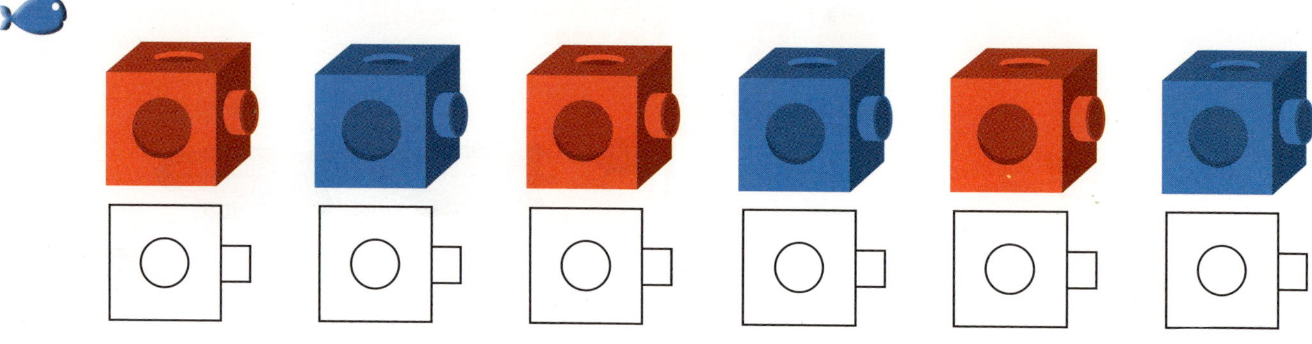

3 4 5

5 6 7

Read the pattern. Color the cubes to copy the pattern.
Draw lines to match the animals in the group. Compare the groups. Circle the group that has fewer.
Count the shapes. Circle the number that tells how many.
Count the bees. Draw more bees to make a group of ten.

Name ______________________

Before and After on a Number Line

5 ___ 7 8 ___ 10

Write the number that is after 6.
Write the number that is after 5.
Write the number that is before 10.
Write the number that is before 6.
Write the number that is after 7.

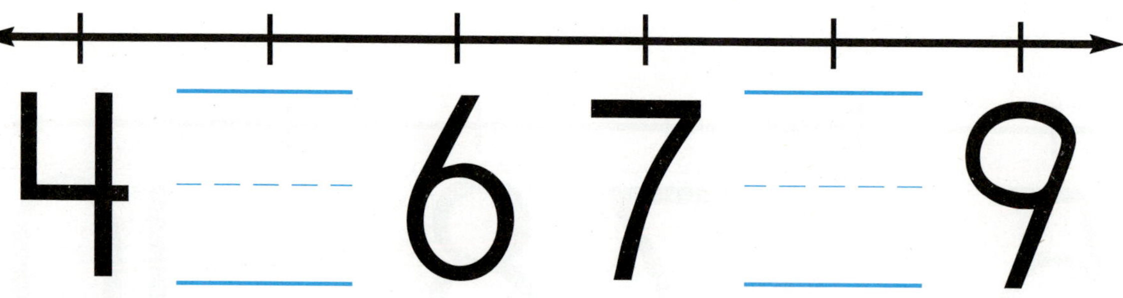

Write the number that is before 8.
Write the number that is after 9.
Write the number that is after 4.
Write the number that is before 9.
Write the number that is after 3.
Write the number that is before 7.

HOME ACTIVITY • Ask your child to use the words *before* and *after* to describe numbers on a number line.

Name ______________________________

Write Numbers 0 to 10

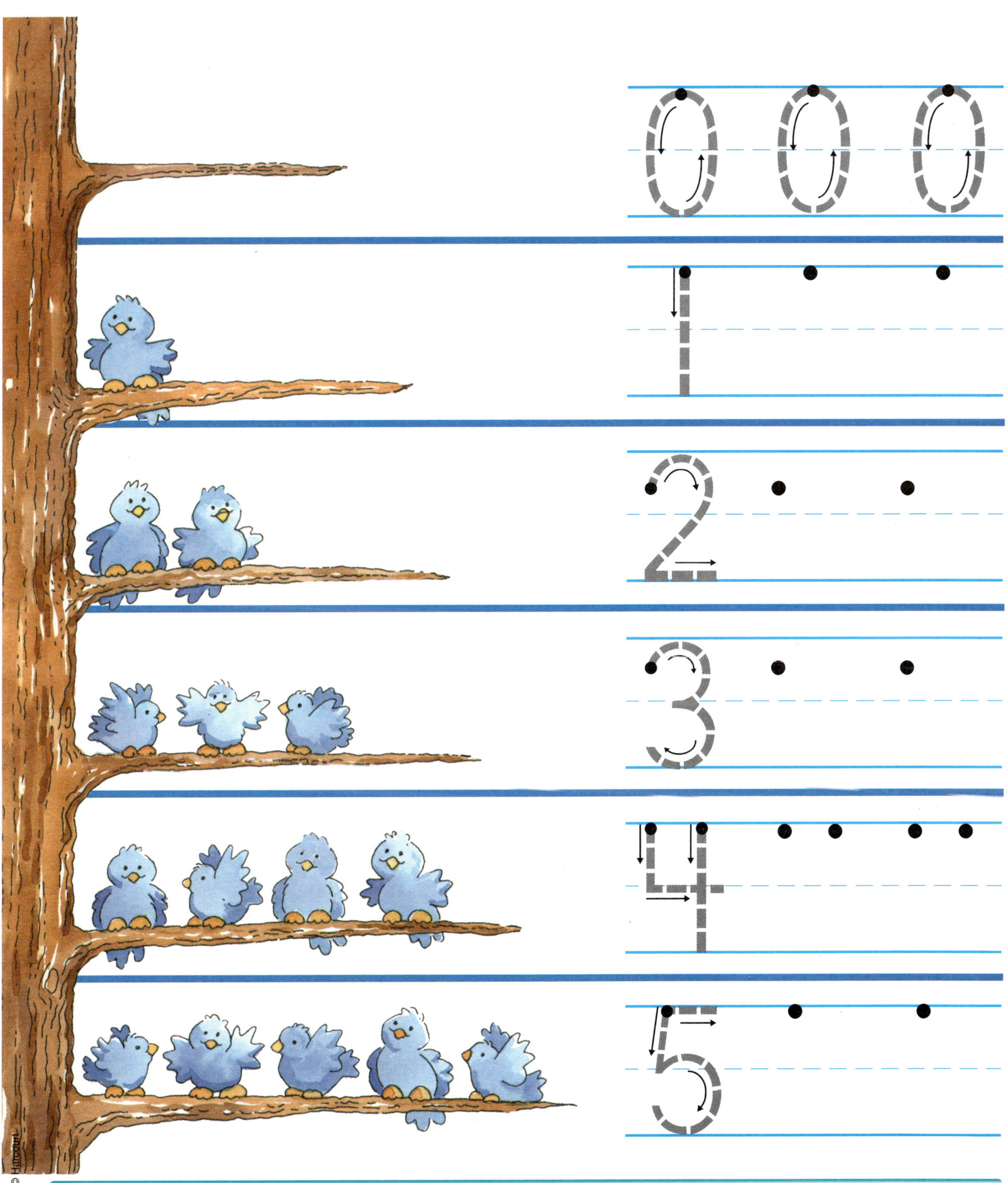

Trace the number that means none in a group. Now, count the birds and write the number that tells how many birds in each group.

Count the birds and write the number that tells how many birds in each group.

HOME ACTIVITY • Have your child count aloud from 0 to 10. Then have him or her try counting from 10 to 0.

Name ______________________________

Algebra: Missing Numbers

4 5 6 ■ 8

2
7

■ 7 8 9 10

5
6

0 1 ■ 3 4

2
5

3 4 5  7

3
6

Circle the missing number.

7 6 5  3

4
8

9 8 7  5

10
6

■ 6 5 4 3

7
8

10  8 7 6

5
9

Circle the missing number.

HOME ACTIVITY • Say several numbers in order, leaving out one number. Ask your child to tell you what number is missing.

Name ______________________________

Problem Solving Skill
Use Data from a Graph

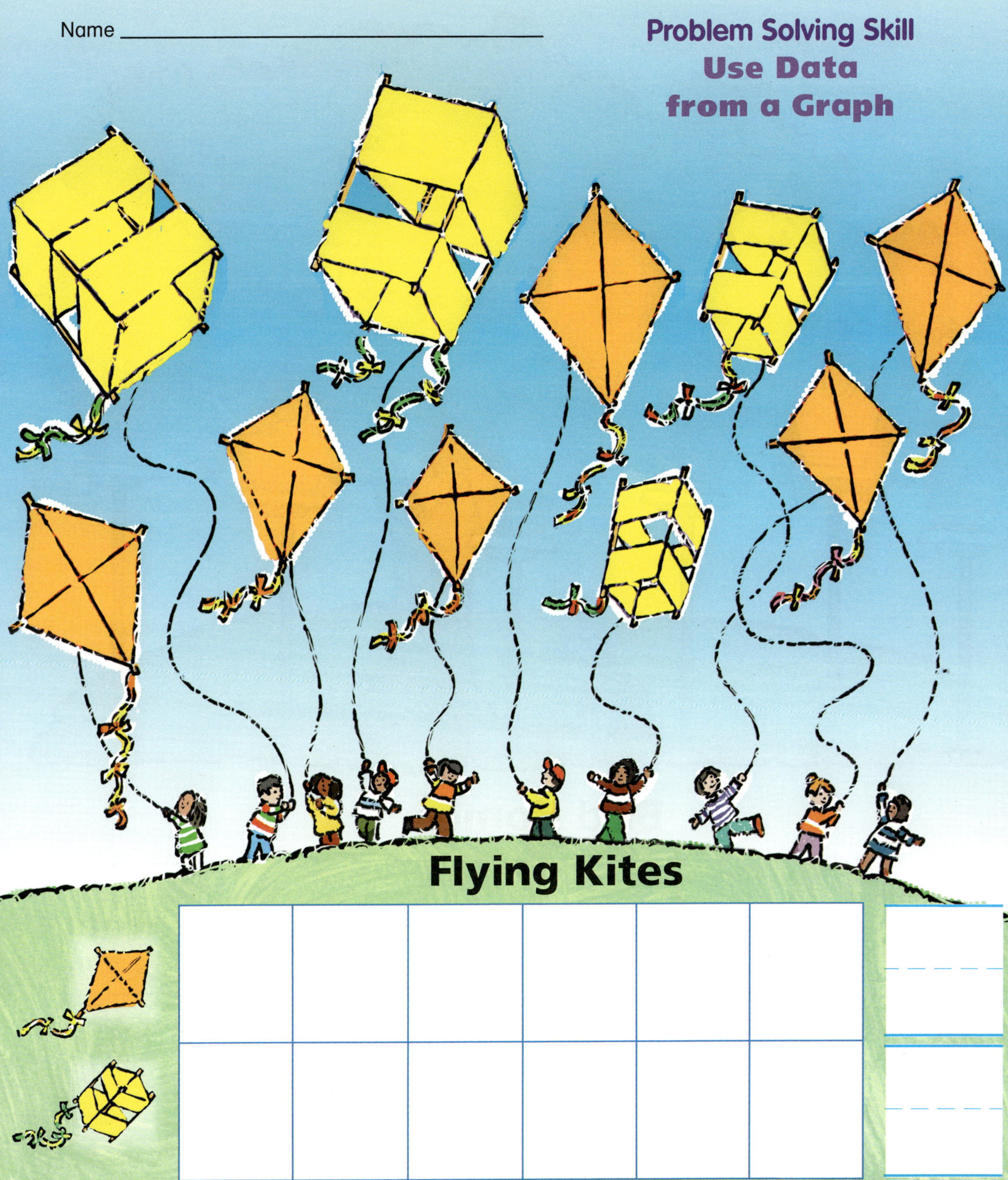

Put an orange cube on each orange kite and a yellow cube on each yellow kite. Move the cubes to the graph. Count the cubes in each row and write the number. Are there more orange kites or more yellow kites? Circle the number that is greater.

Bird Homes

Put a red cube on each birdhouse and a yellow cube on each nest. Move the cubes to the graph. Count the cubes in each row and write the number. Are there more nests or more birdhouses? Circle the number that is less.

HOME ACTIVITY • Have your child find out whether each family member would rather have milk or juice and then use the information to draw a simple graph.

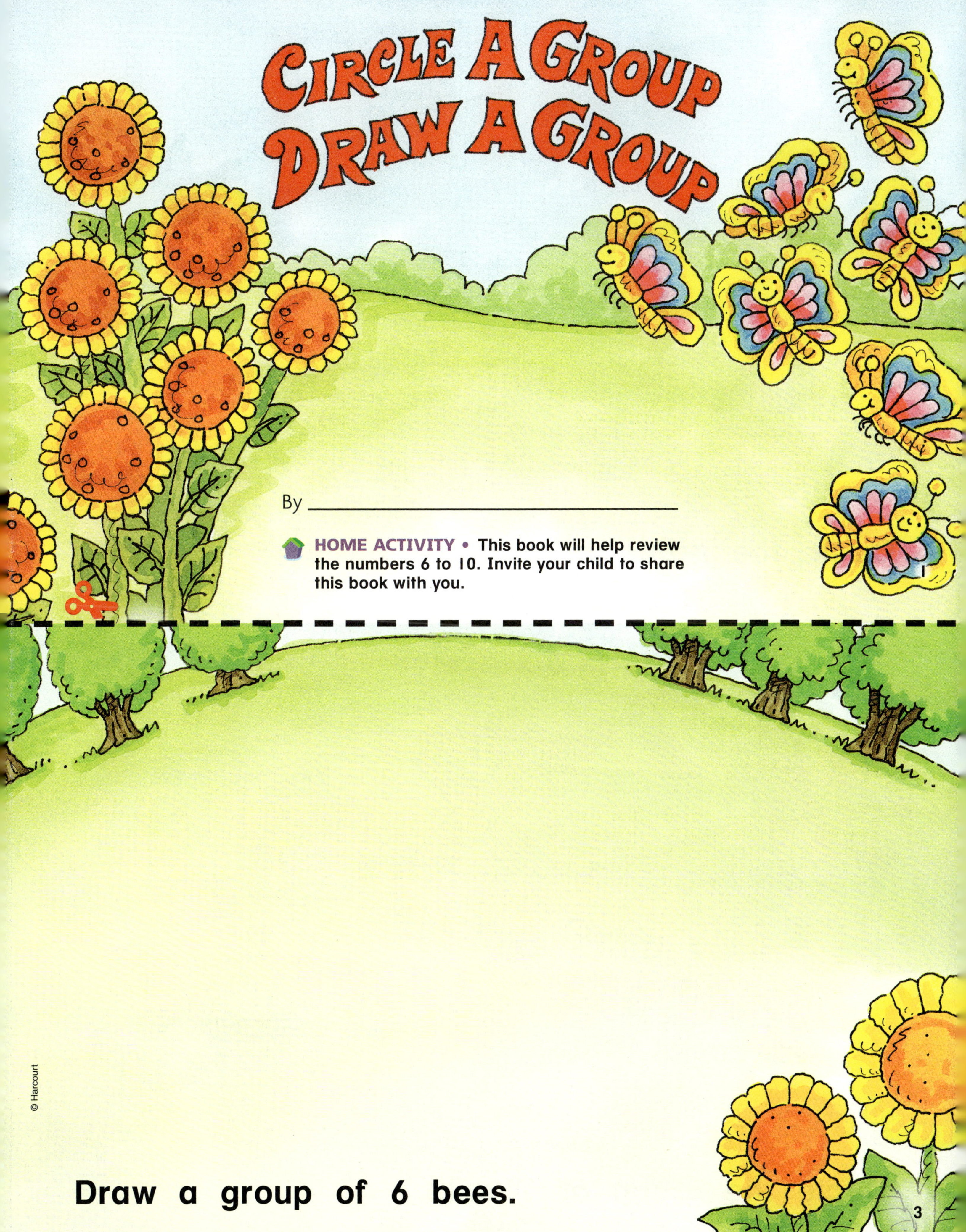

By ______________________________

HOME ACTIVITY • **This book will help review the numbers 6 to 10. Invite your child to share this book with you.**

Draw a group of 6 bees.

Circle the group of 6 trees.

Circle the group of 7 ants.

Draw a group of 7 plants.

Draw a group of 8 balloons.

Circle the group of
8 raccoons.

Circle the group of
9 frogs.

Draw a group of 9 logs.

Draw a group of 10 tops.

Circle the group of 10 raindrops.

6 7 8 9 10

Name ______________________________

Review

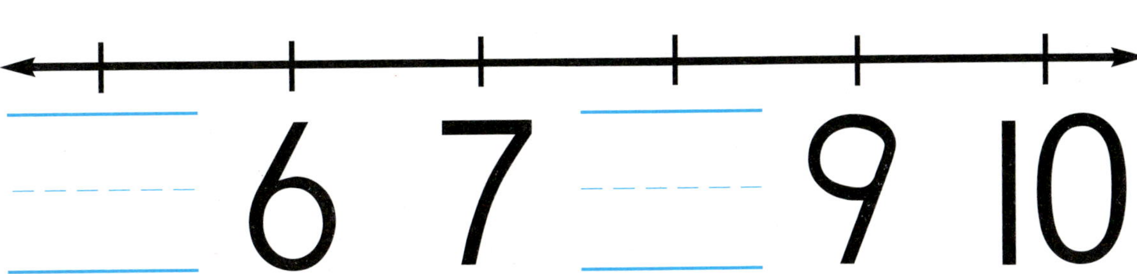

10  8 7 6

5
9

Flying Kites

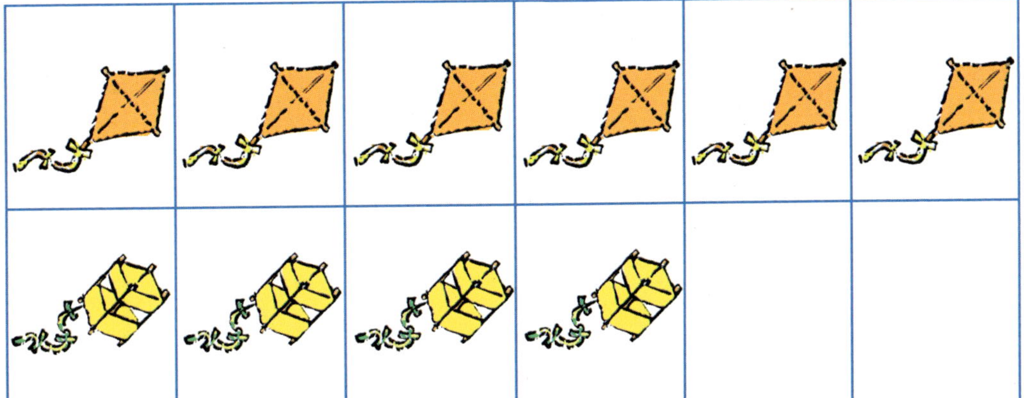

Write the number that is before 6. Write the number that is after 7.
Circle the missing number.
Count the kites in each row of the graph and write the numbers. Are there more orange kites or yellow kites? Circle the number that is greater.

Cumulative Review

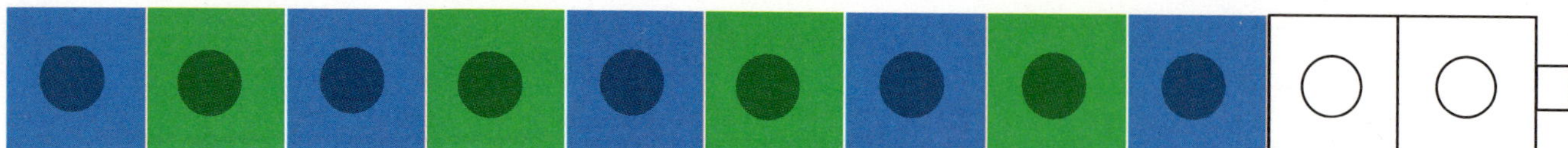

3 4 5  7

3

6

Color the cubes to show what most likely comes next.

Look at the card with 5 dots at the beginning of the row. Without counting, circle the card with fewer dots.

Count the butterflies. Write the number.

Circle the missing number.

Name ______________________________

Test

6 7 ___ 9 10

___ 6 7 ___ 9 10

6 7  9 10

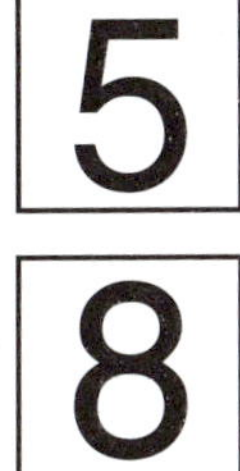

Count the shapes. Write how many.
Count the cubes in each group and write the numbers.
Circle the number that is greater.
Write the number that is before 6. Write the number that is after 7.
Circle the missing number.

CHALLENGE

In the Park

Flowers, Birds, and Butterflies

Color the boxes in the graph to show how many are in the park.

HARCOURT
Math

CHAPTER 5

Geometry and Fractions

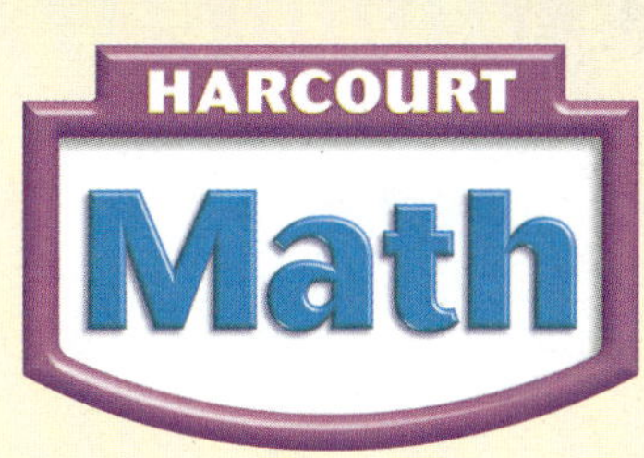

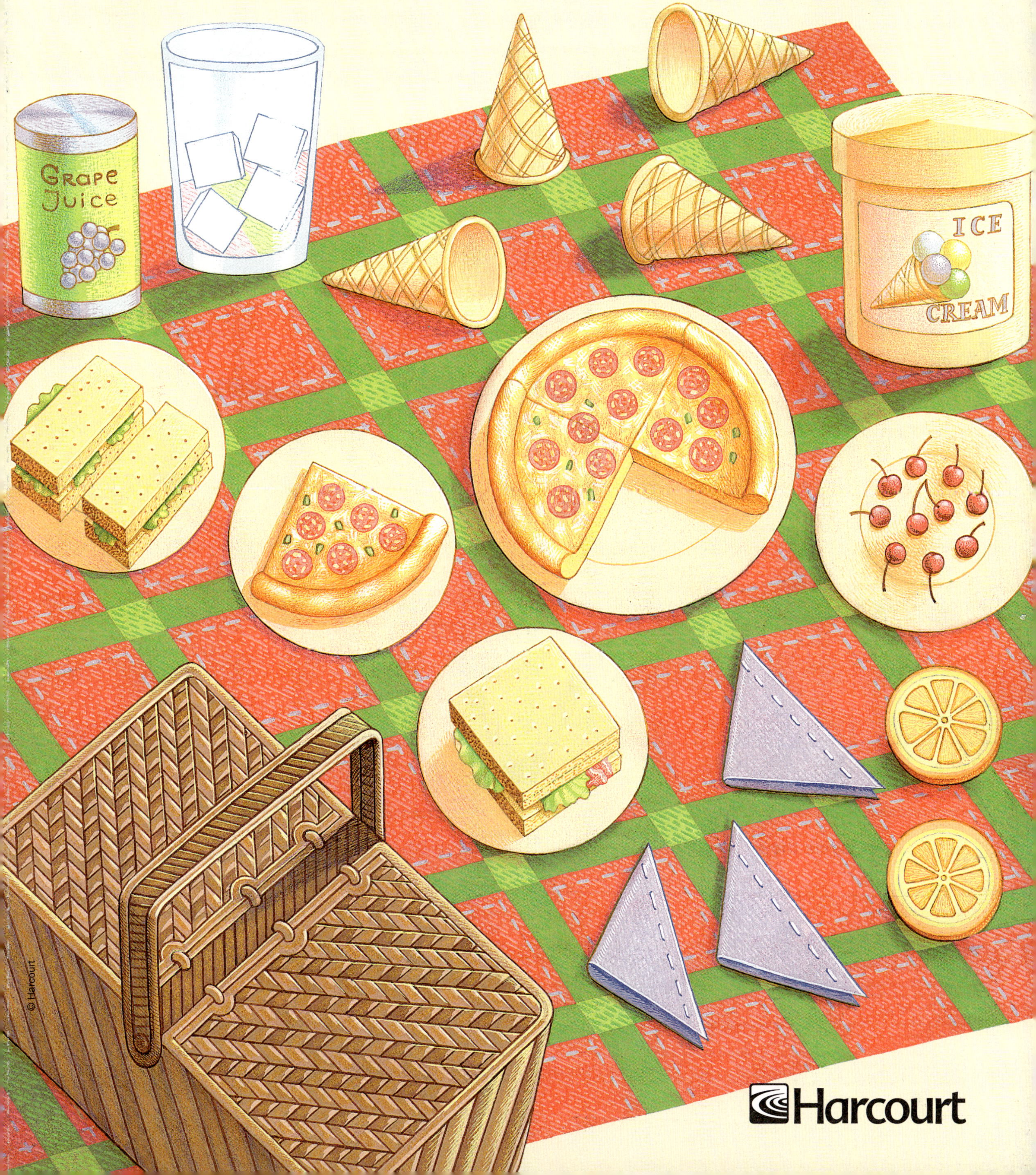

Grape Juice
ICE CREAM

Harcourt

🐟 🐢 ⭐ ❤ **Circle the shapes that are the same.**

Printed in the United States of America

Photography Credits:

All photography by Harcourt photographers listed, © Harcourt: Weronica Ankarorn, Victoria Bowen, Ken Kinzie, Sheri O'Neal, Quebecor Imaging, and Terry Sinclair.

Nan Brooks: 112; **Heidi King:** 117, 129, 130; **Jill Meyerhoff:** 123; **Stephanie Peterson**; 117, 118, 124, 125, 126; **Pattie Silver:** 120; **Valerie Sokolova:** cover; **Paige Billin-Frye:** storybook.

15 16 17 18 19 20 1678 16 15 14 13 12 11
4500311726

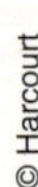

SCHOOL HOME CONNECTION

Dear Family,

Today we started a new chapter, Geometry and Fractions. We will learn to recognize and name geometric shapes and equal parts.

Love,

____

Solid Figures		Plane Shapes	
cone		circle	
sphere		triangle	
cylinder		square	
cube		rectangle	

Visit *The Learning Site* for additional ideas and activities. www.harcourtschool.com

ACTIVITY

- Choose one of the solid figures listed, and help your child find objects that have that shape.

BOOKS TO SHARE

To read about shapes with your child, look for these books at your local library.

Sea Shapes, by Suse MacDonald. Harcourt, 1994.

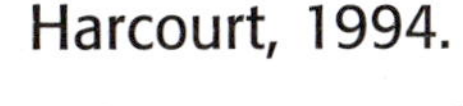

What Is Round? by Rebecca Kai-Dotlich. HarperCollins, 1999.

Color Zoo, by Lois Ehlert. HarperCollins, 1989.

Math Game

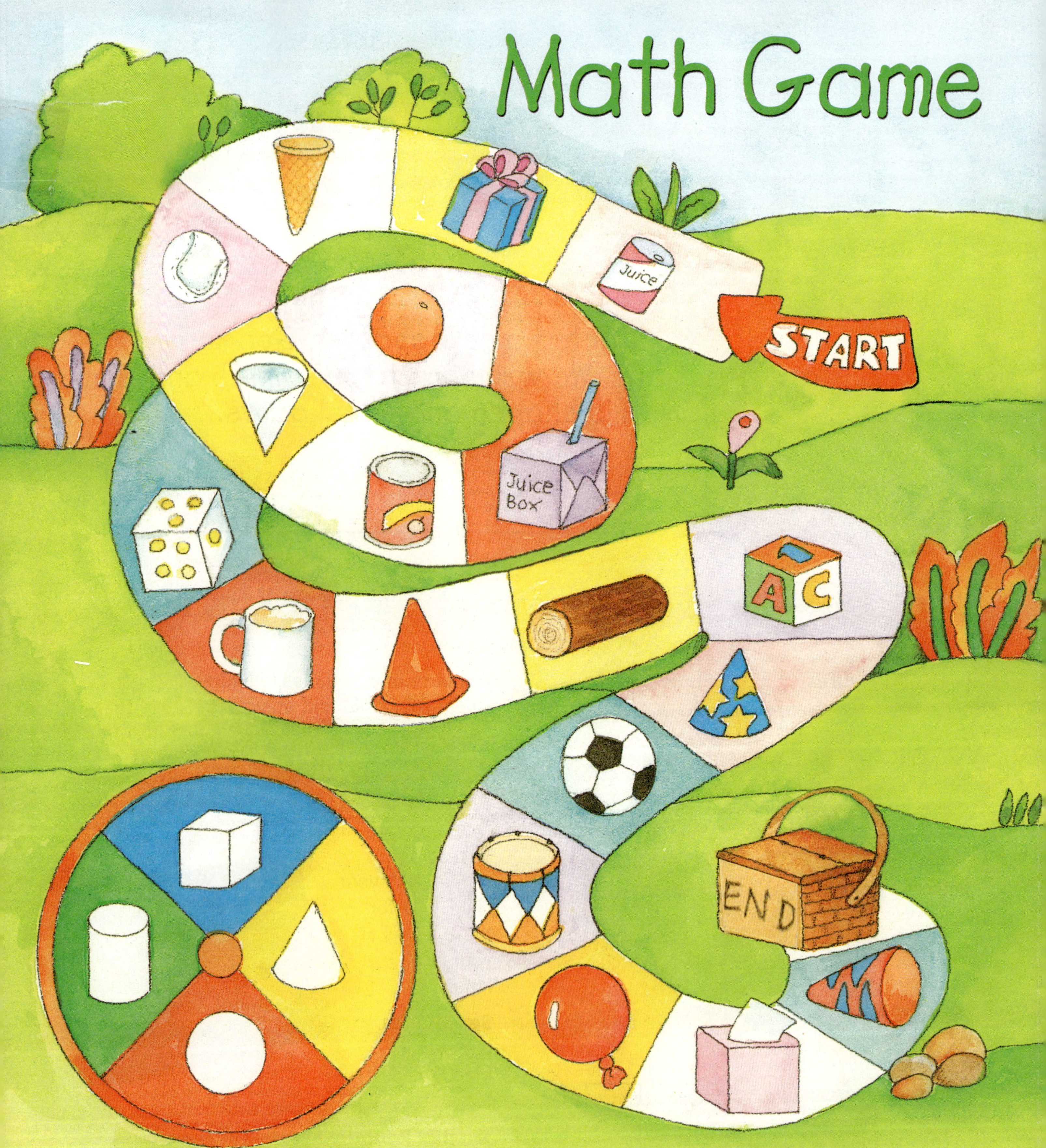

MATERIALS: 2 game markers, paper clip, pencil

DIRECTIONS: Play with a partner. Place your game markers at START and decide who goes first. Players take turns spinning the spinner. Each player names the shape the spinner lands on and moves his or her game marker to the closest object with the same shape. The first player to reach END wins.

Name ______________________________

Algebra: Sort Solid Figures

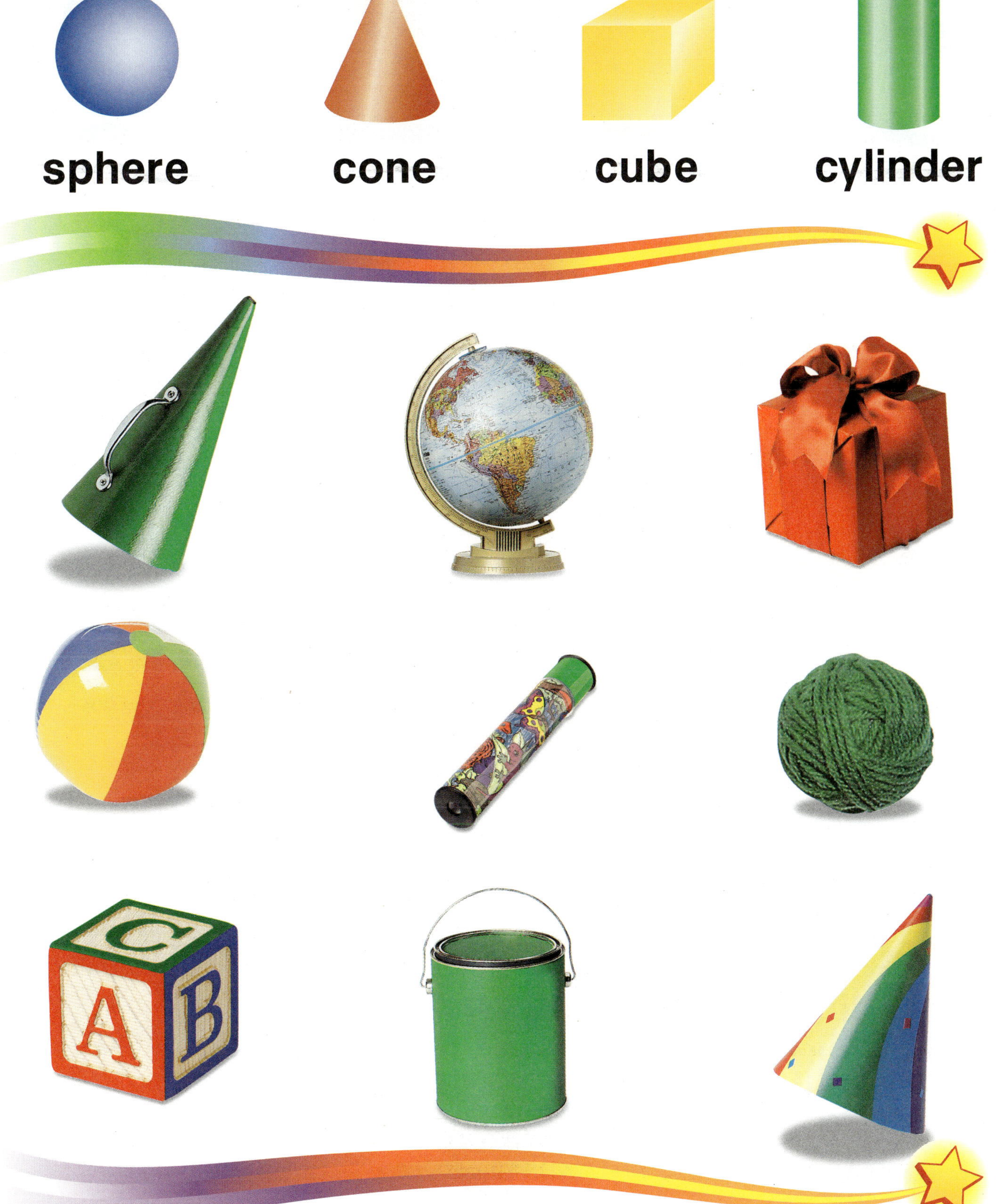

Use blue to circle the objects shaped like spheres.
Use red to circle the objects shaped like cones.
Use yellow to circle the objects shaped like cubes.
Use green to circle the objects shaped like cylinders.

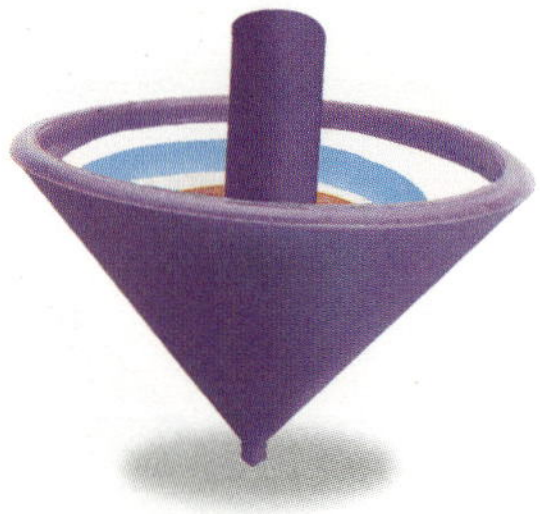

Use blue to circle the objects shaped like spheres.
Use red to circle the objects shaped like cones.
Use yellow to circle the objects shaped like cubes.
Use green to circle the objects shaped like cylinders.

HOME ACTIVITY • Have your child use the words *sphere, cube, cylinder*, and *cone* to tell you about the objects on this page.

Name ___________________________

Move Solid Figures

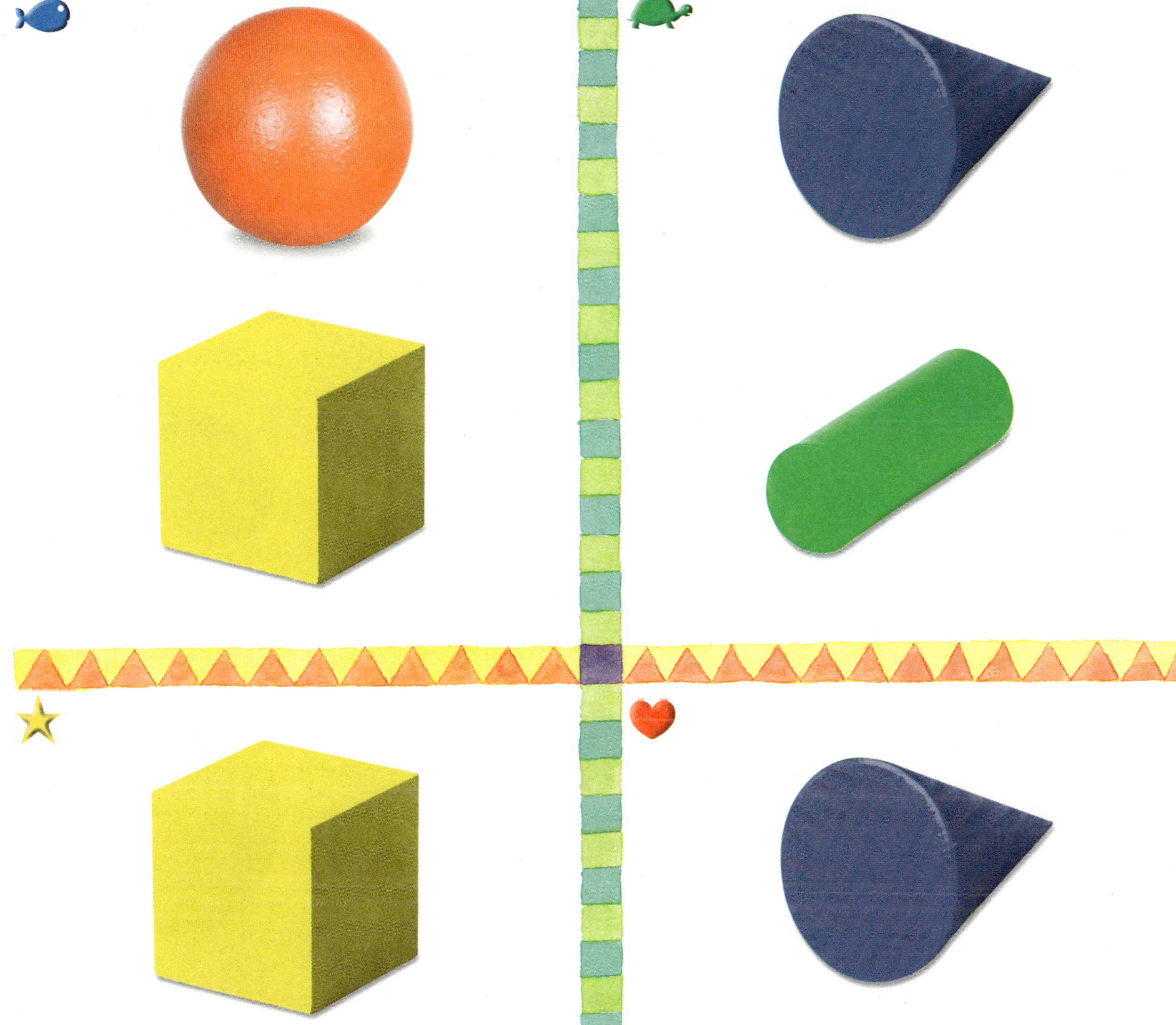

- (fish) Circle the shape that rolls.
- (turtle) Circle the shape that stacks.
- (star) Circle the shape that slides.
- (heart) Circle the shape that rolls and slides.

- Circle the shapes that roll.
- Circle the shapes that stack.
- Circle the shapes that slide.
- Circle the shapes that stack and slide.

HOME ACTIVITY • Have your child find and name shapes in your home that roll, stack, or slide.

Name ______________________________

Problem Solving Skill
Use Visual Thinking

JUICE

YIELD

Look at the object at the beginning of the row. Color in the outline that matches the shape of the object.

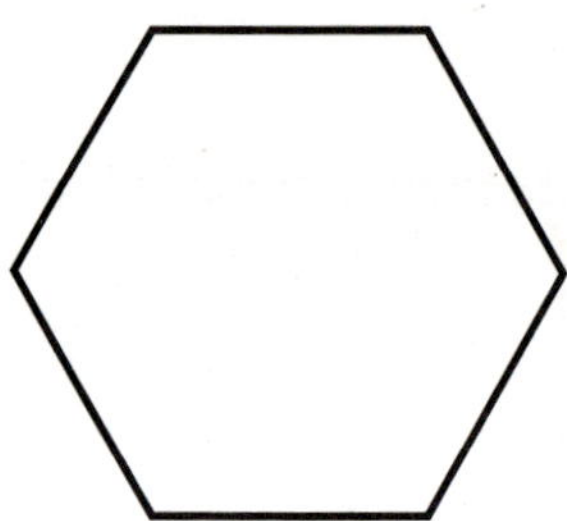

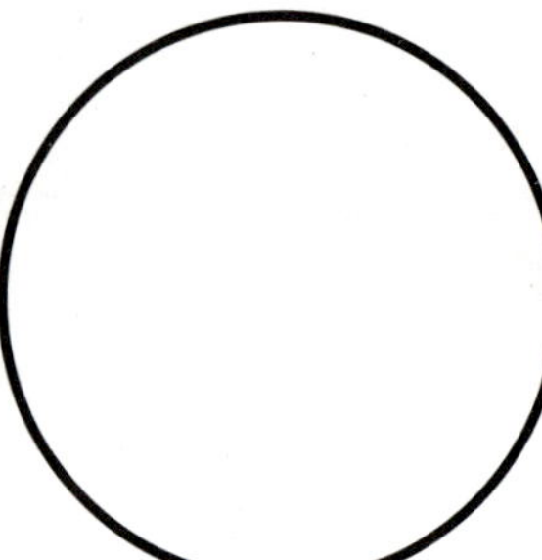

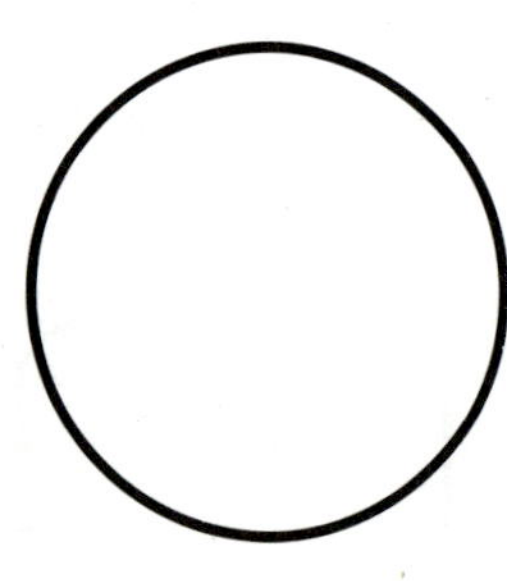

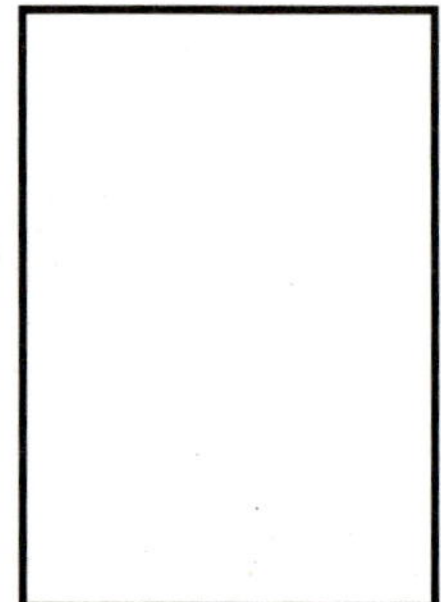

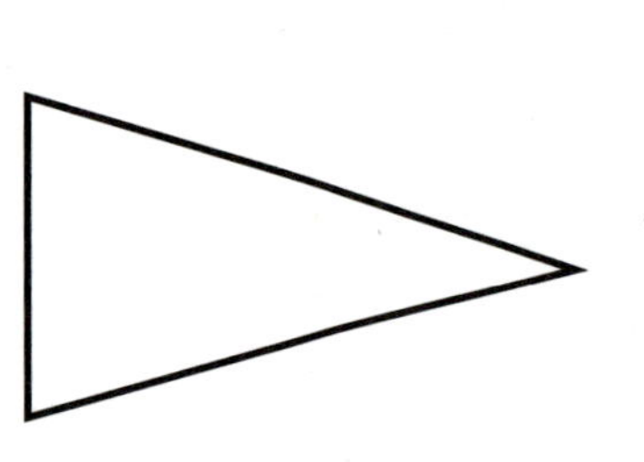

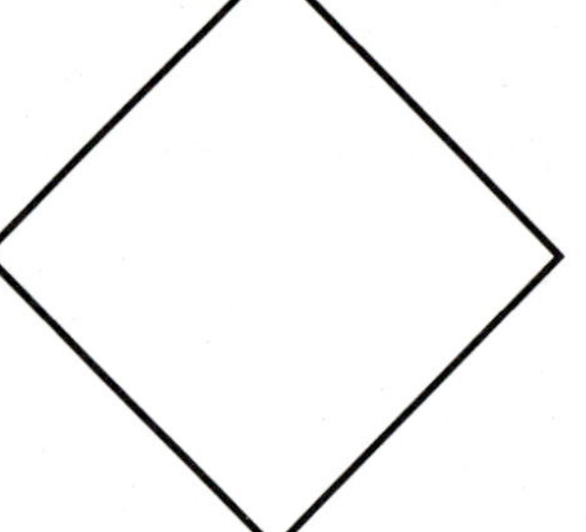

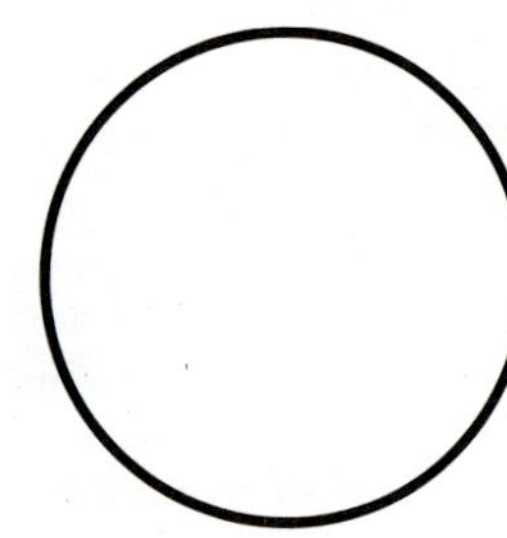

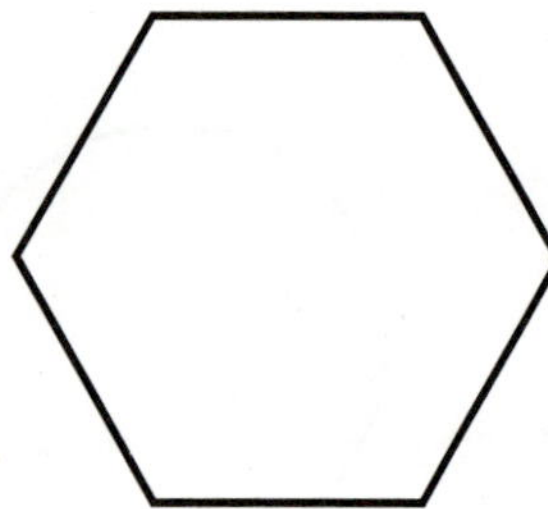

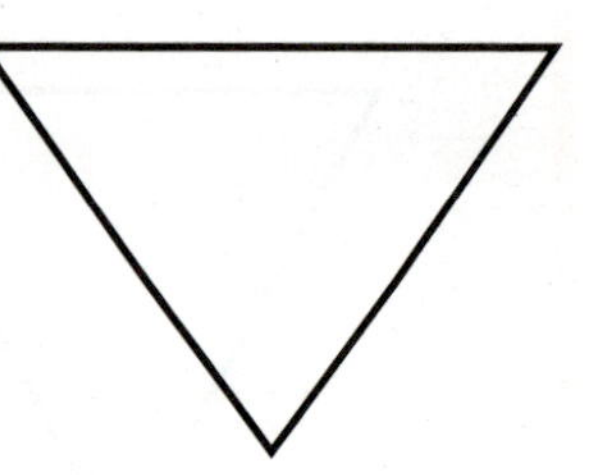

Look at the object at the beginning of the row. Color in the outline that matches the shape of the object.

HOME ACTIVITY • Have your child trace around objects to explore shapes and their outlines.

Name ______________________________

Algebra: **Sort Plane Shapes**

circle

square

triangle

rectangle

Use the words *curves, sides,* and *corners* to describe each shape.
Use orange to circle the shapes with curves.
Use purple to circle the shapes with four sides.
Use green to circle the shapes with three corners.

Color the circles yellow. Color the squares and rectangles blue. Color the triangles green.

HOME ACTIVITY • Go on a "Shape Hunt." Help your child find and name shapes in your home.

Name ______________________________

Plane Shapes in Different Positions

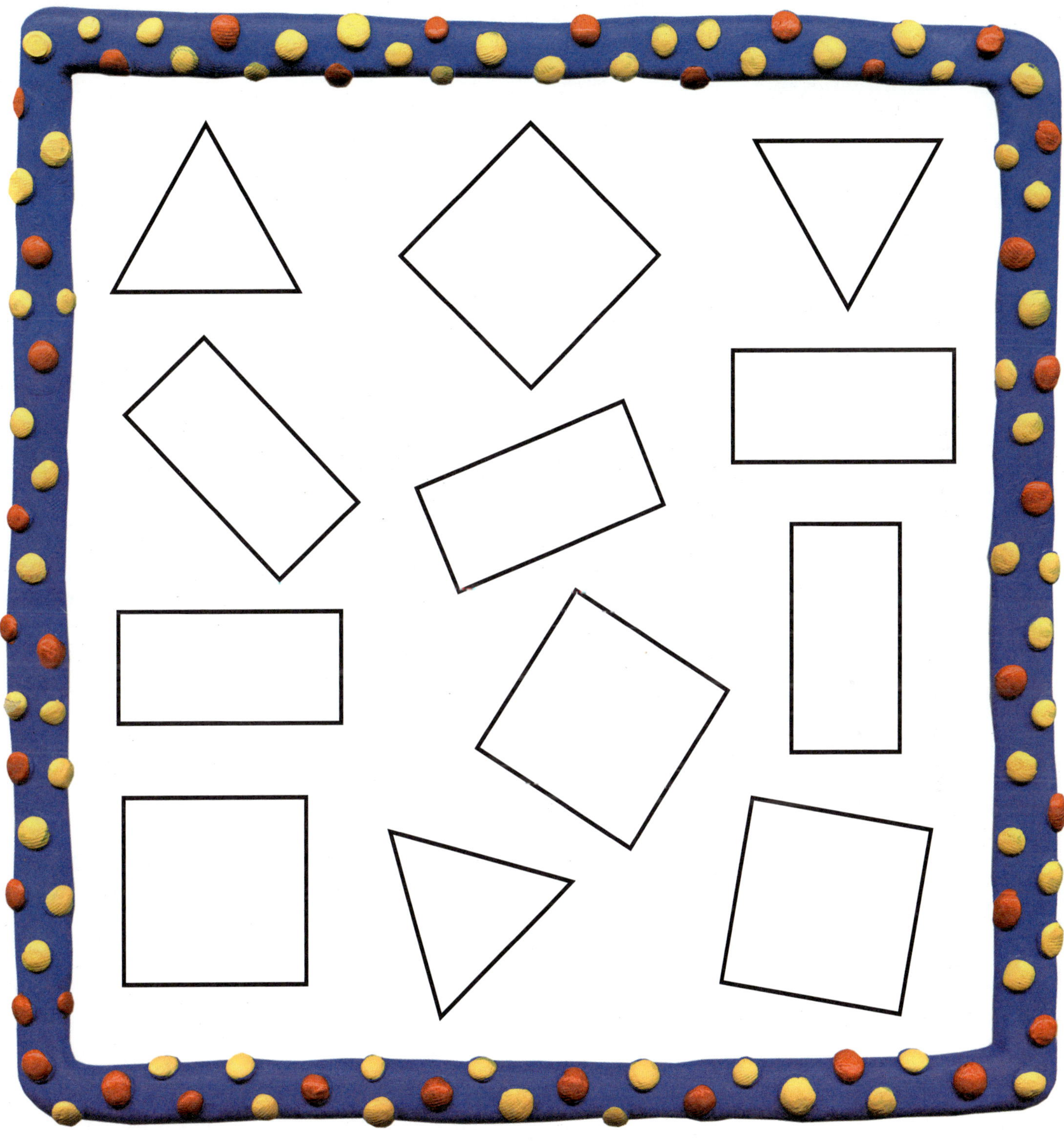

Color the triangles blue, color the squares red, and color the rectangles orange.

Use plane shapes to finish the puzzle. What shapes did you use? Use the same color to color the shapes that are alike.

HOME ACTIVITY • Have your child find triangles, squares, and rectangles in your home and community.

Name ________________________________

Review

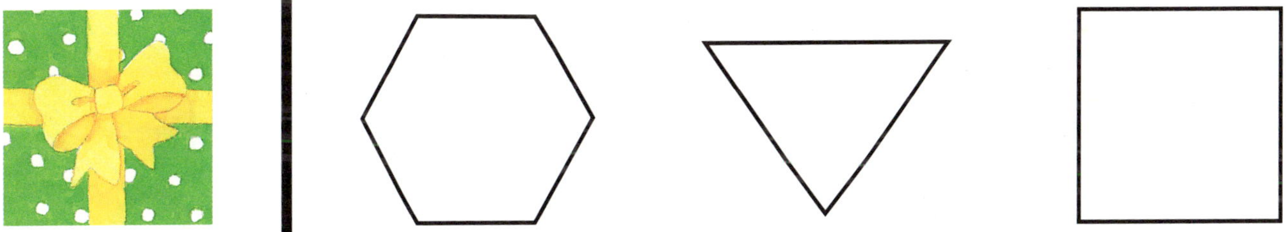

- Look at the shape at the beginning of the row. Circle the objects shaped like spheres.
- Circle the shapes that stack.
- Look at the object at the beginning of the row. Color the outline that matches the shape of the object.
- Circle the shapes with three corners.

Cumulative Review

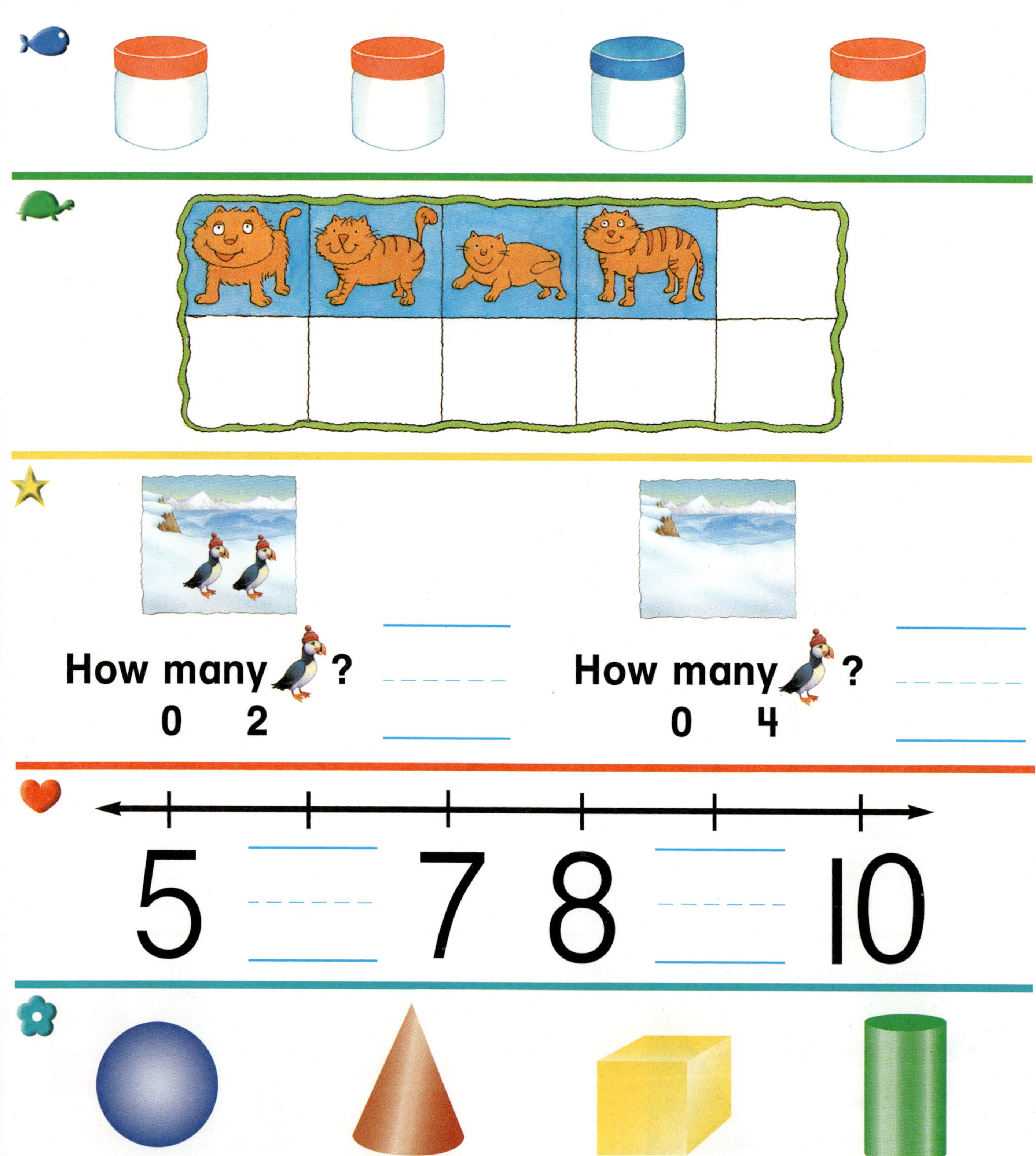

- Mark an X on the object that does not belong.
- Color one box for each cat.
- Count the puffins. Circle the number that tells how many. Then write the number.
- Write the number that is after 5. Write the number that is before 10.
- Use red to circle the cone. Use green to circle the cylinder.

Name ___________________________

Symmetry

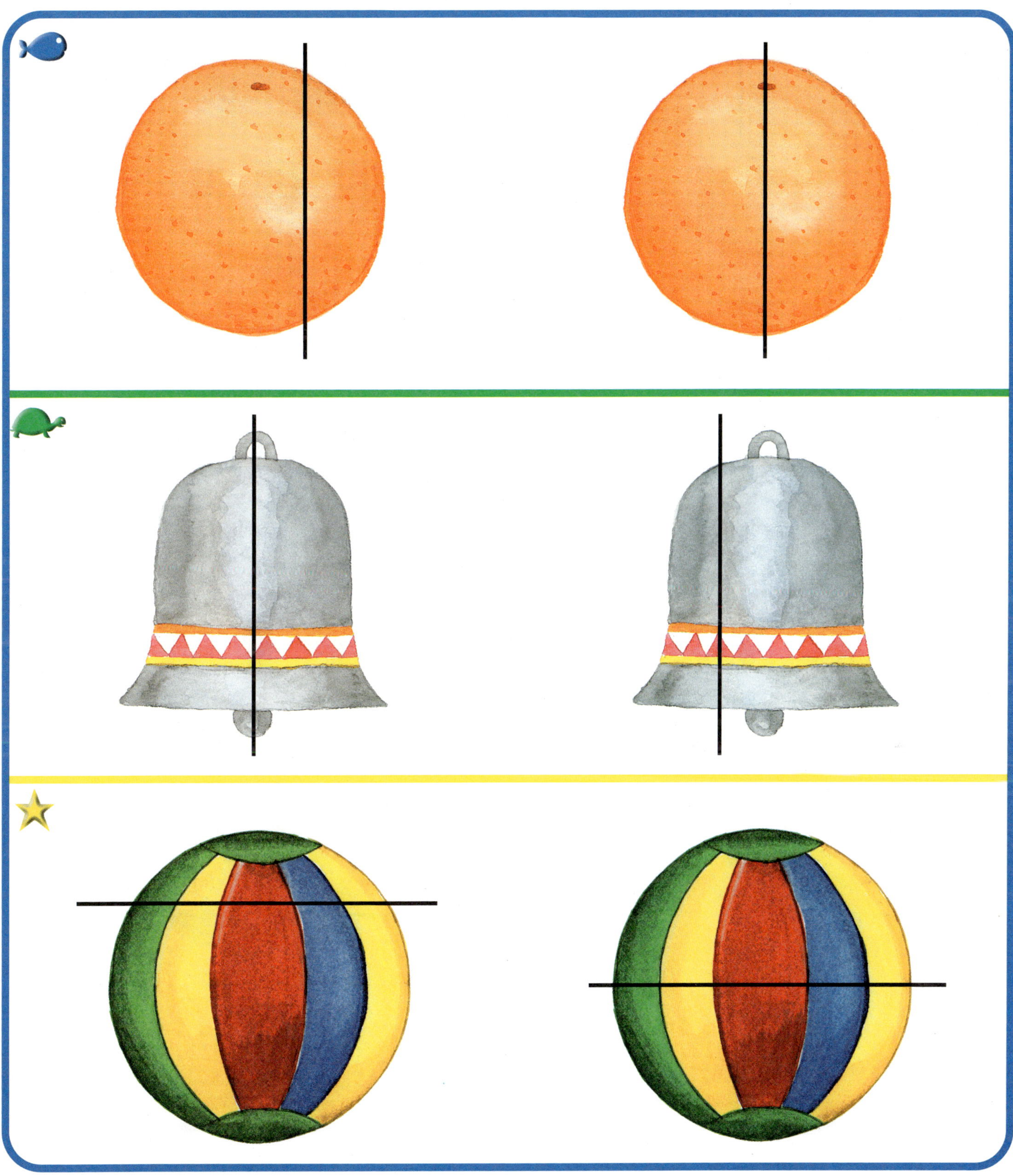

Circle the objects that have a line that divides them into two matching parts.

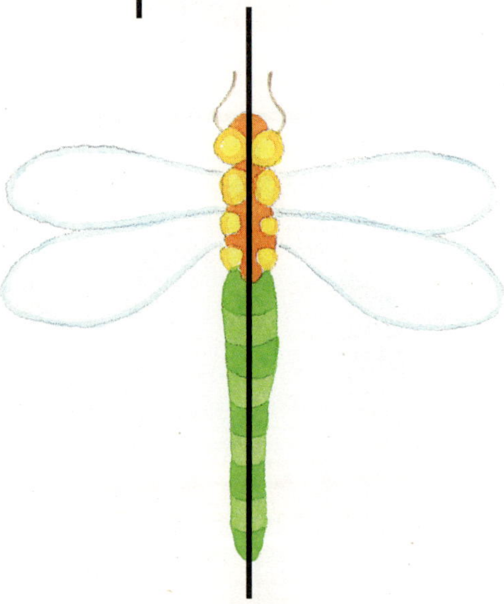

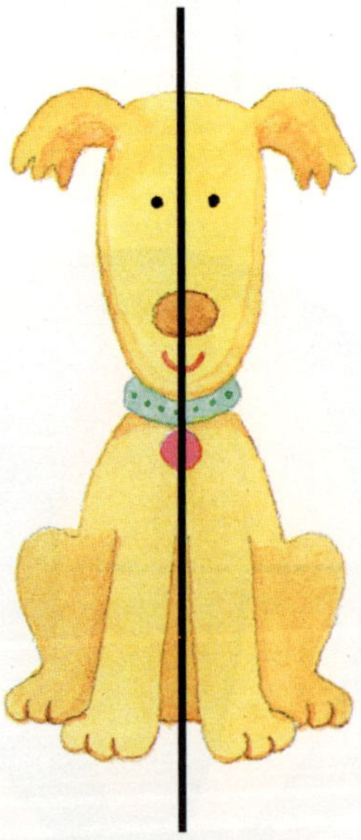

Circle the objects that have a line that divides them into two matching parts.

HOME ACTIVITY • Cut out a paper square or circle. Help your child fold the shape to show two matching parts.

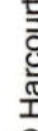

Name ______________________________

Equal Parts

Circle the shape that shows equal parts. How do you know?

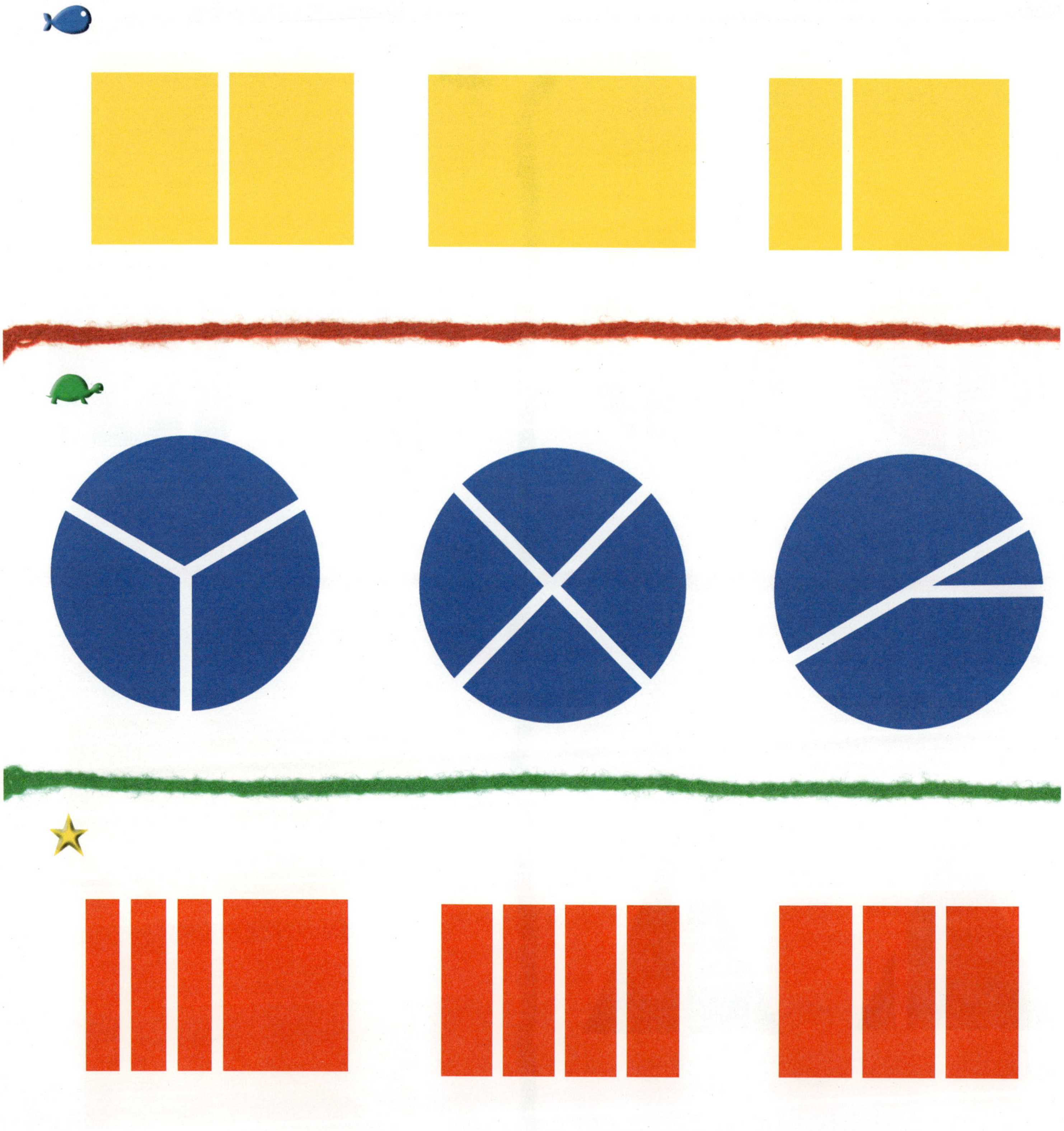

Circle the shape that is divided into two equal parts. How do you know?

Circle the shape that is divided into three equal parts. How do you know?

Circle the shape that is divided into four equal parts. How do you know?

HOME ACTIVITY • Cut some food items into equal parts and others into unequal parts. Have your child point out the items that are cut into equal parts.

Name ______________________________

Problem Solving Strategy
Make a Model

Use your pizza pieces to find the pizza that shows 2 equal parts, or halves. Color one half.
Use your pizza pieces to find the pizza that shows 4 equal parts, or fourths. Color one fourth.

Use green to color one part of each shape. Use red to circle the shapes that show one half. Use blue to circle the shapes that show one fourth.

HOME ACTIVITY • As you prepare meals or snacks, show your child how you divide foods, such as fruits and sandwiches, into halves or fourths.

By ______________________

HOME ACTIVITY • **This book will help review shapes. Invite your child to share this book with you. Have him or her point to each shape.**

YIELD

Find the objects shaped like triangles.

Find the objects shaped like squares.

Find the objects shaped like circles.

Find the objects shaped like rectangles.

Find the objects shaped like cubes.

Find the objects shaped like circles, squares, triangles, and rectangles.

Find the objects shaped like spheres.

Find the objects shaped like cones.

Find the objects shaped like cubes, spheres, cones, and cylinders.

Find the objects shaped like cylinders.

Tell about each shape.

Name ____

Review

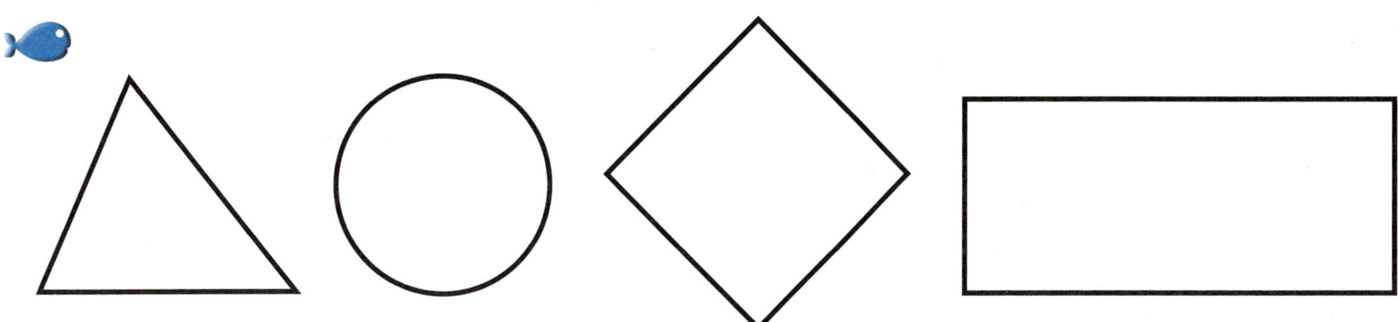

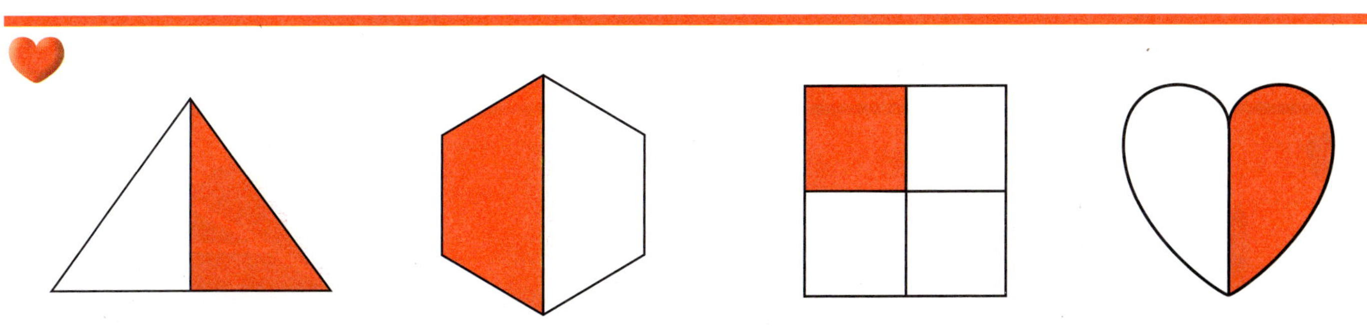

Color the circle red. Color the square yellow. Color the triangle blue. Color the rectangle green.

Circle the pictures that have a line that makes two matching parts.

Circle the shapes that show equal parts.

Circle the shapes that show one half red. Draw a line under the shape that shows one fourth red.

Cumulative Review

1 2   4 5

■ 6 5 4 3 | 7 8

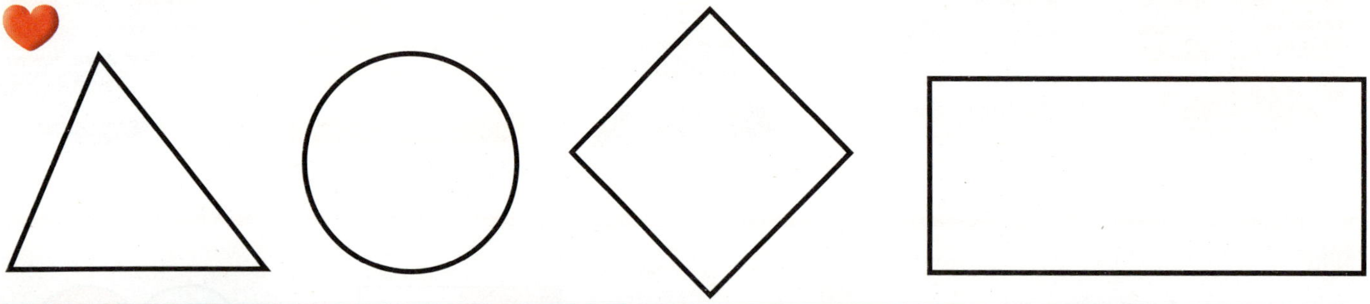

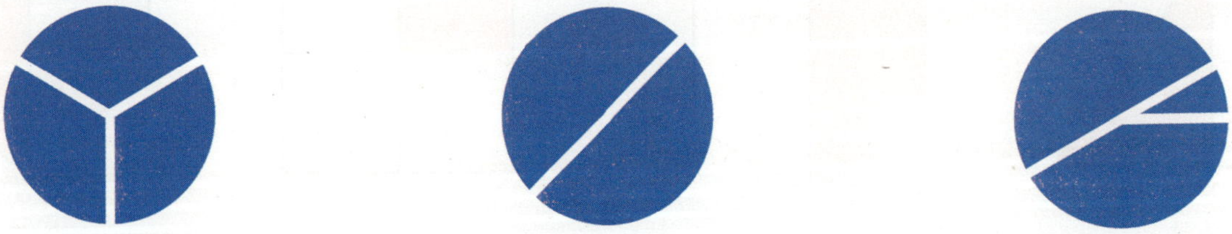

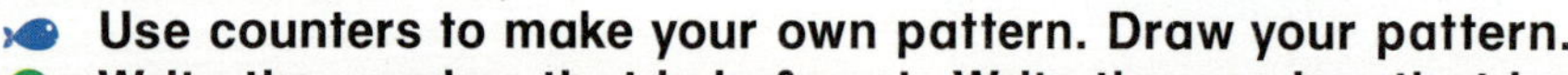

- Use counters to make your own pattern. Draw your pattern.
- Write the number that is before 1. Write the number that is after 2.
- Circle the missing number.
- Color the circle red. Color the square yellow. Color the triangle blue. Color the rectangle green.
- Circle the shape that is divided into three equal parts.

Name ________________________________

Test

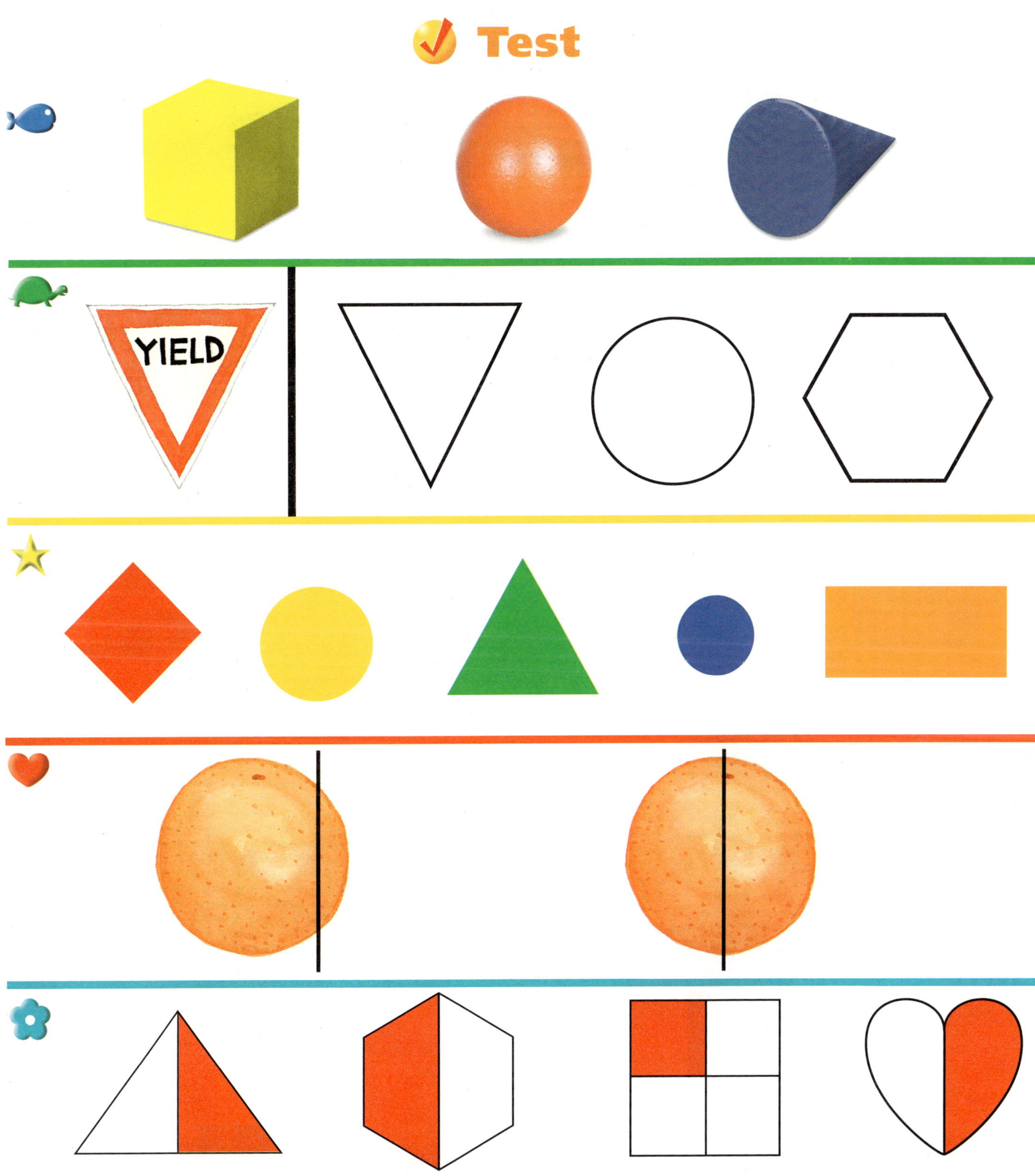

Circle the shapes that roll.
Look at the object at the beginning of the row. Color in the outline that matches the shape of the object.
Circle the square.
Circle the orange that has a line that makes two matching parts.
Circle the shapes that show one half red. Draw a line under the shape that shows one fourth red.

CHALLENGE

Shape Prints

Circle the solid figures that could make the plane shape print.

CHAPTER
6
Numbers 10 to 30
HARCOURT
Math
© Harcourt
Harcourt

Circle the groups with ten animals.

Grateful acknowledgment is made to The Millbrook Press for permission to reprint the cover illustration from *Bears at the Beach: Counting 10 to 20* by Niki Yektai. Copyright © 1996 by Niki Yektai.

Printed in the United States of America

Photography Credits:

All photography by Harcourt photographers listed, © Harcourt: Weronica Ankarorn, Victoria Bowen, Ken Kinzie, Sheri O'Neal, Quebecor Imaging, and Terry Sinclair.

Illustration Credits:

Paige Billin-Frye: Storybook; **Joe Boddy:** 138; **Daniel Del Valle:** 145, 146; **Patty Silver:** 139, 140, 141, 142; **Geraldo Suzan:** 143, 144; **Stan Tusan:** cvr, 136, 147, 148; **Jane Yamada:** 151, 152 .

15 16 17 18 19 20 1678 16 15 14 13 12 11
4500311726

SCHOOL HOME CONNECTION

Dear Family,

Today we started a new chapter, Numbers 10 to 30. In this chapter, we will learn about numbers to 30 and how to see these numbers on ten frames.

Love,

____

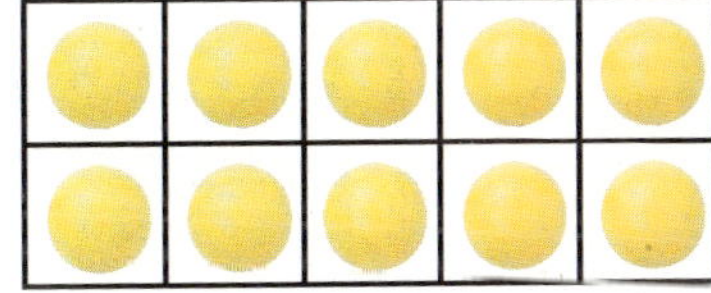

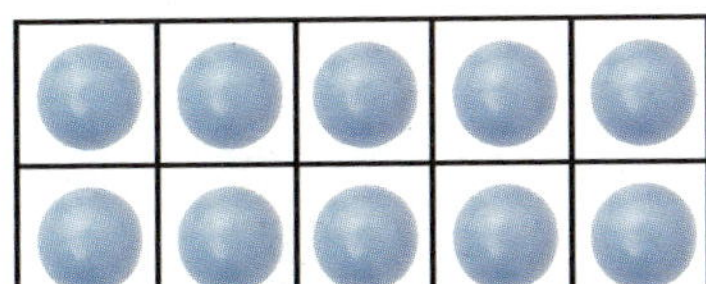

groups of 10 on ten-frames

The names for 11, 12, 13, and 15 may be harder for children to remember since they do not contain the familiar number names *one, two, three,* and *five.*

Visit *The Learning Site* for additional ideas and activities. www.harcourtschool.com

- Count aloud often with your child.

BOOKS TO SHARE

To read about numbers with your child, look for these books at your local library.

Let's Count It Out, Jesse Bear,
by Nancy White Carlstrom. Simon & Schuster, 1996.

Count!
by Denise Fleming. Henry Holt, 1997.

Bears at the Beach,
by Niki Yektai. Millbrook, 1996.

MATERIALS: a different colored pencil for each player
DIRECTIONS: Play with a partner. Each player takes a turn drawing lines to connect the numbers 10 to 30 in order. If one player cannot continue, the partner takes over and draws lines as far as possible. The first player to reach 30 wins.

Name ______________________________

Problem Solving Strategy
Make a Model

10

ten

PROBLEM SOLVING

Place 10 cubes on the ten frame. Trace the number.

Use cubes to model the number that is 1 less than 9. Write the number.

Use cubes to model the number that is 2 more than 8. Write the number.

Use cubes to model the number that is 1 less than 10. Write the number.

Use cubes to model the number that is 1 more than 9. Write the number.

Use cubes to model the number that is 3 more than 7. Write the number.

HOME ACTIVITY • Draw a ten frame on a sheet of paper. Model numbers from 1 to 10, using small objects such as dried beans. Each time, ask your child if the ten frame shows a group of 10.

Name ___________________________

11, 12, 13

11

12

13

Say the number. Count the color tiles. Write the number.

Draw more color tiles to make 13. Write the number.
Draw more color tiles to make 11. Write the number.
Draw more color tiles to make 13. Write the number.
Draw more color tiles to make 12. Write the number.

HOME ACTIVITY • Draw two ten frames side by side on a sheet of paper. Have your child show the numbers 11 and 12, using small objects such as buttons.

Name ____________________

14, 15, 16

14

15

16

14

15

16

Count the objects. Trace the numbers.
Draw more Xs to show the numbers. Write the numbers.

15

13

16

14

Draw more Xs to show the number. Write the number.

HOME ACTIVITY • Cut away two sections of two egg cartons to make two ten frames. Have your child use small objects such as paper clips to show the numbers 15 and 16 in the ten frames.

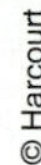

Name ______________________

Forward and Backward on a Number Line

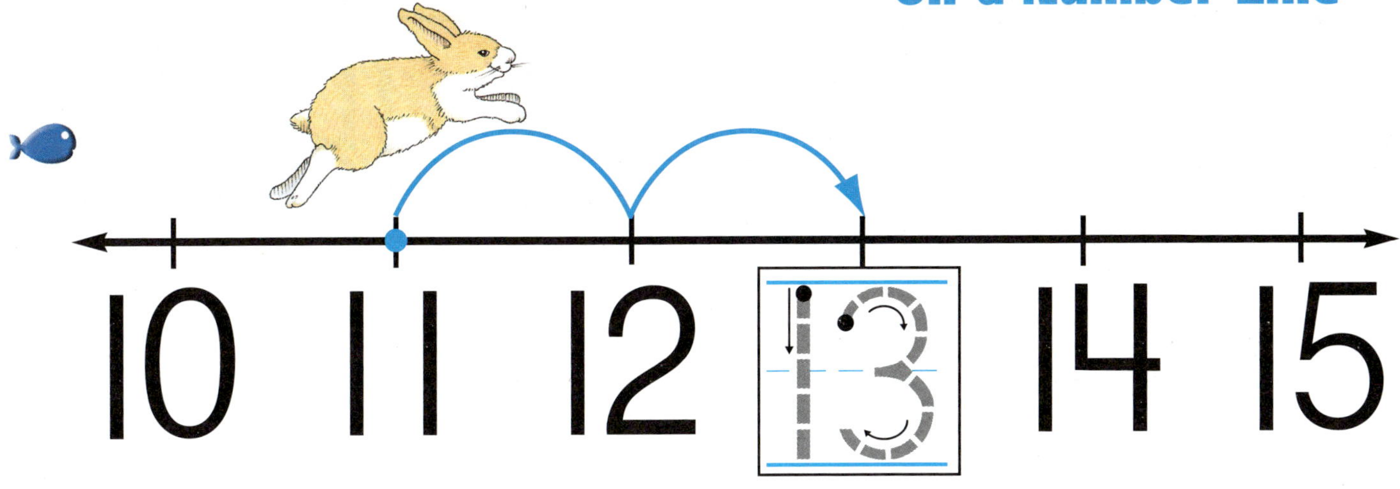

10 11 12 13 ☐ 15

10 ☐ 12 13 14 15

- Start at 11. Count 2 numbers forward. Write the number.
- Start at 10. Count 4 numbers forward. Write the number.
- Start at 14. Count 3 numbers back. Write the number.

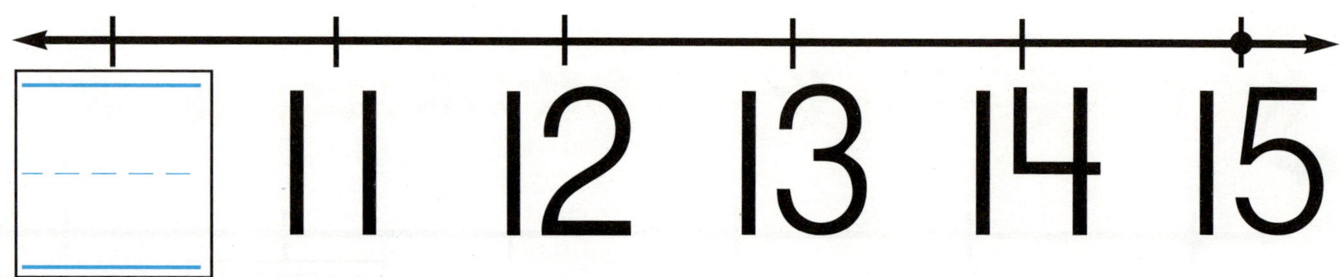

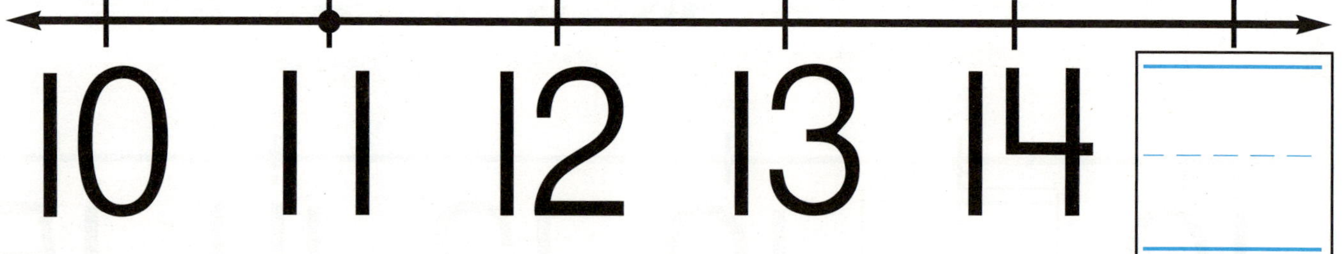

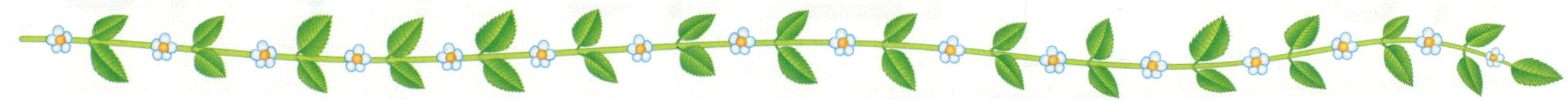

Start at 10. Count 2 numbers forward. Write the number.
Start at 15. Count 5 numbers back. Write the number.
Start at 11. Count 4 numbers forward. Write the number.

HOME ACTIVITY • Draw a number line from 0 to 16. Invite your child to read the numbers on the number line.

Name ______________________________

17 and 18

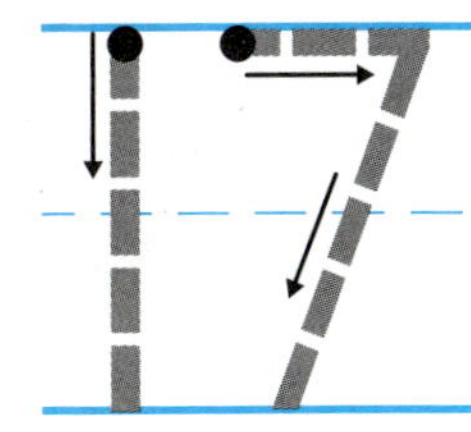

Draw more chicks to show 7 more than 10. Trace the number.
Draw more chicks to show 8 more than 10. Trace the number.

16 17 18

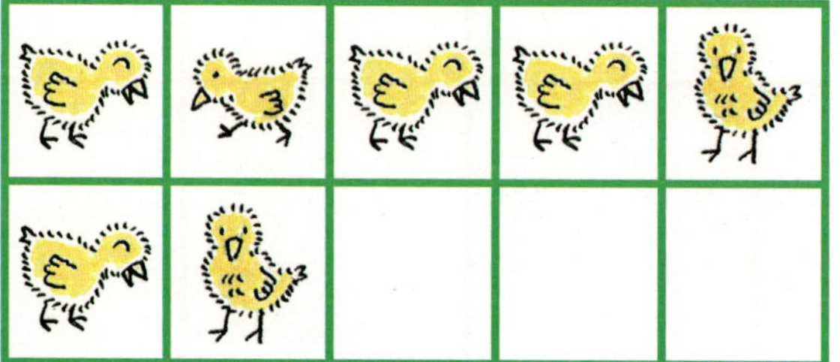

16 17 18

16 17 18

Count the chicks.
Circle the number that tells how many.
Write the number.

HOME ACTIVITY • Draw two ten frames on a sheet of paper. Have your child use coins or other small objects to show 17 and 18.

Name ____________________

- Draw more color tiles to make 13. Write the number.
- Draw more color tiles to make 15. Write the number.
- Draw more color tiles to make 17. Write the number.
- Start at 10. Count two numbers forward. Write the number.

Cumulative Review

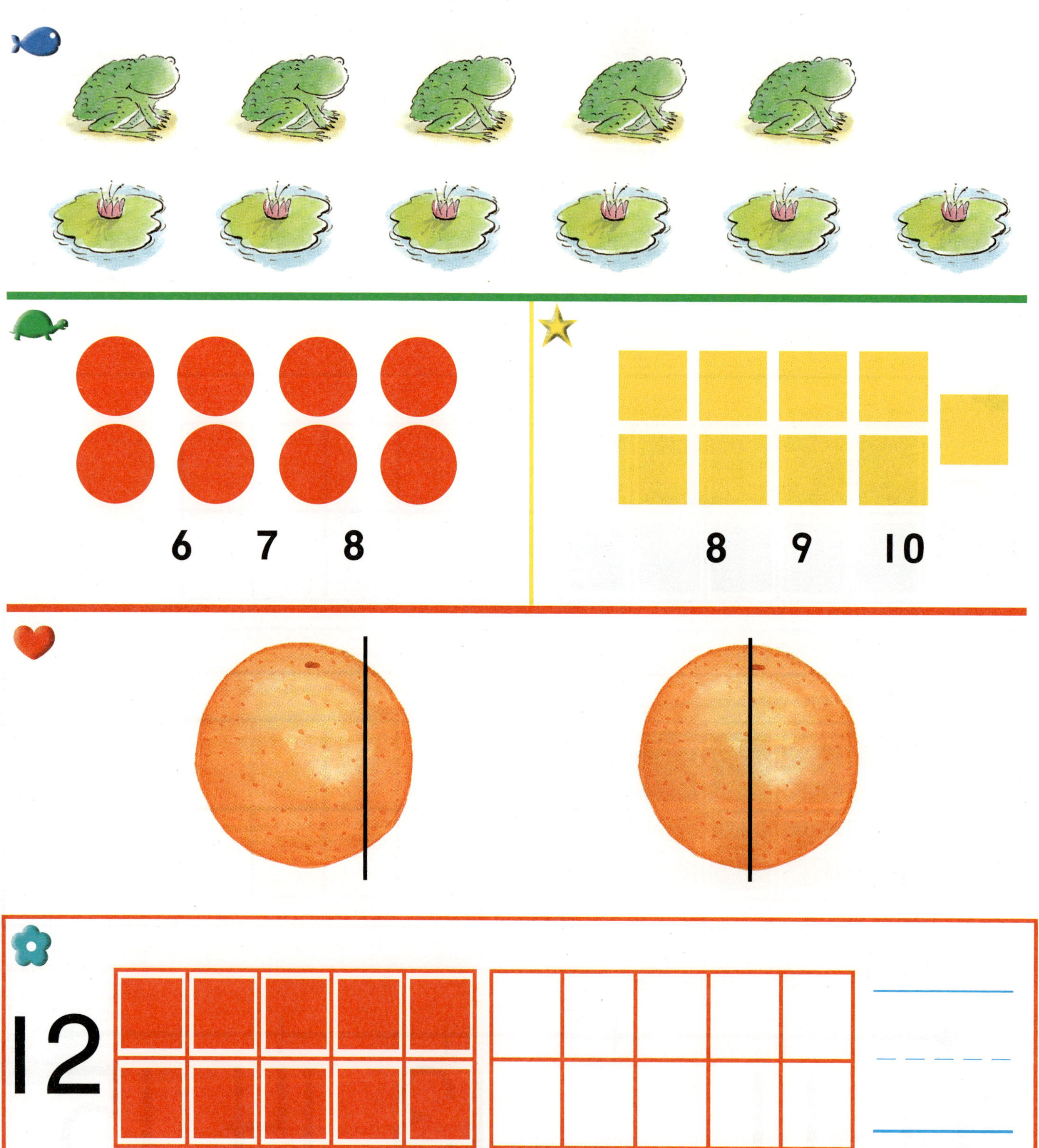

Draw lines to match the objects in the two groups. Compare the groups. Circle the group that has more.
Count. Circle the number that tells how many.
Circle the orange that is divided into two matching parts.
Draw more color tiles to make 12. Write the number.

Name ______________________________

Use Data from a Graph

Shirts

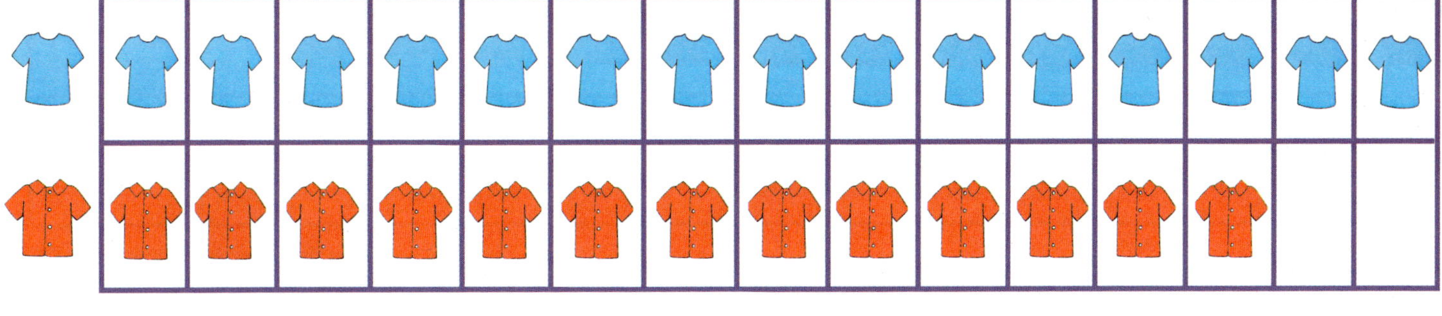

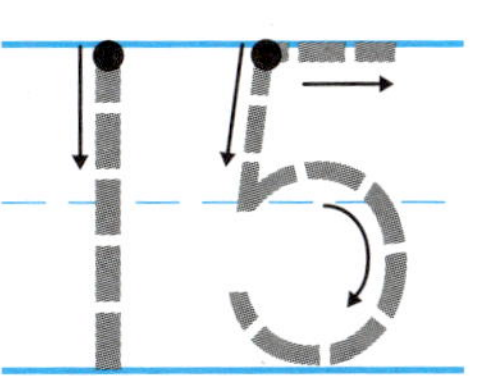

Weather

Count and write how many. Circle the number that shows more. Mark an X on the number that shows fewer.

Count and write how many. Circle the number that shows the most. Mark an X on the number that shows the fewest.

Pets

Shoes

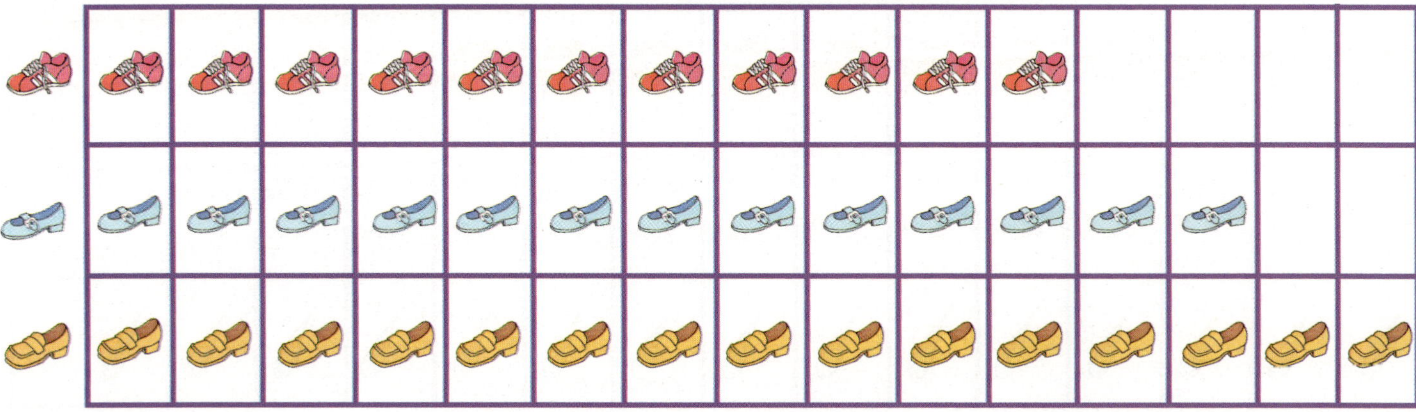

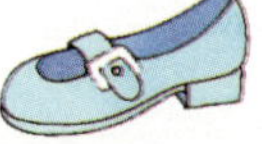

Count and write how many. Circle the number that shows the most. Mark an X on the number that shows the fewest.

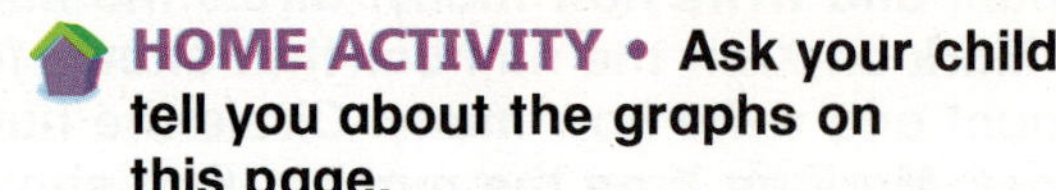

HOME ACTIVITY • Ask your child to tell you about the graphs on this page.

Name ______________________

19 and 20

Count. Trace the number.

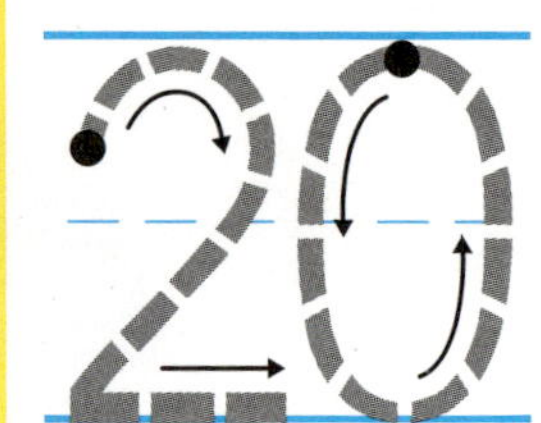

18 19 20

18 19 20

18 19 20

18 19 20

Count the objects. Circle the number that tells how many. Write the number.

HOME ACTIVITY • Set out small objects in groups of 11 to 20, and invite your child to count them.

Name ____________________

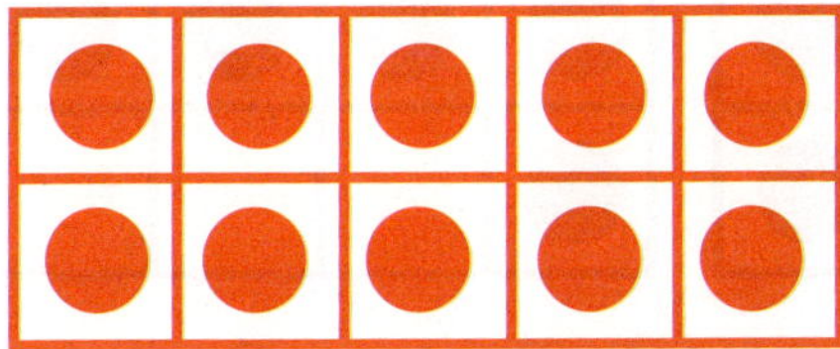 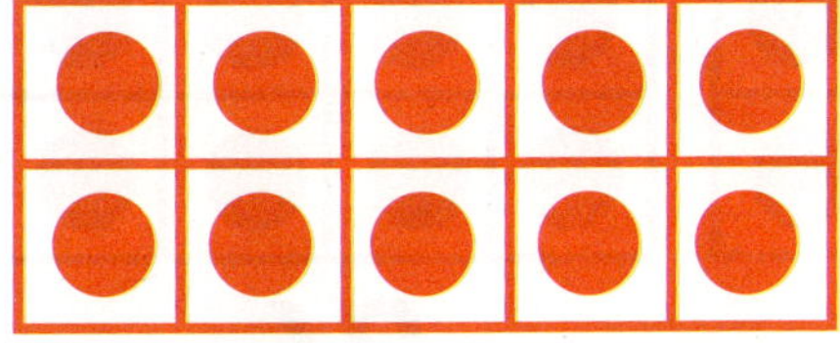 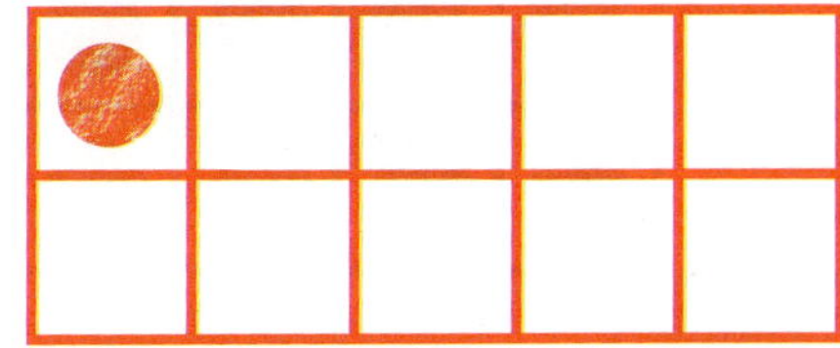

21

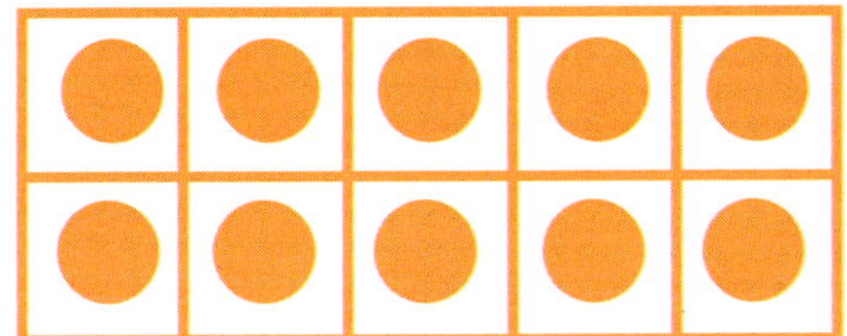 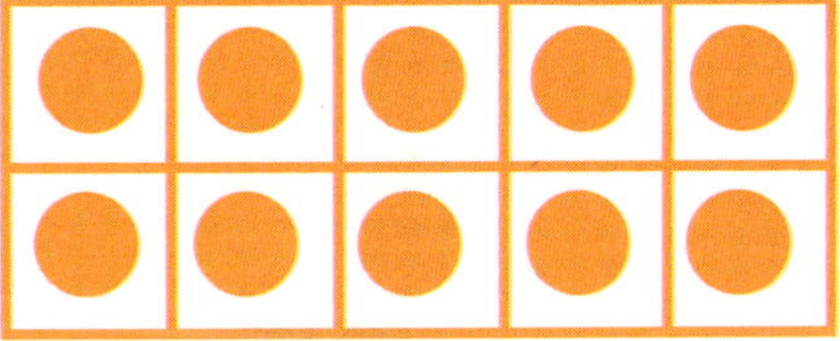 

22

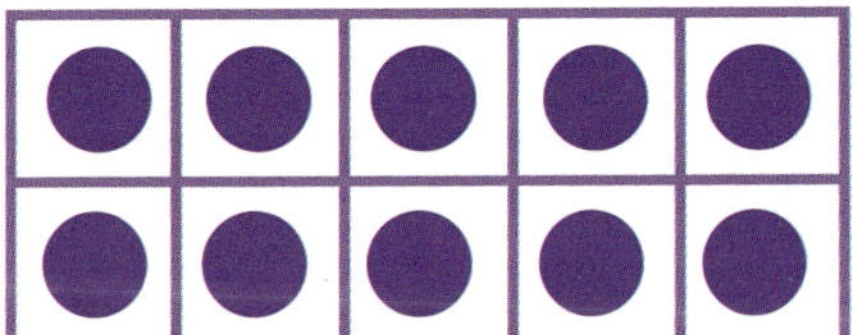 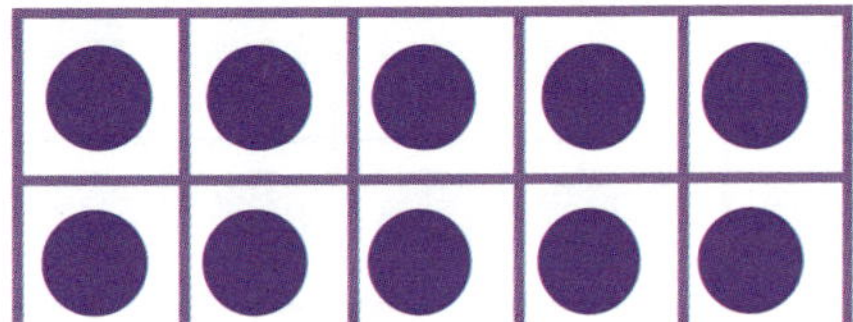 

23

 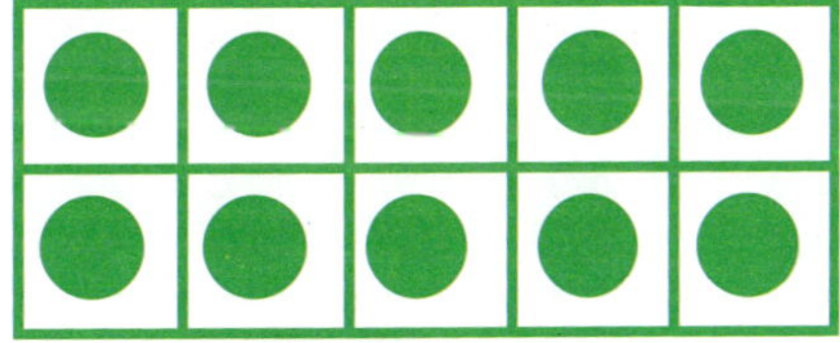 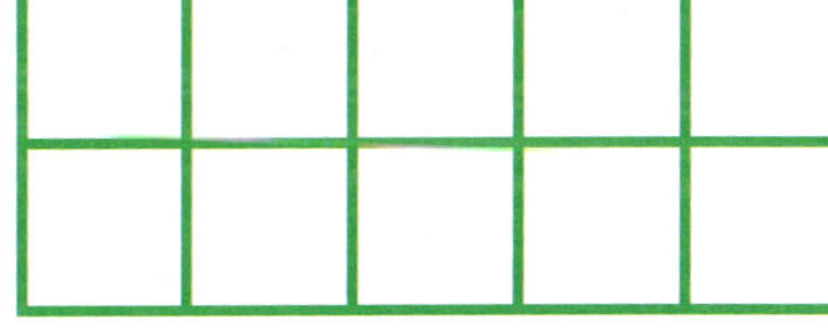

24

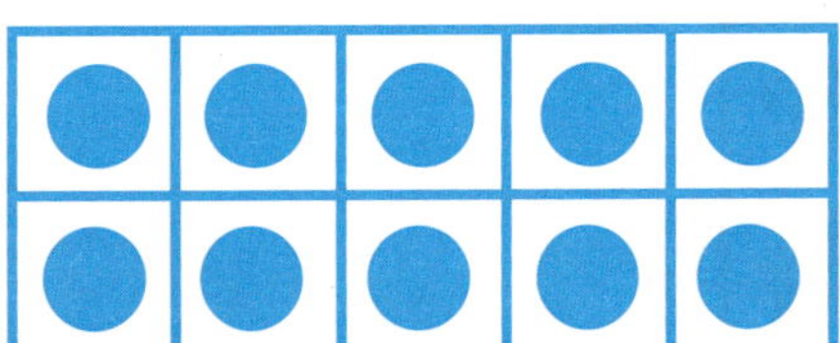 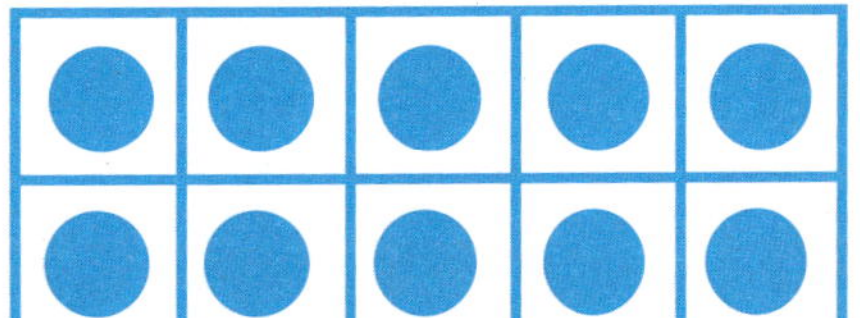 

25

Draw more counters to make 21.
Draw more counters to make 22.
Draw more counters to make 23.
Draw more counters to make 24.
Draw more counters to make 25.

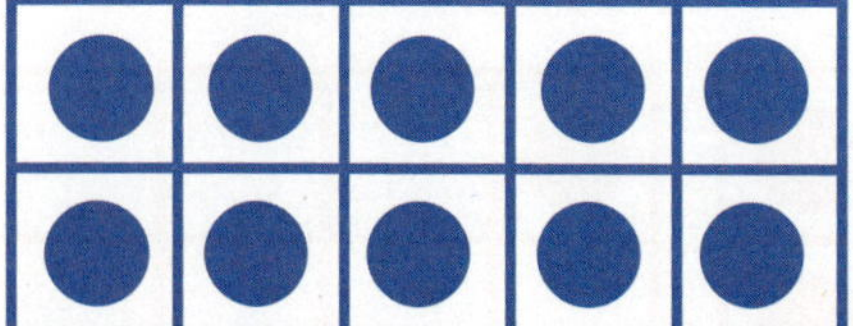 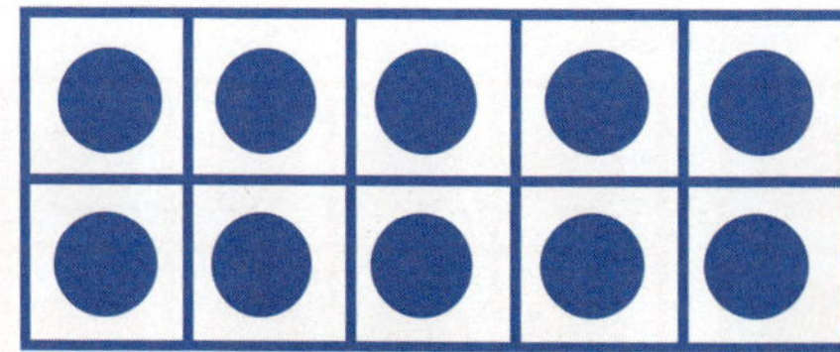 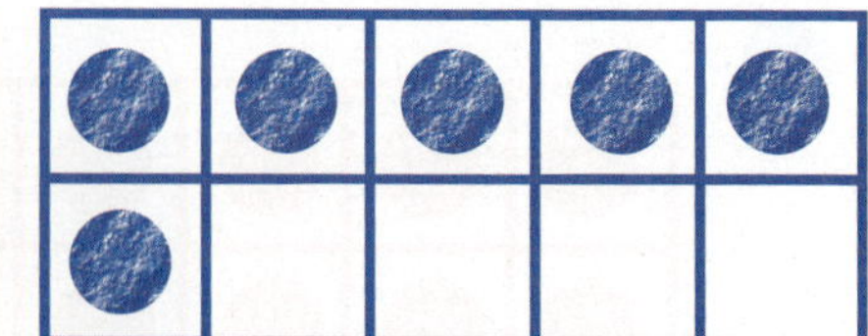

26

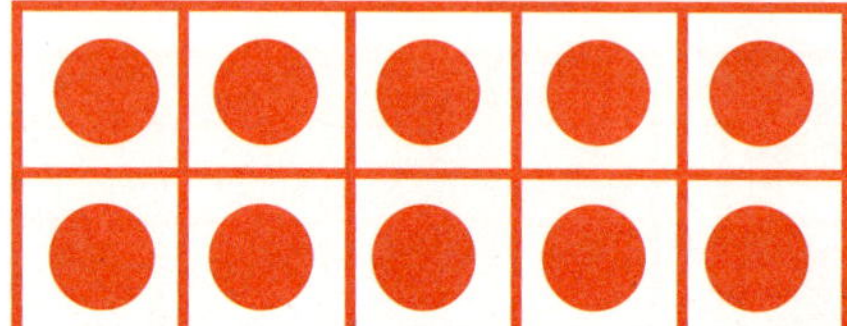 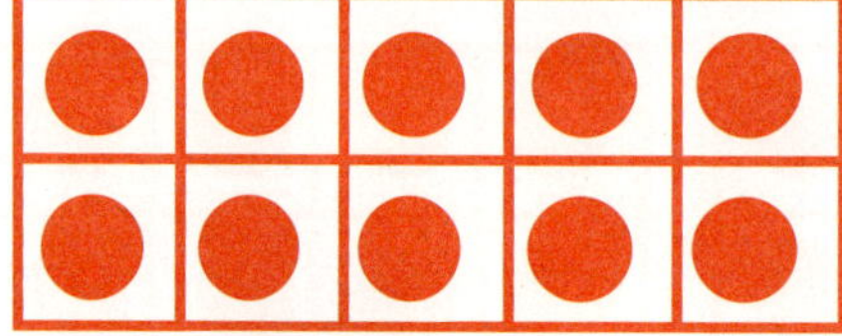 

27

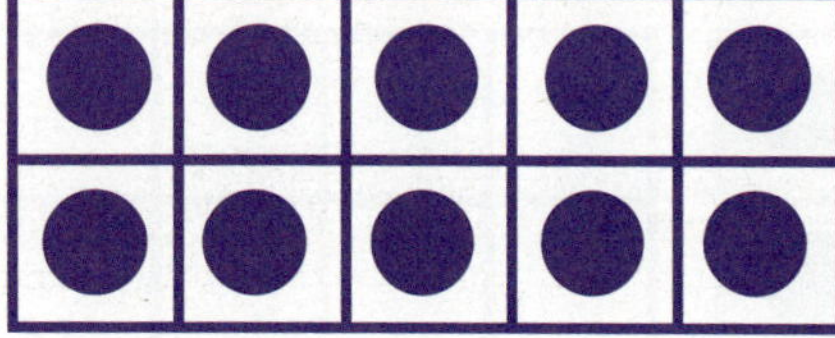 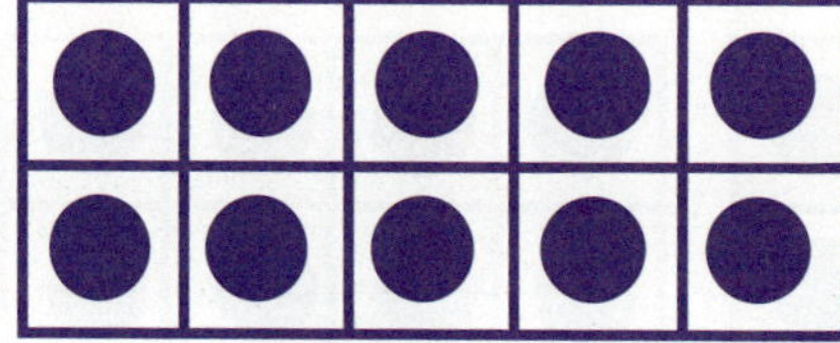 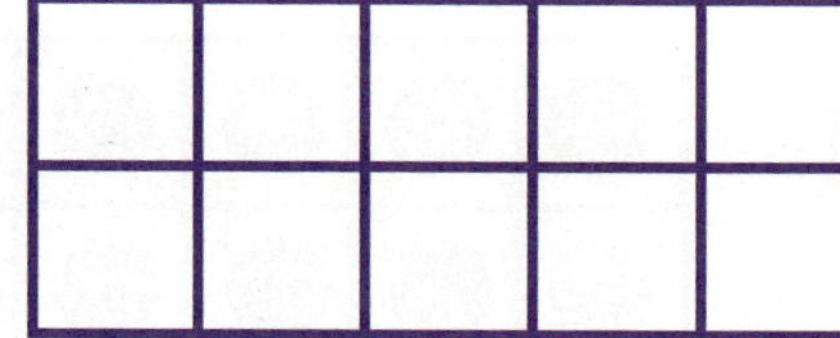

28

  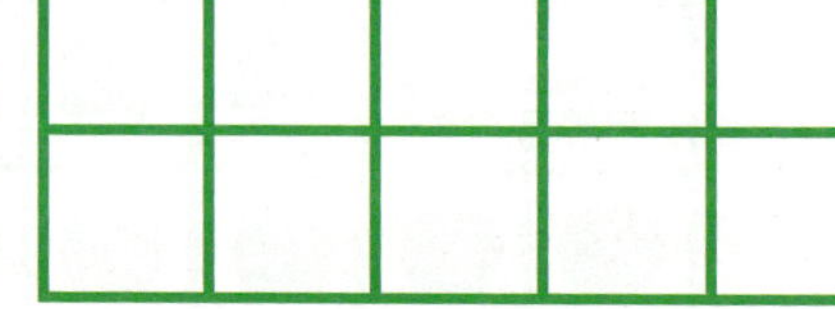

29

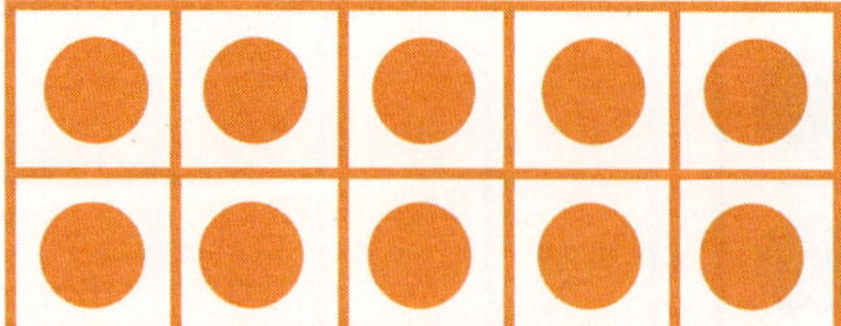 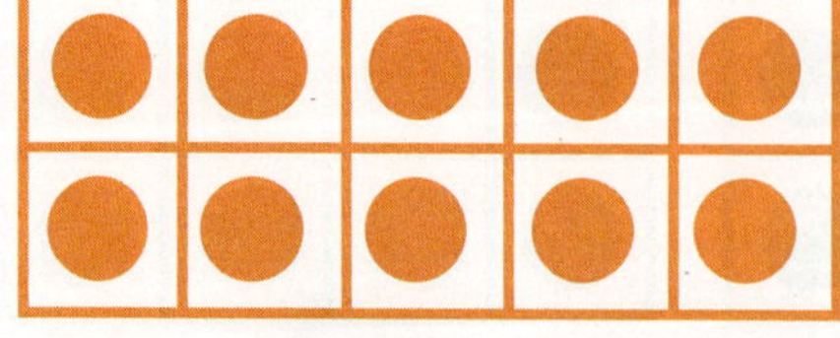 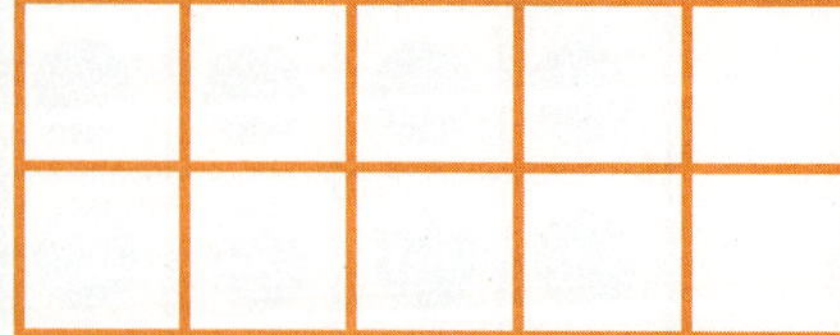

30

Draw more counters to make 26.
Draw more counters to make 27.
Draw more counters to make 28.
Draw more counters to make 29.
Draw more counters to make 30.

HOME ACTIVITY • Help your child count aloud from 1 to 30.

Ten and More
By
HOME ACTIVITY • This book will help review counting on ten frames. Invite your child to share this book with you.
1
How many eggs?

How many windows? 11

© Harcourt

How many horses? ____

How many horseshoes? ______

How many bells? ______

How many cows? ______

How many geese? ______

How many sheep? ______

How many chickens? ______

Country Store

How many hats? ______

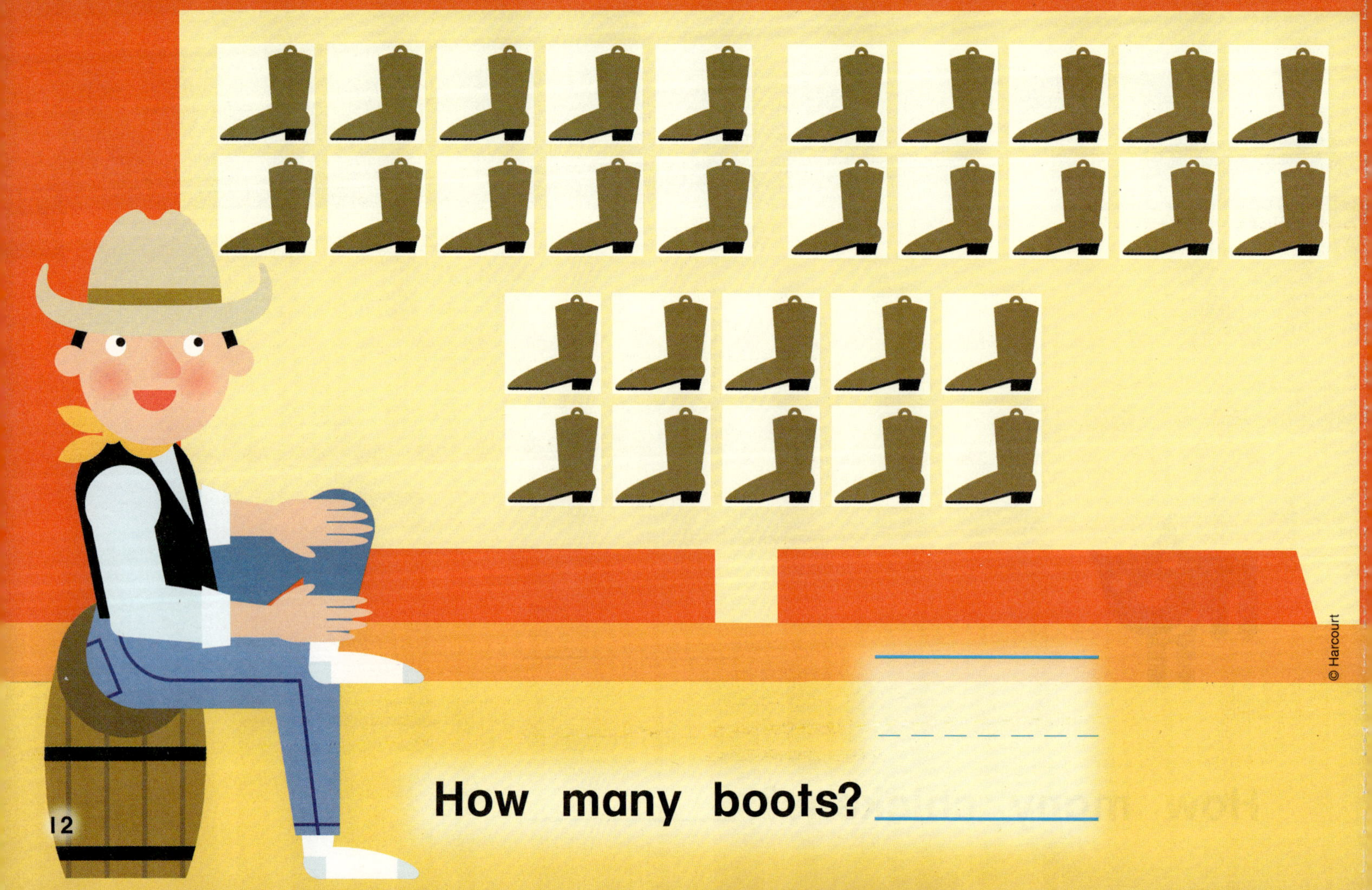

How many boots? ______

Name ______________________________

Review

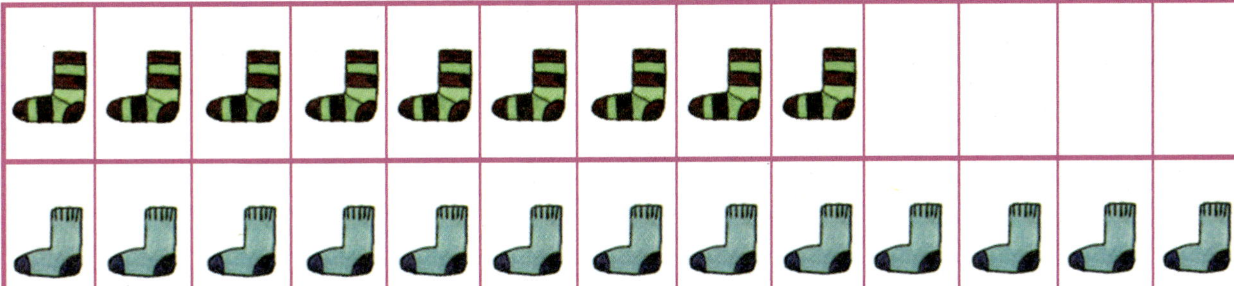

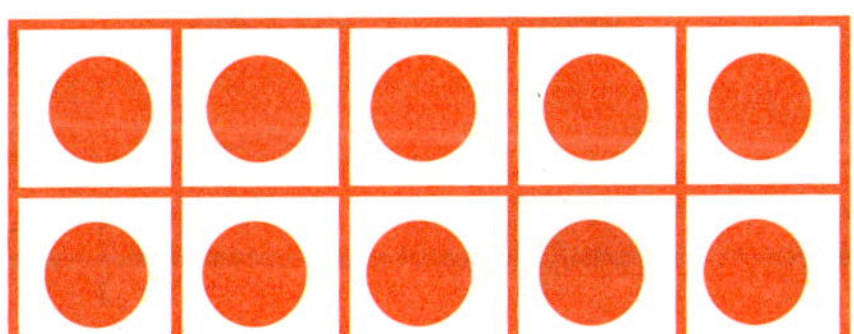

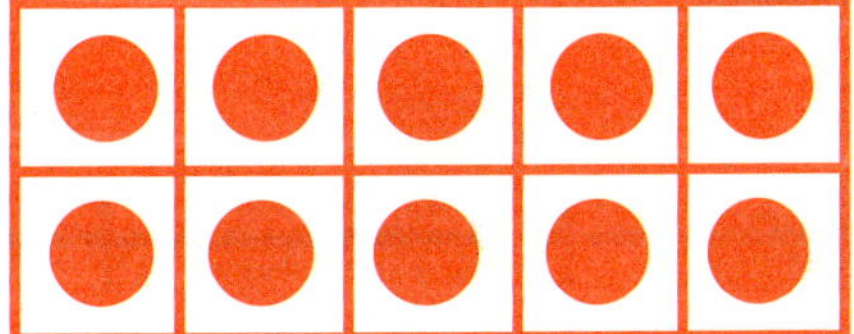

21

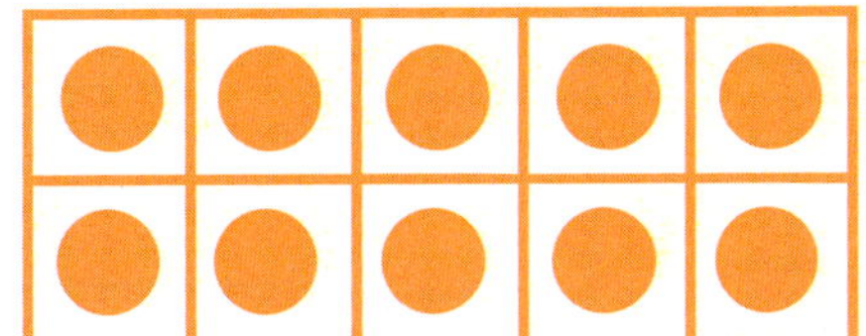

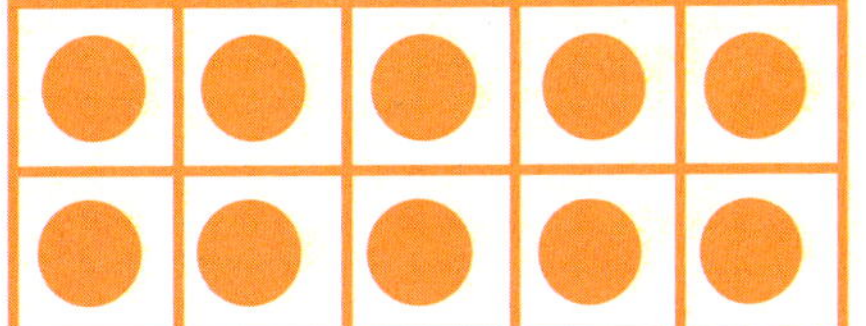

30

Count and write how many. Circle the number that shows more. Mark an X on the number that shows fewer.

Draw more counters to make 21.

Draw more counters to make 30.

Cumulative Review

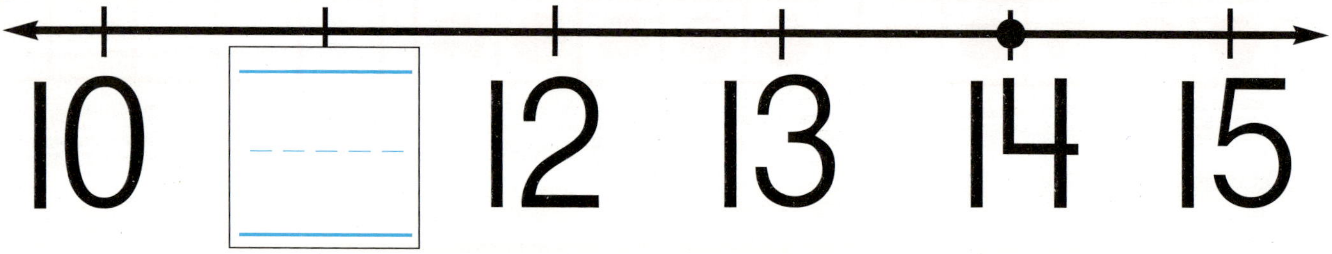

10 ___ 12 13 14 15

18 19 20

Use two colors of counters to make your own pattern. Draw your pattern.
Count the cubes. Write the numbers. Circle the number that is greater.
Circle the shape with curves. Color the shapes with four edges. Mark an X on the shape with three corners.
Start at 14. Count three numbers back. Write the number.
Count the flowers. Circle the number that tells how many. Write the number.

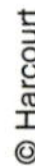

Name ___________________________

Test

13

14

17

18

24

25

30

31

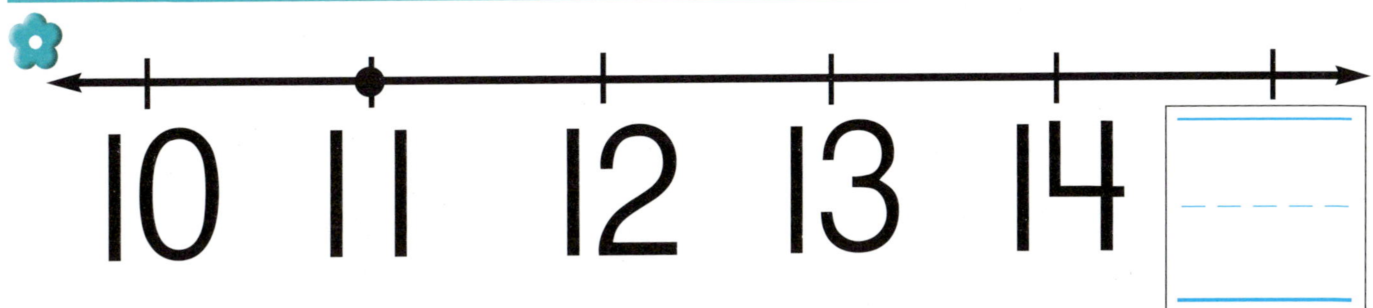

Count. Circle the number that tells how many.

Start at 11. Count four numbers forward. Write the number.

CHALLENGE

Color by Number

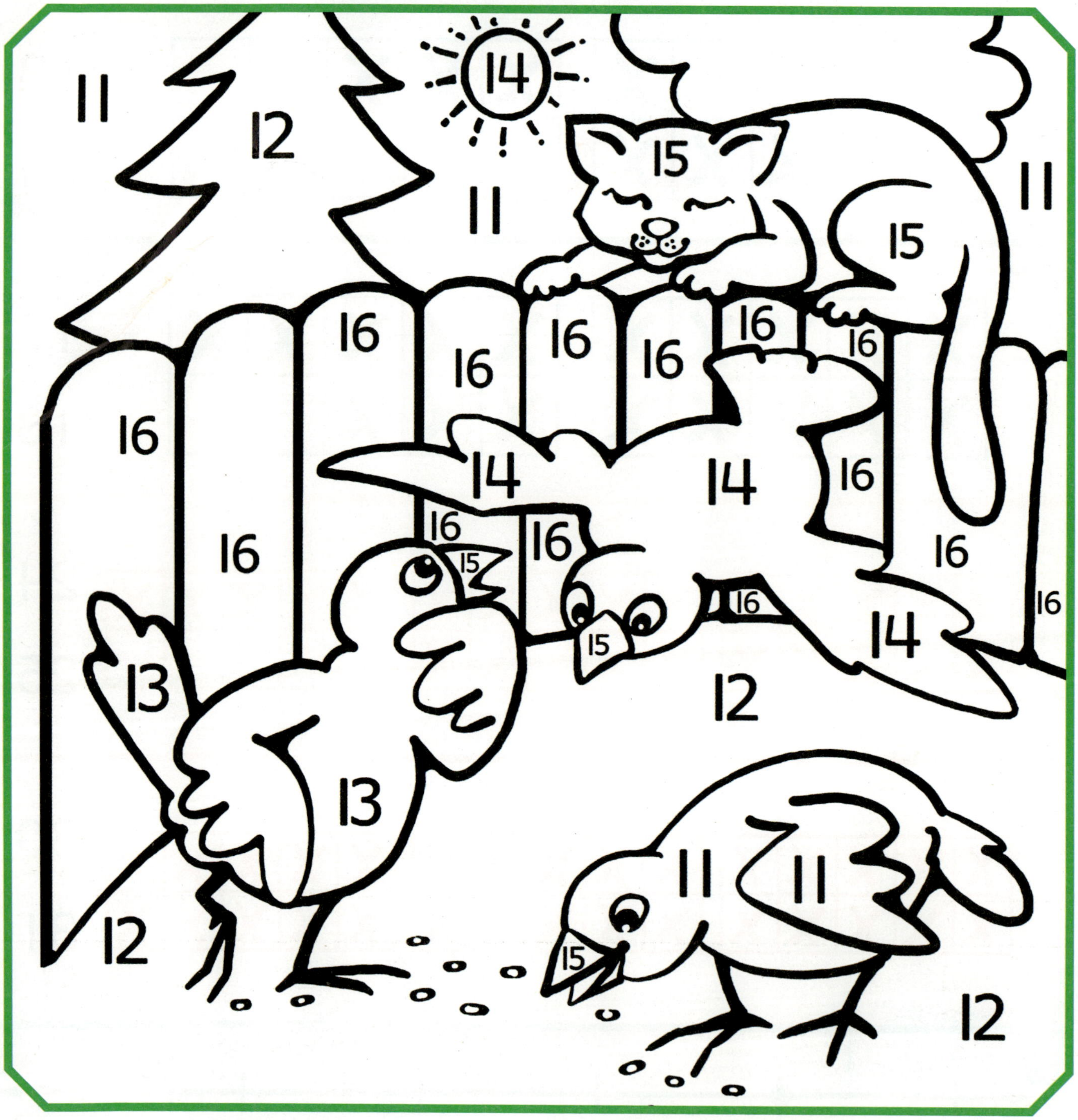

Use these colors to color by number.

11
12
13

14
15
16

Number Patterns

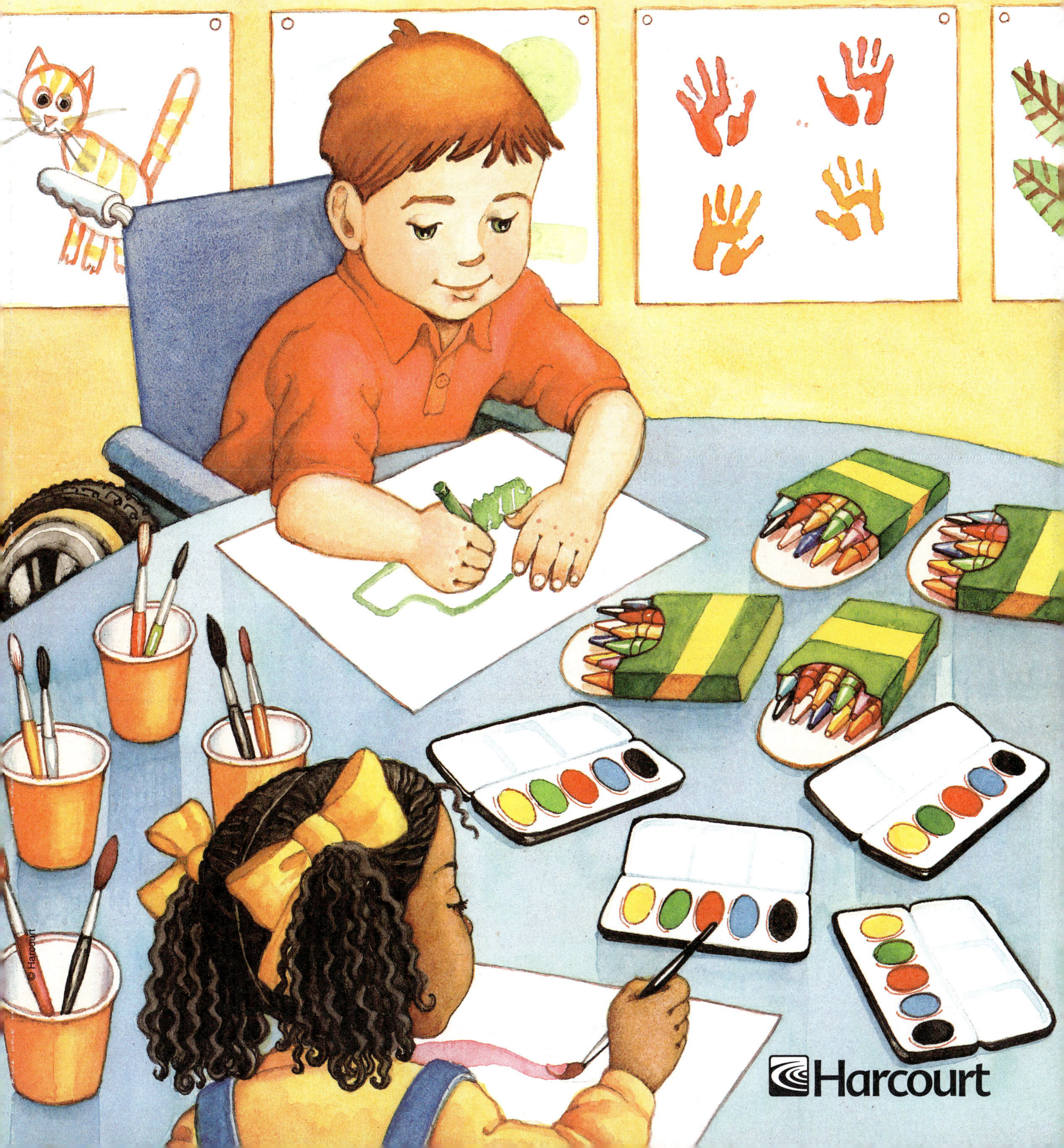

Harcourt

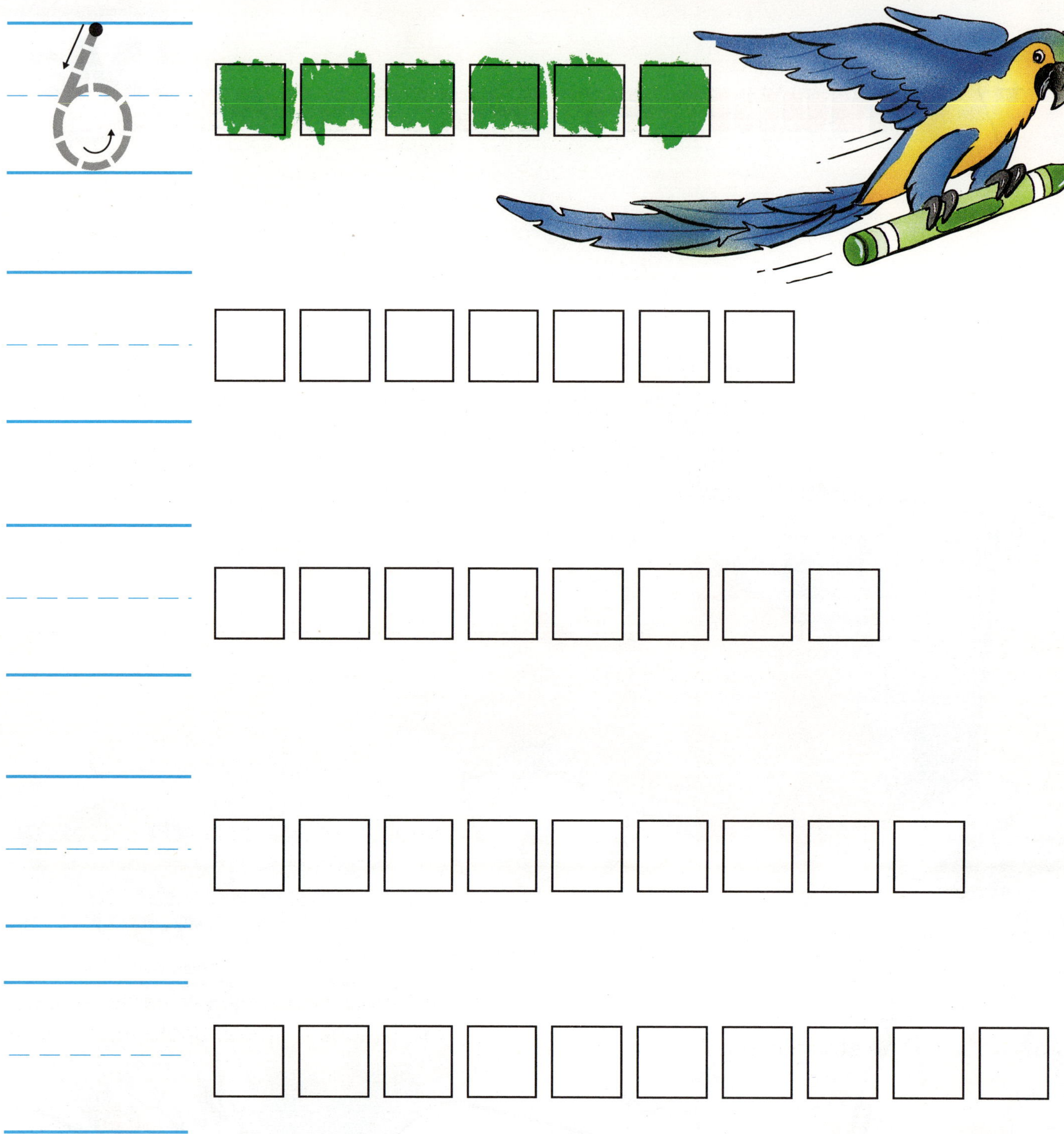

Count and color the boxes. Write the numbers.

Printed in the United States of America

Photography Credits:

All photography by Harcourt photographers listed, © Harcourt: Weronica Ankarorn, Victoria Bowen, Ken Kinzie, Sheri O'Neal, Quebecor Imaging, and Terry Sinclair.

Illustration Credits:

Daniel DelValle: 164; **Franklin Hammond:** Storybook; **Heidi King:** 170; **Richard Kolding:** 172; **Claude Martinot:** 165, 166, 167, 168, 169, 171, 173, 174, 177, 178, 182, 183, 184; **Stephanie Peterson:** 164; **Dorothy Stott:** 181; **Jay Veno:** 162.

15 16 17 18 19 20 1678 16 15 14 13 12 11
4500311726

SCHOOL HOME CONNECTION

Dear Family,

Today we started a new chapter, Number Patterns. In this chapter we will learn to skip count by tens, fives, and twos. We will also learn about even and odd numbers.

Love,

____

even

4 is an even number

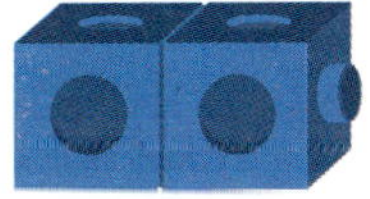
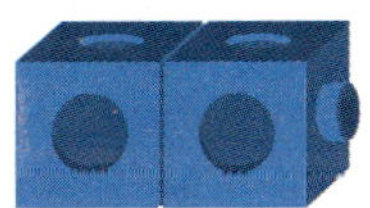

An even number of cubes can be grouped in pairs.

odd

7 is an odd number

An odd number of cubes can be grouped in pairs but has one left over.

Visit *The Learning Site* for additional ideas and activities. www.harcourtschool.com

ACTIVITY

- Have your child count fingers and toes by fives and then by tens.

BOOKS TO SHARE

To read more about number patterns with your child, look for these books in your local library.

One Potato: A Counting Book of Potato Prints,
by Diana Pomeroy.
Harcourt, 1996.

Hundredth Day Worries,
by Margery Cuyle.
Simon and Schuster, 2000.

The King's Commissioners
by Aileen Friedman. Scholastic, 1995.

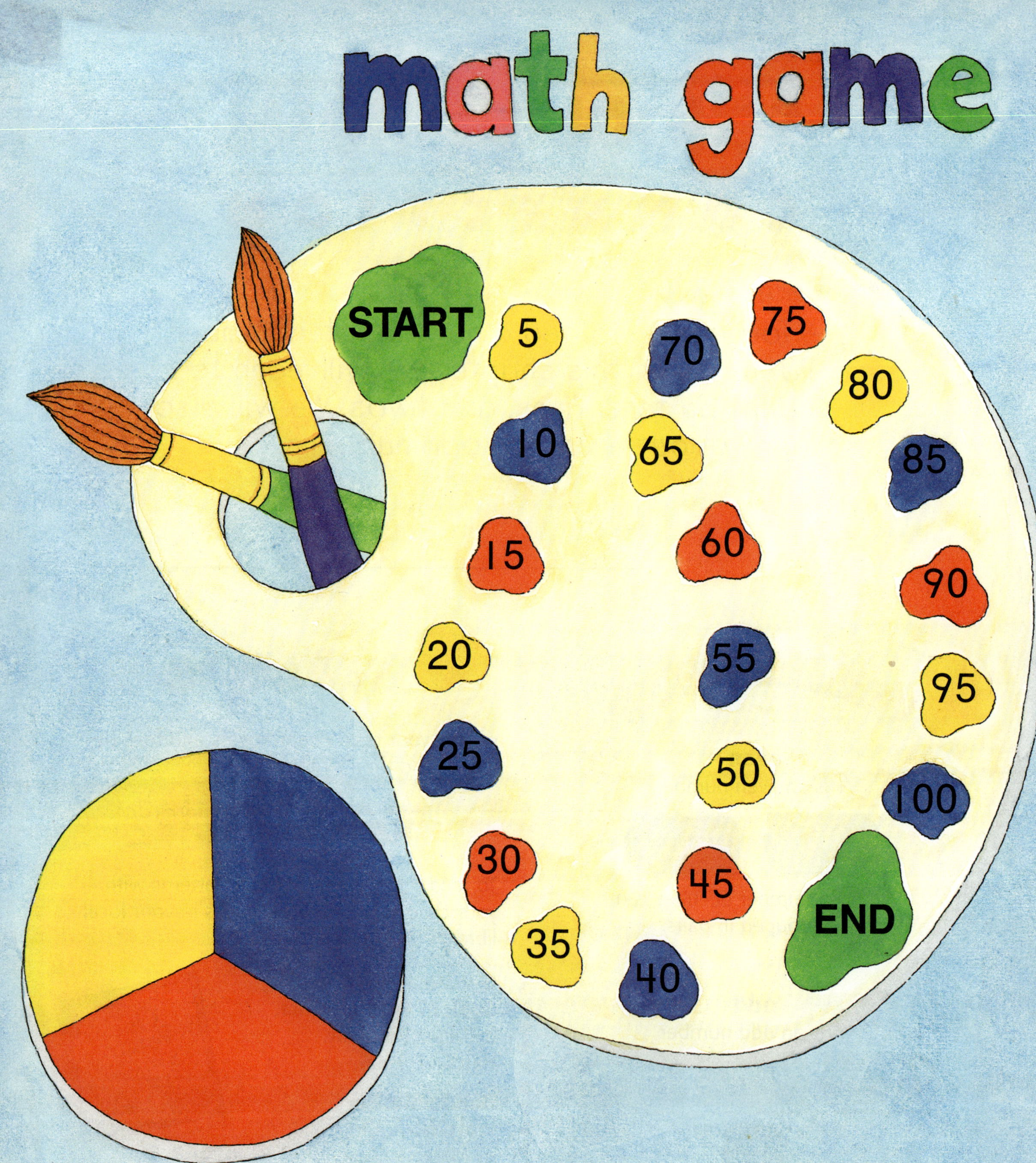

MATERIALS: 2 game markers, pencil, paper clip
DIRECTIONS: Play with a partner and decide who goes first. Put your game marker on START. Players take turns spinning the spinner. Move your game marker and count by fives to get to that color. The first player to get to END wins.

Name ______________________________

Count Orally Using a Hundred Chart

1	2	3	4	5	6	7	8	9	10
11	12	13	14	15	16	17	18	19	20
21	22	23	24	25	26	27	28	29	30
31	32	33	34	35	36	37	38	39	40
41	42	43	44	45	46	47	48	49	50
51	52	53	54	55	56	57	58	59	60
61	62	63	64	65	66	67	68	69	70
71	72	73	74	75	76	77	78	79	80
81	82	83	84	85	86	87	88	89	90
91	92	93	94	95	96	97	98	99	100

Touch each number as you count from 1 to 35. Circle each number you say. Touch and count from 36 to 68. Circle each number you say. Touch and count from 69 to 100. Circle each number you say.

1	2	3	4	5	6	7	8	9	10
11	12	13	14	15	16	17	18	19	20
21	22	23	24	25	26	27	28	29	30
31	32	33	34	35	36	37	38	39	40
41	42	43	44	45	46	47	48	49	50
51	52	53	54	55	56	57	58	59	60
61	62	63	64	65	66	67	68	69	70
71	72	73	74	75	76	77	78	79	80
81	82	83	84	85	86	87	88	89	90
91	92	93	94	95	96	97	98	99	100

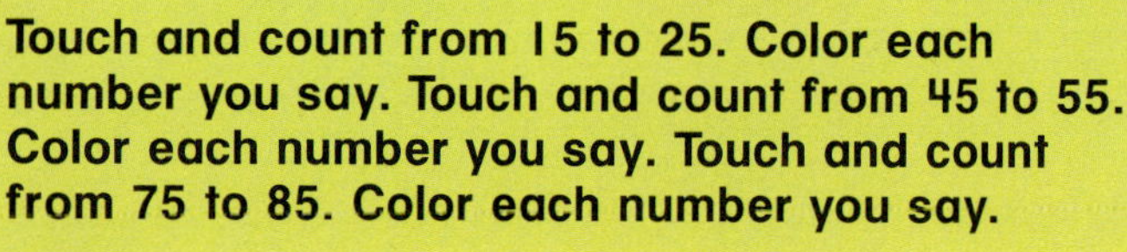
Touch and count from 15 to 25. Color each number you say. Touch and count from 45 to 55. Color each number you say. Touch and count from 75 to 85. Color each number you say.

HOME ACTIVITY • Count out loud with your child from 1 to 100.

Name ____________________

Algebra: **Count by 10s**

1	2	3	4	5	6	7	8	9	10
11	12	13	14	15	16	17	18	19	20
21	22	23	24	25	26	27	28	29	30
31	32	33	34	35	36	37	38	39	40
41	42	43	44	45	46	47	48	49	50
51	52	53	54	55	56	57	58	59	60
61	62	63	64	65	66	67	68	69	70
71	72	73	74	75	76	77	78	79	80
81	82	83	84	85	86	87	88	89	90
91	92	93	94	95	96	97	98	99	100

Touch and count by tens. Use blue to color the numbers you say.

1	2	3	4	5	6	7	8	9	10
11	12	13	14	15	16	17	18	19	20
21	22	23	24	25	26	27	28	29	30
31	32	33	34	35	36	37	38	39	40
41	42	43	44	45	46	47	48	49	50
51	52	53	54	55	56	57	58	59	60
61	62	63	64	65	66	67	68	69	70
71	72	73	74	75	76	77	78	79	80
81	82	83	84	85	86	87	88	89	90
91	92	93	94	95	96	97	98	99	100

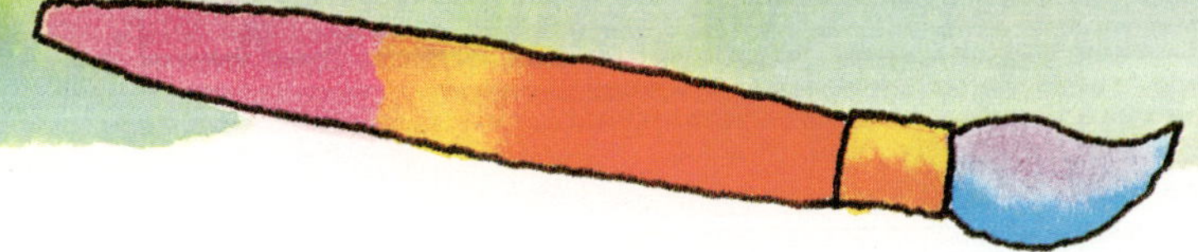

Touch and count by tens. Finish writing the numbers.

HOME ACTIVITY • Help your child count by tens to 100.

Name ______________________

Algebra: Count by 5s

1	2	3	4	5	6	7	8	9	10
11	12	13	14	15	16	17	18	19	20
21	22	23	24	25	26	27	28	29	30
31	32	33	34	35	36	37	38	39	40
41	42	43	44	45	46	47	48	49	50
51	52	53	54	55	56	57	58	59	60
61	62	63	64	65	66	67	68	69	70
71	72	73	74	75	76	77	78	79	80
81	82	83	84	85	86	87	88	89	90
91	92	93	94	95	96	97	98	99	100

Put a red cube on each number that ends with a 5 or a 0. Color these boxes red. Touch and count by fives.

Put 5 connecting cubes above each hand. Count by fives. Trace the numbers.

HOME ACTIVITY • Help your child practice counting by fives.

Name ______________________________

Algebra: Count by 2s

1	2	3	4	5	6	7	8	9	10
11	12	13	14	15	16	17	18	19	20
21	22	23	24	25	26	27	28	29	30
31	32	33	34	35	36	37	38	39	40
41	42	43	44	45	46	47	48	49	50
51	52	53	54	55	56	57	58	59	60
61	62	63	64	65	66	67	68	69	70
71	72	73	74	75	76	77	78	79	80
81	82	83	84	85	86	87	88	89	90
91	92	93	94	95	96	97	98	99	100

Put a yellow cube on the 2, 4, 6, 8, 10, 12, and 14.
Color these boxes yellow. Color to finish the pattern.
Touch and count by twos.

Count by twos. Trace the numbers.

HOME ACTIVITY • Give your child a handful of pennies. Have him or her group the pennies in pairs and then count them by twos.

Name ______________________________

Problem Solving Strategy
Find a Pattern

1	2	3	4	5	6	7	8	9	10
11	12	13	14	15	16	17	18	19	20
21	22	23	24	25	26	27	28	29	30
31	32	33	34	35	36	37	38	39	40
41	42	43	44	45	46	47	48	49	50
51	52	53	54	55	56	57	58	59	60
61	62	63	64	65	66	67	68	69	70
71	72	73	74	75	76	77	78	79	80
81	82	83	84	85	86	87	88	89	90
91	92	93	94	95	96	97	98	99	100

Use yellow to color the numbers you say when you count by fives. Use blue to circle the numbers you say when you count by tens. What patterns do you see?

1	2	3	4	5	6	7	8	9	10
11	12	13	14	15	16	17	18	19	20
21	22	23	24	25	26	27	28	29	30
31	32	33	34	35	36	37	38	39	40
41	42	43	44	45	46	47	48	49	50
51	52	53	54	55	56	57	58	59	60
61	62	63	64	65	66	67	68	69	70
71	72	73	74	75	76	77	78	79	80
81	82	83	84	85	86	87	88	89	90
91	92	93	94	95	96	97	98	99	100

Use yellow to color the numbers you say when you count by twos. Use red to color the other numbers. What pattern do you see?

HOME ACTIVITY • Encourage your child to count by ones, twos, fives, and tens while you shop, walk, or ride together.

Name ______________________________

Review

1	2	3	4	5	6	7	8	9	10
11	12	13	14	15	16	17	18	19	20
21	22	23	24	25	26	27	28	29	30
31	32	33	34	35	36	37	38	39	40
41	42	43	44	45	46	47	48	49	50
51	52	53	54	55	56	57	58	59	60
61	62	63	64	65	66	67	68	69	70
71	72	73	74	75	76	77	78	79	80
81	82	83	84	85	86	87	88	89	90
91	92	93	94	95	96	97	98	99	100

Touch and count by tens. Finish writing the numbers. Use blue to circle the numbers you say. Touch and count by fives. Use green to color the numbers you say.

Cumulative Review

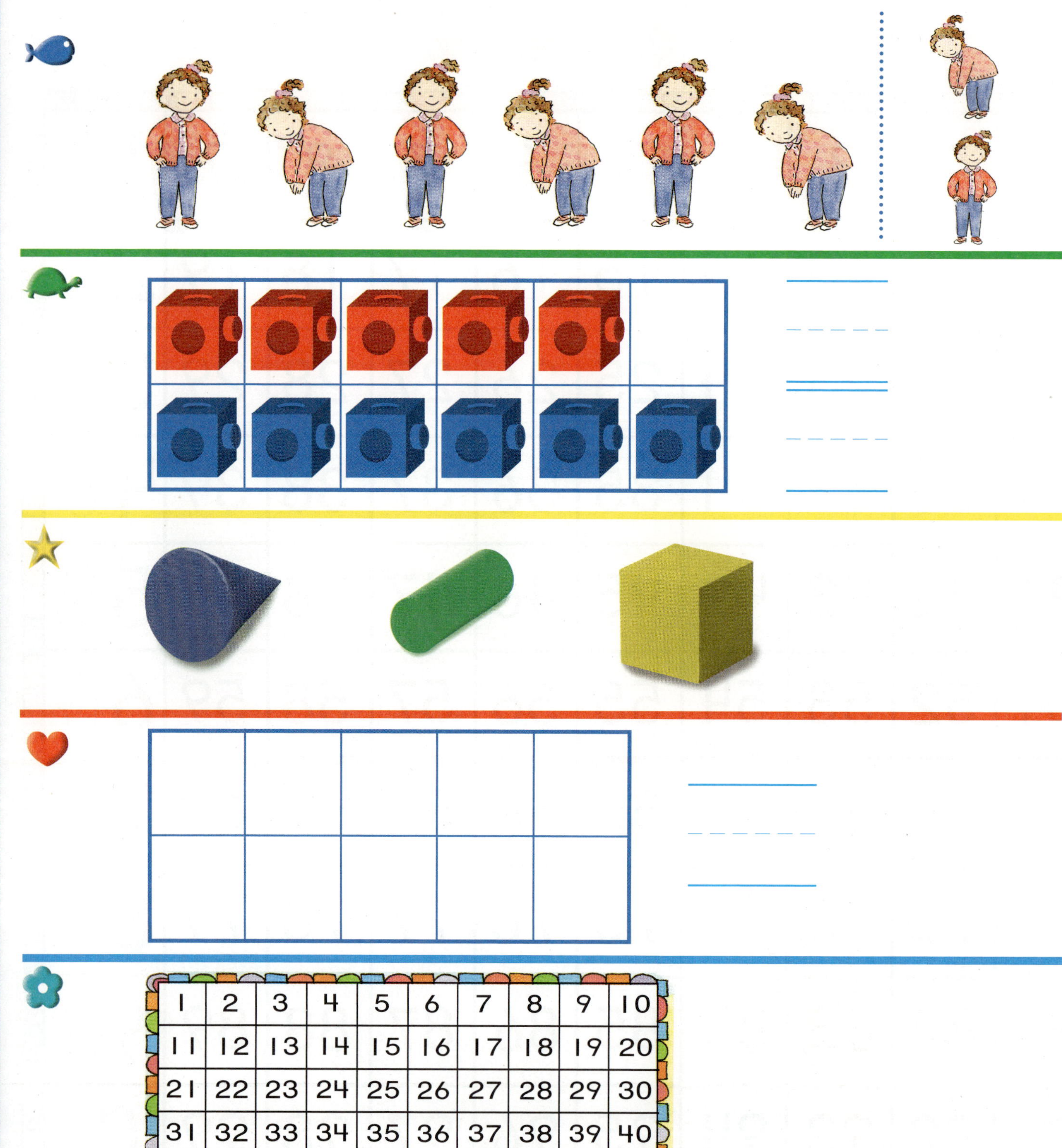

1	2	3	4	5	6	7	8	9	10
11	12	13	14	15	16	17	18	19	20
21	22	23	24	25	26	27	28	29	30
31	32	33	34	35	36	37	38	39	40
41	42	43	44	45	46	47	48	49	50

- Circle what you would most likely do next.
- Count the cubes in each row and write the number. Circle the number that is greater.
- Circle the shapes that stack and slide.
- Draw counters in the ten frame to show the number that is two more than eight. Write the number.
- Touch and count by tens. Use blue to color the numbers you say.

Name ______________________________

Counting by 10s and 5s

Count by tens to connect the dots in order.

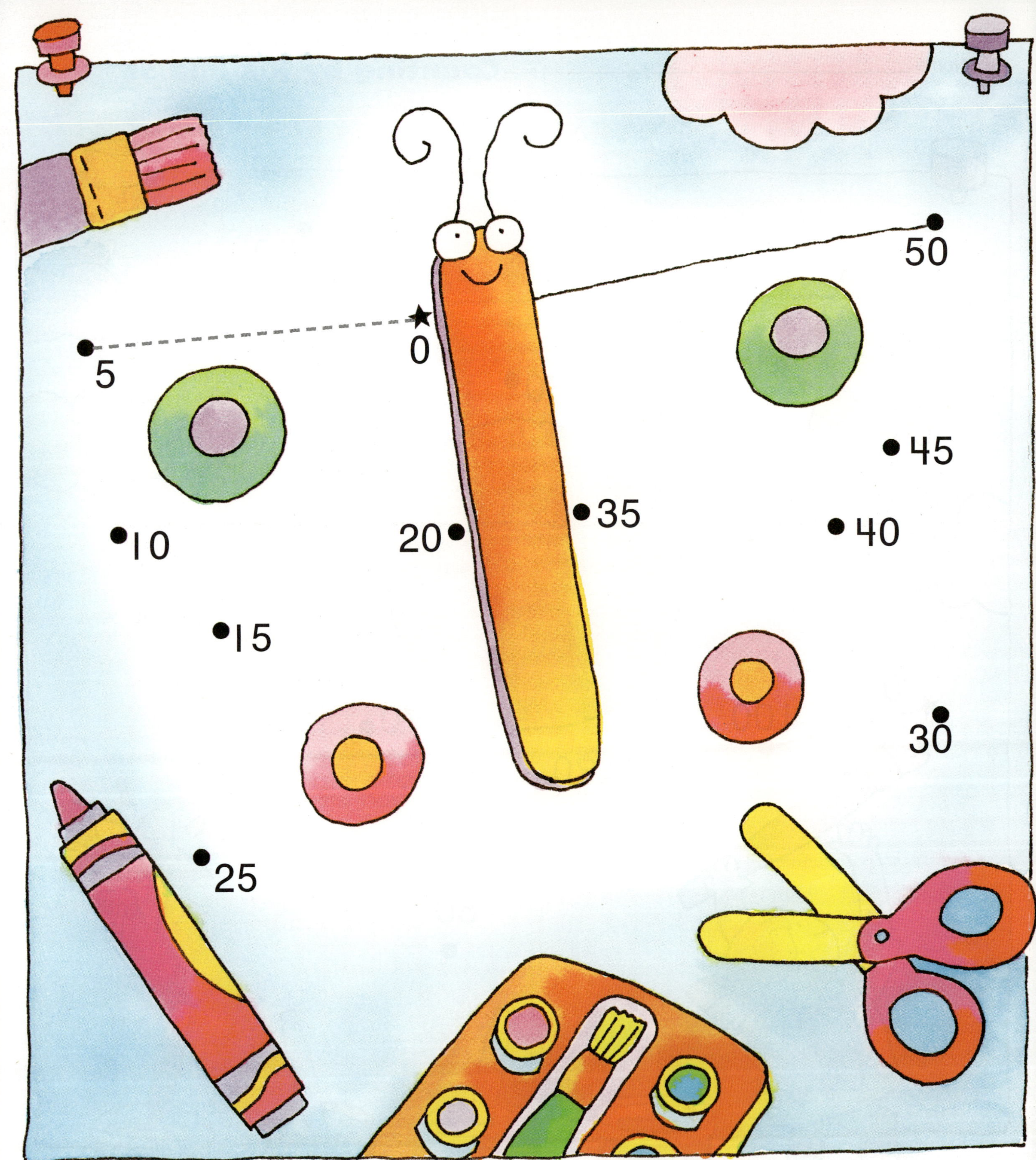

Count by fives to connect the dots in order.

HOME ACTIVITY • Have your child show you how he or she counted by fives to connect the dots.

Name ___________________________

Even and Odd Numbers

3 

4 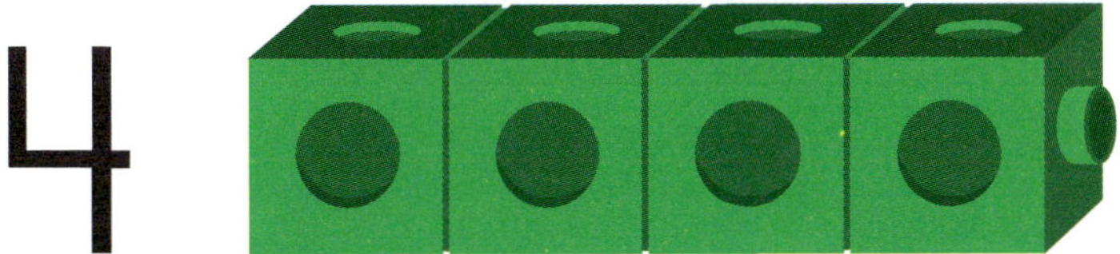

5 

6 

Build the cube train. Take one cube from each end of the train and snap these cubes together. Do this as many times as you can. If you have only pairs, the number is even. Circle the number. If you have one cube left over, the number is odd. Mark an X on the number.

7

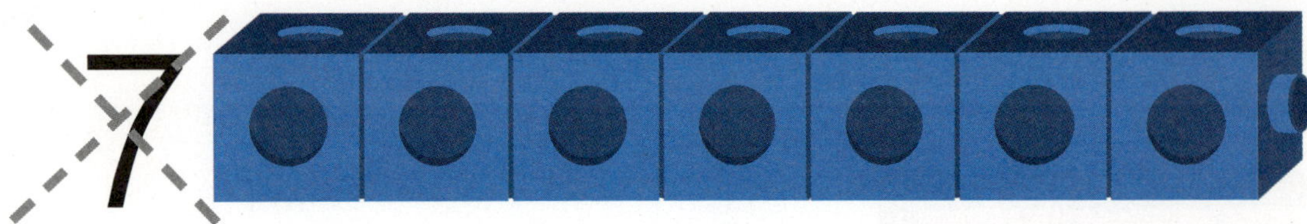

8

9

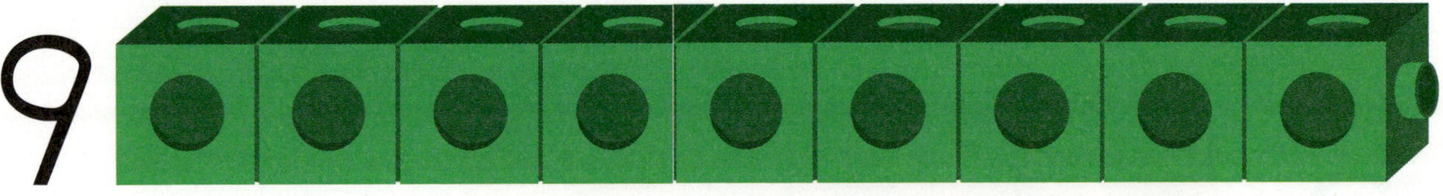

10

Build the cube train. Take one cube from each end of the train and snap these cubes together. Do this as many times as you can. If you have only pairs, the number is even. Circle the number. If you have one cube left over, the number is odd. Mark an X on the number.

HOME ACTIVITY • Say a number. Have your child make pairs with pennies to find out if the number has a "leftover."

Name ______________________________

Ordinal Numbers

first

Circle the fifth child. Draw a line under the seventh child. Mark an X on the tenth child.

Circle the first bear. Draw a line under the sixth bear. Mark an X on the ninth bear.

Circle the fifth ladybug. Circle the second butterfly. Circle the seventh duck. Circle the ninth frog.

HOME ACTIVITY • Have your child use position words such as *first* and *third* to tell the order of the animals in each line.

Name ______________________________

Problem Solving Skill
Use a Model

2 3 4 5 6 7 8

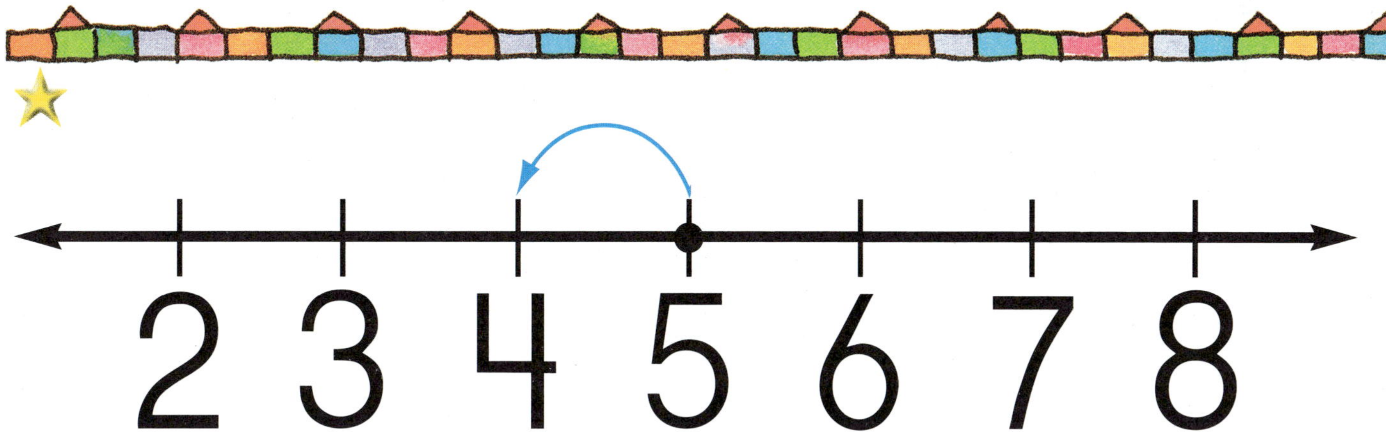

Put your finger on 5. Count up 1. What number are you on? Circle the number.

Put your finger on 5. Count up 2. What number are you on? Circle the number.

Put your finger on 5. Count back 1. What number are you on? Circle the number.

7 8 9 10 11 12 13

Put your finger on 10. Count back 1. What number are you on? Circle the number.
Put your finger on 10. Count back 2. What number are you on? Circle the number.
Put your finger on 10. Count up 1. What number are you on? Circle the number.

HOME ACTIVITY • Ask your child to show you how to count up and back on a number line.

Counting Is Fun

2

5

10

By ______________________________

HOME ACTIVITY • This book will help review skip-counting. Invite your child to share this book with you.

2 4 6 8 10

Let's count by twos.

5 10 15 20 25

Let's count by fives.

5
10
15
20
25
10
20
30
40
50

Let's count by twos, fives, and tens.

Name ____________________

Review

5

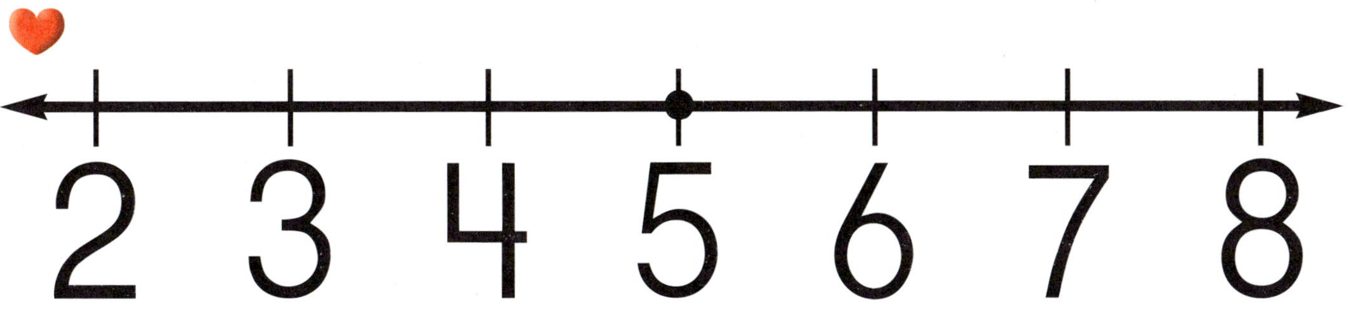

Build the cube train. Take a cube from each end of the train and snap these cubes together. Do this as many times as you can. If you have only pairs, the number is even. Circle the number. If you have one cube left over, the number is odd. Mark an X on the number.

Circle the seventh child.

Put your finger on 10. Count up 1. What number are you on? Circle the number.

Put your finger on 5. Count back 1. What number are you on? Circle the number.

Cumulative Review

Circle the fish that is in the fishbowl.
Circle the bird that is over the tree.
Use counters to show the same pattern. Draw the pattern.
Look at the object at the beginning of the row. Color in the outline that matches the shape of the object.
Color to continue the pattern. Touch and count by twos.
Circle the fifth ladybug. Draw a line under the seventh ladybug. Mark an X on the tenth ladybug.

Name ________________________________

Test

1	2	3	4	5	6	7	8	9	10
11	12	13	14	15	16	17	18	19	20
21	22	23	24	25	26	27	28	29	30

7

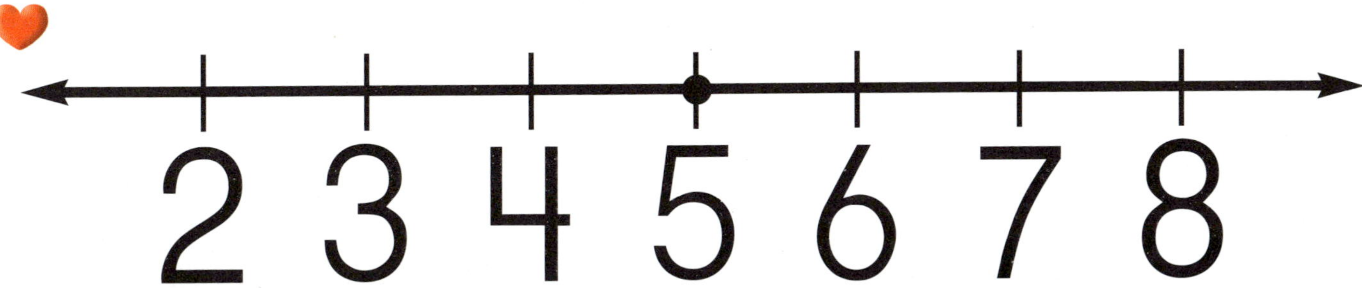

Use green to color the numbers you say when you count by fives.

Build the cube train. Take one cube from each end of the train and snap these cubes together. Do this as many times as you can. If you have only pairs, the number is even. Circle the number. If you have one cube left over the number is odd. Mark an X on the number.

Circle the tenth child.

Put your finger on 5. Count up 2. What number are you on? Circle the number.

CHALLENGE

Counting on the Calculator

Use a calculator. Press ON/C 0 + 1 =. Now, keep pressing =. Write the missing numbers. What number pattern do you see?

Use a calculator. Press ON/C 0 + 2 =. Now, keep pressing =. Write the missing numbers. What number pattern do you see?

CHAPTER
8
Money and Time
HARCOURT
Math
BUG BANK
MARCH
Harcourt

Draw a line to match the front of each coin to its back.

Grateful acknowledgment is made to Random House Children's Books, a division of Random House, Inc. for permission to reprint the cover illustration by Bob Barner from *Benny's Pennies* by Pat Brisson. Illustration copyright © 1993 by Bob Barner.

Printed in the United States of America

Photography Credits:

All photography by Harcourt photographers listed, © Harcourt: Weronica Ankarorn, Victoria Bowen, Ken Kinzie, Sheri O'Neal, Quebecor Imaging, and Terry Sinclair.

Illustration Credits:

Liz Allen: 207, 208; **Russel Bencati:** 193; **Ken Bowser:** 198; **Susan Calitri:** 199, 200; **Carolyn Croll:** Storybook; **Obadinah Heavner:** 205; **C.D. Hullinger:** cvr, 190; **Judy Love:** 203, 204; **Claude Martinot:** 192; **Peggy Tagel:** 194; **Sally Vitsky:** 206.

15 16 17 18 19 20 1678 16 15 14 13 12 11
4500311726

SCHOOL HOME CONNECTION

Dear Family,

Today we started a new chapter, Money and Time. We will learn to recognize coins and their value. We will also learn about time, using a calendar and a clock.

Love,

____

Heads		Tails
	penny	
	nickel	
	dime	

Visit *The Learning Site* for additional ideas and activities. www.harcourtschool.com

ACTIVITY

- Have your child sort a handful of change so that all the coins that are alike are together.
- Choose a "coin of the day," and talk about what is shown on both sides of the coin.

BOOKS TO SHARE

To read about money with your child, look for these books at your local library.

Benny's Pennies, by Pat Brisson. Yearling, 1993.

26 Letters and 99 Cents, by Tana Hoban. Morrow, 1995.

Jelly Beans for Sale, by Bruce McMillan. Scholastic, 1996.

Math Game

MATERIALS: number cube (1–6), game marker for each player
DIRECTIONS: Players take turns tossing the number cube and moving their game marker that number of spaces. Players are to name the coin and tell its value. If a player lands on a flower with a coin, he or she should tell how many pennies the coin is worth. The first player to get to the wishing well wins.

Name ______________________________

Penny

or

1¢

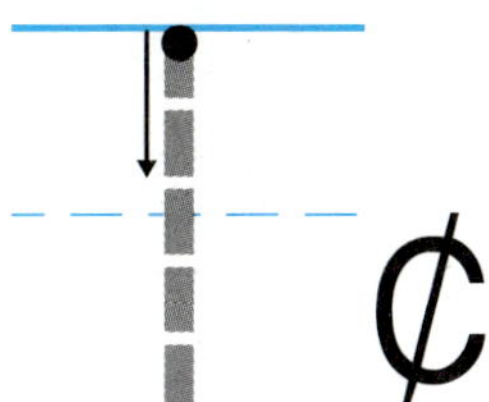

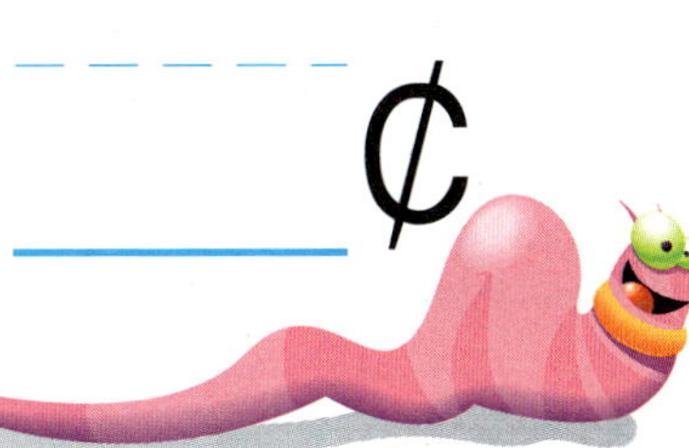

Count the pennies. Write how many cents.

8 ¢

¢

¢

¢

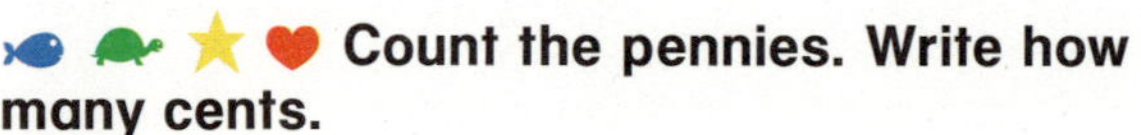
Count the pennies. Write how many cents.

HOME ACTIVITY • Place a handful of coins on a table. Ask your child to sort out the pennies, count them, and tell you how many cents there are.

Name ______________________________

Nickel

5¢

 or 

5¢

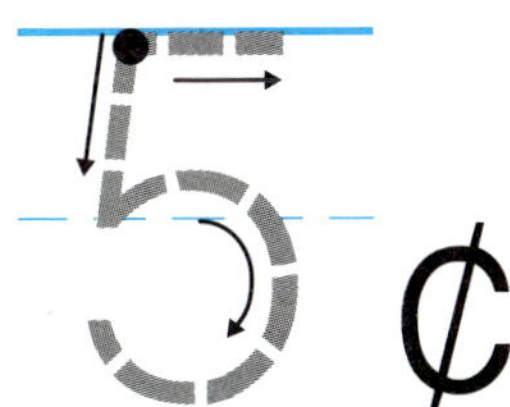

¢

Write how many cents. Circle the coins that show 5¢.

5 ¢

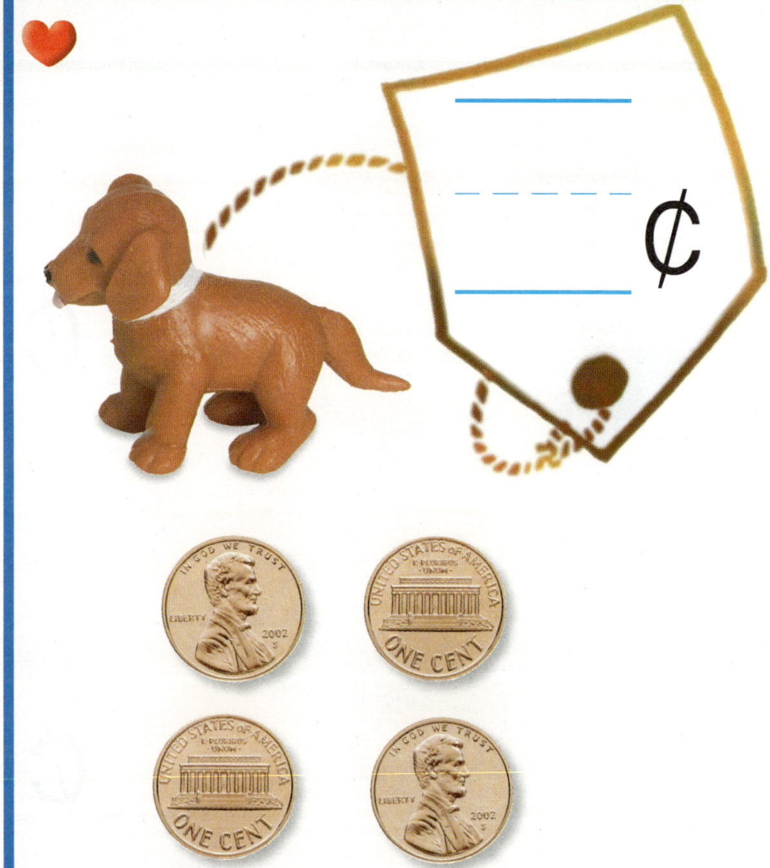

¢

¢

¢

Write how many cents. Circle the coins that show 5¢.

HOME ACTIVITY • Show your child a handful of coins. Have him or her sort out the nickels and tell how many cents they stand for.

Name ______________________

Dime

10¢

 or 

10¢

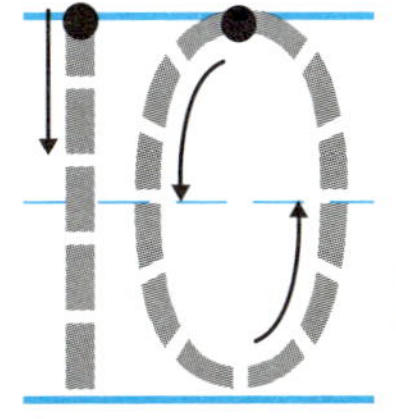

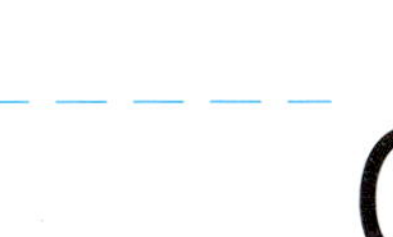

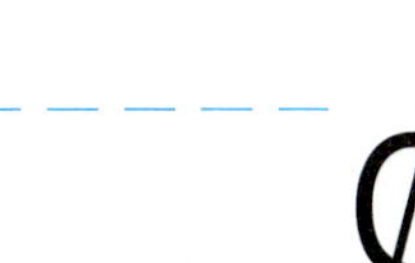

 Write how many cents. Circle the coins that show 10¢.

10¢

¢

¢

¢

¢

¢

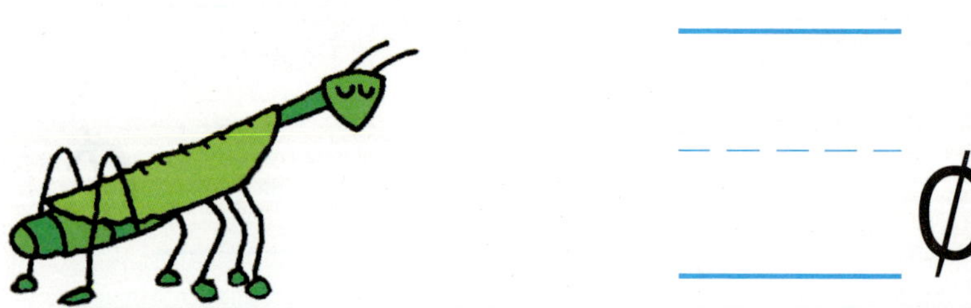

Write how many cents. Circle the coins that show 10¢.

HOME ACTIVITY • Using 10 pennies, 1 nickel, and 1 dime, ask your child to sort the coins and tell how many cents are in each group.

Name ___________________________

Problem Solving Strategy
Draw a Picture

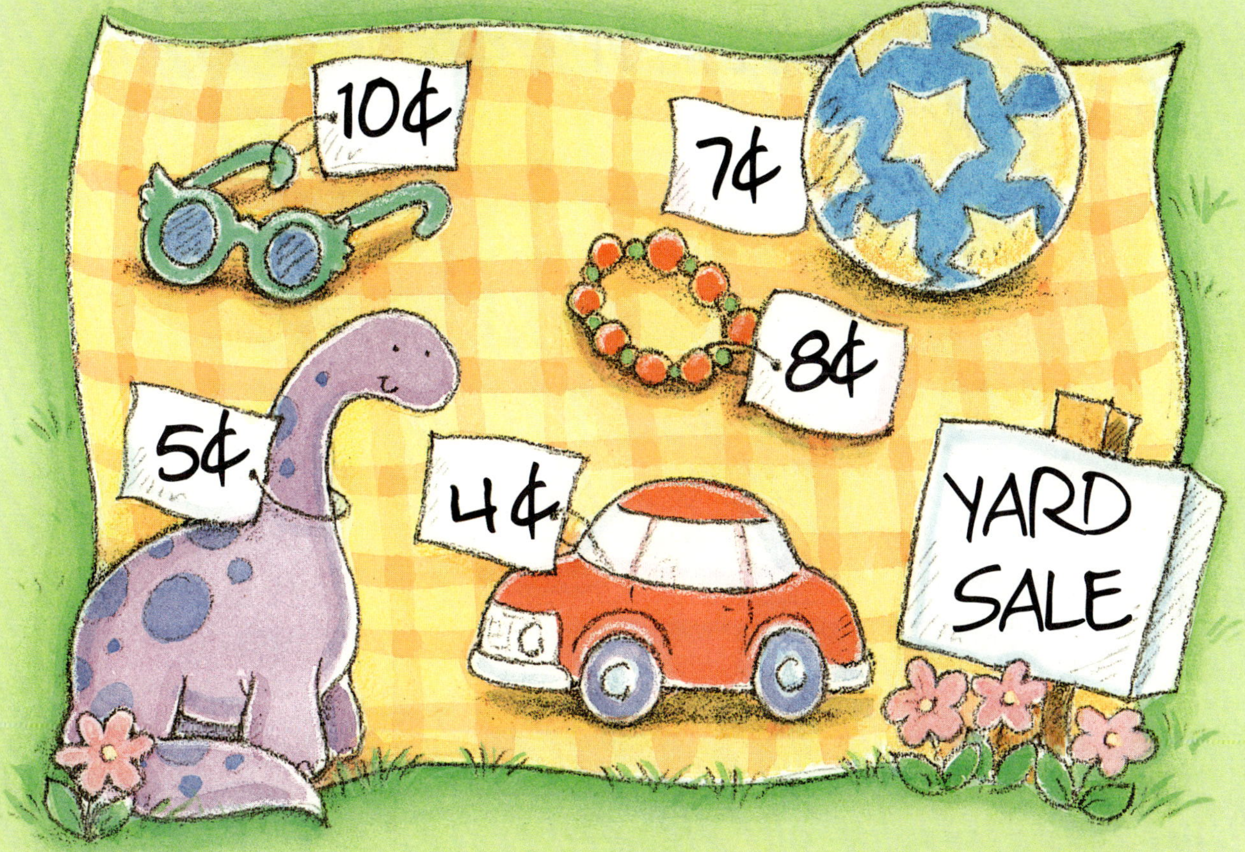
10¢
7¢
8¢
5¢
4¢
YARD SALE

	______ ¢
	______ ¢

Choose a toy to buy. Circle the toy. Then draw the coins you would use to buy it. Write how many cents.

PROBLEM SOLVING

Choose a plant to buy. Circle the plant. Then draw the coins you would use to buy it. Write how many cents.

HOME ACTIVITY • Have your child use pennies, nickels, and dimes to practice "buying" objects in your home.

Name ____________________

Review

____ ¢

____ ¢

____ ¢

____ ¢

____ ¢

Count the pennies. Write how many cents.

Write how many cents. Circle the coins that show 5¢.

Write how many cents. Circle the coins that show 10¢.

Cumulative Review

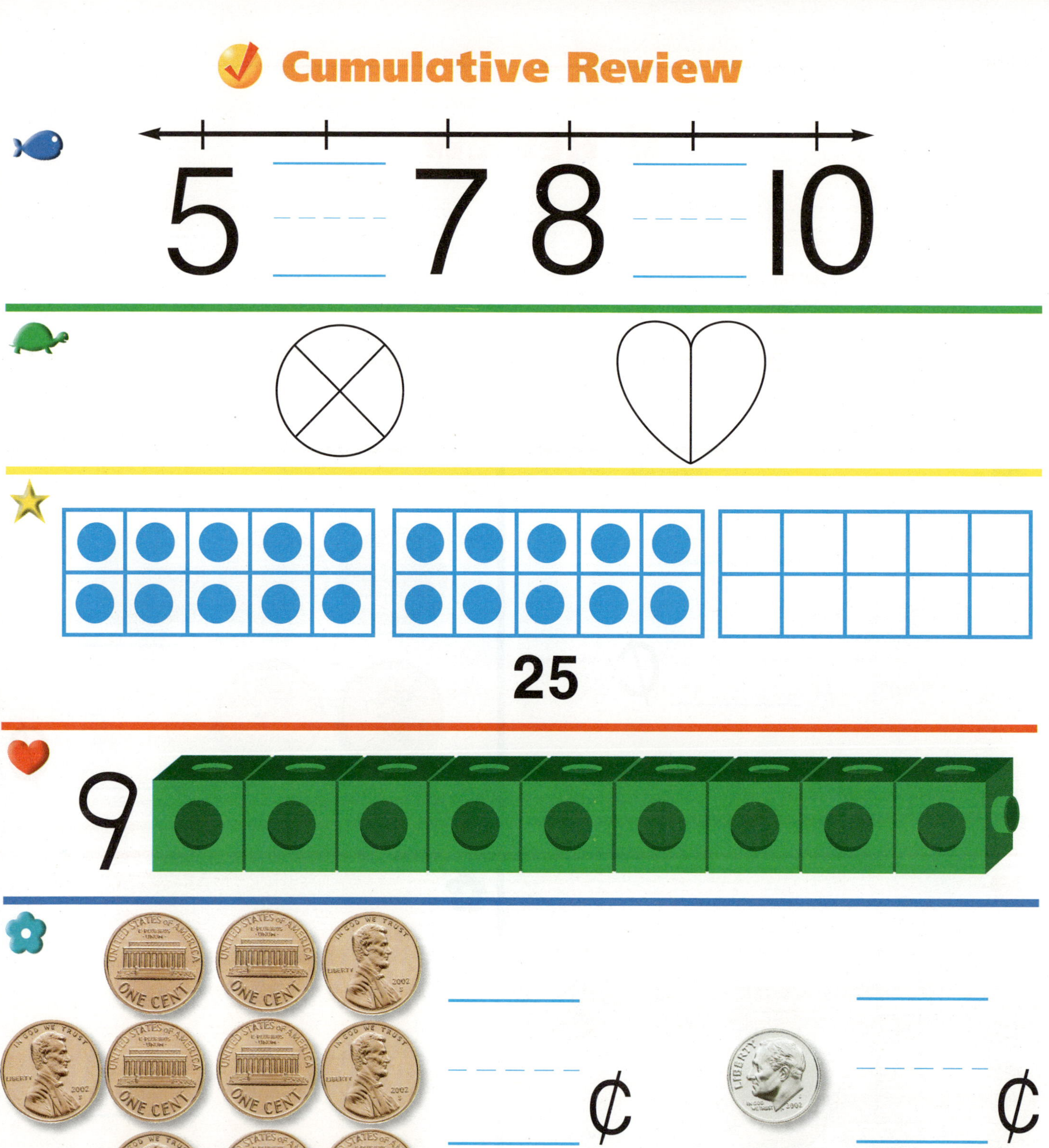

Write the number that is after 5. Write the number that is before 10.

Use green to color one part of each shape. Use red to circle the shape that shows one half. Use blue to circle the shape that shows one fourth.

Draw more counters to make 25.

Build the cube train. Take one cube from each end of the train and snap these cubes together. Do this as many times as you can. If you have only pairs, the number is even. Circle the number. If you have one cube left over, the number is odd. Mark an X on the number.

Write how many cents.

Name ______________________________

Morning, Afternoon, Evening

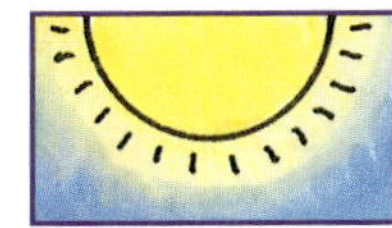

What times of day do the pictures show? Circle the time of day that is missing.

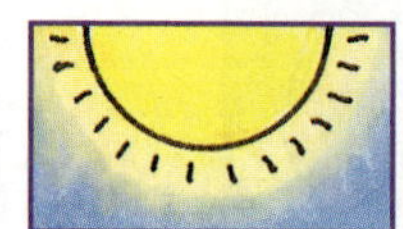

What times of day do the pictures show? Circle the time of day that is missing.

HOME ACTIVITY • In any order, name three activities, such as playing after school, eating breakfast, and taking a bath. Ask your child to put them in order from morning to afternoon to evening.

Name ______________________________

Use a Calendar

March

Sunday	Monday	Tuesday	Wednesday	Thursday	Friday	Saturday
	1	2	3	4	5	6
7	8	9	10	11	12	13
14	15	16	17	18	19	20
21	22	23	24	25	26	27
28	29	30	31			

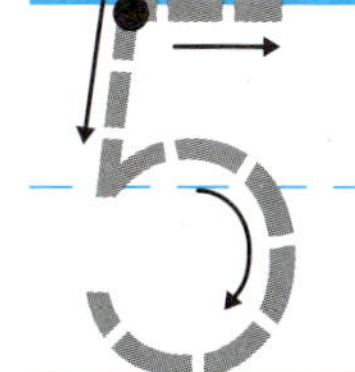

Wednesdays

______ Fridays

______ Saturdays

______ Days in March

Count the Wednesdays. Write how many.
Count the Fridays. Write how many.
Count the Saturdays. Write how many.
Write how many days in March.

April

Sunday	Monday	Tuesday	Wednesday	Thursday	Friday	Saturday
				1	2	3
4	5		7	8	9	10
	12	13	14	15		17
18	19	20		22	23	24
	26	27	28	29	30	

Trace the numbers and fill in the missing numbers.
Circle the name of the month.
Color the first day of the month green.
Color the last day of the month red.

HOME ACTIVITY • Show your child the calendar page for this month. Help him or her find and name today's day and date.

Name ______________________

More Time, Less Time

 **Circle the activity that takes more time.**

Circle the activity that takes less time.

HOME ACTIVITY • Have your child predict which of two chores will take more time. Then have him or her act out the chores to see which took longer.

Name ____________________

Use a Clock

3 o'clock

3:00

3 o'clock

Write the numbers on the clock. Circle the number that tells where the hour hand is pointing.

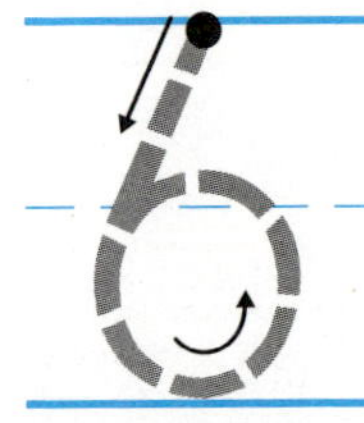

o'clock

o'clock

o'clock

o'clock

o'clock

o'clock

Write the number that tells the hour. Circle the two clocks that show the same time.

HOME ACTIVITY • Help your child tell time on clocks at home and in the community.

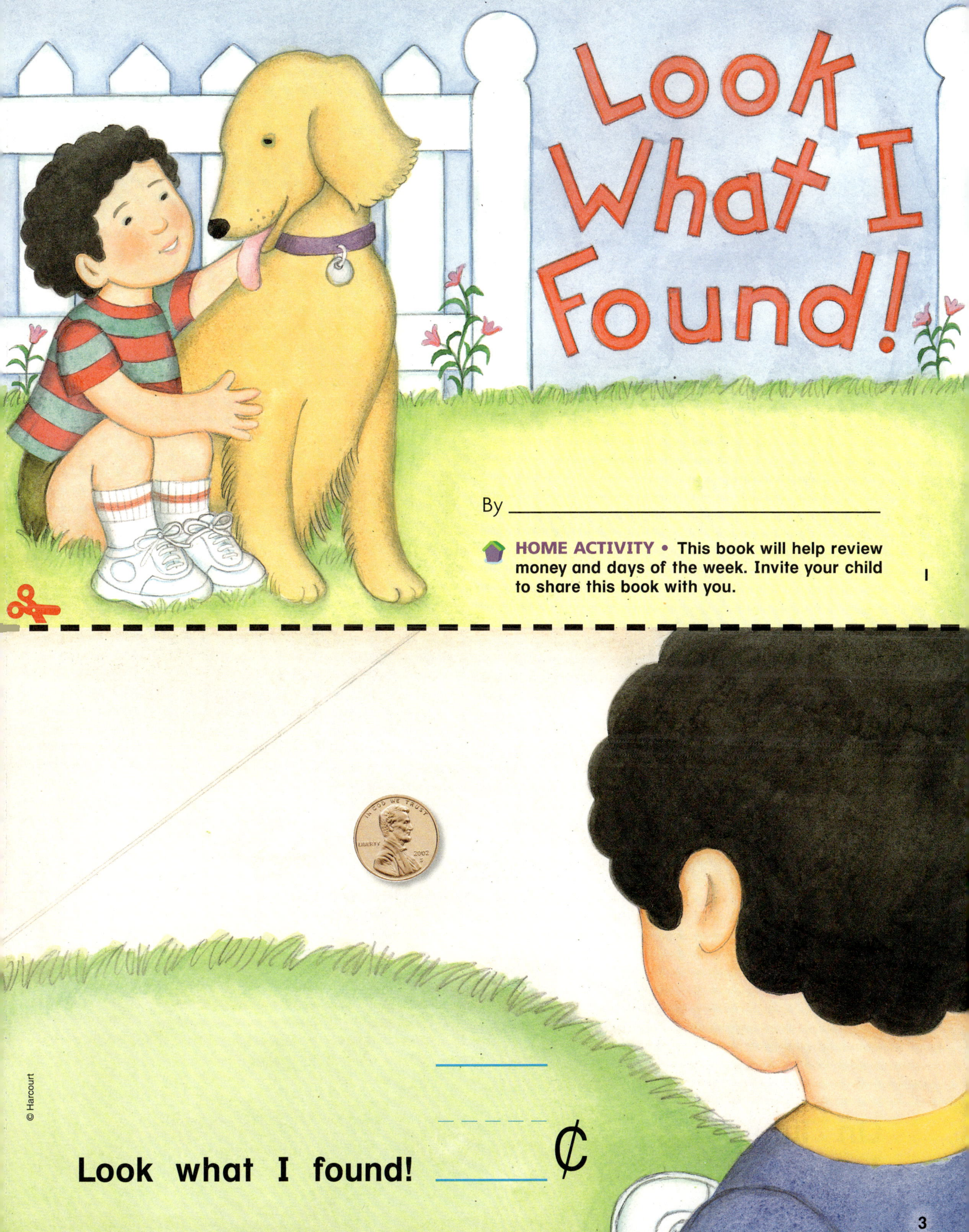

By ______________________

HOME ACTIVITY • This book will help review money and days of the week. Invite your child to share this book with you.

Look what I found! ______ ¢

On Monday
I went with Grandpa.

On Tuesday
I went with Mom.

Look what I found! ____ ¢

Look what I found! ____ ¢

On Wednesday
I went with Uncle Gary.

6

On Thursday
I went with Nana.

8

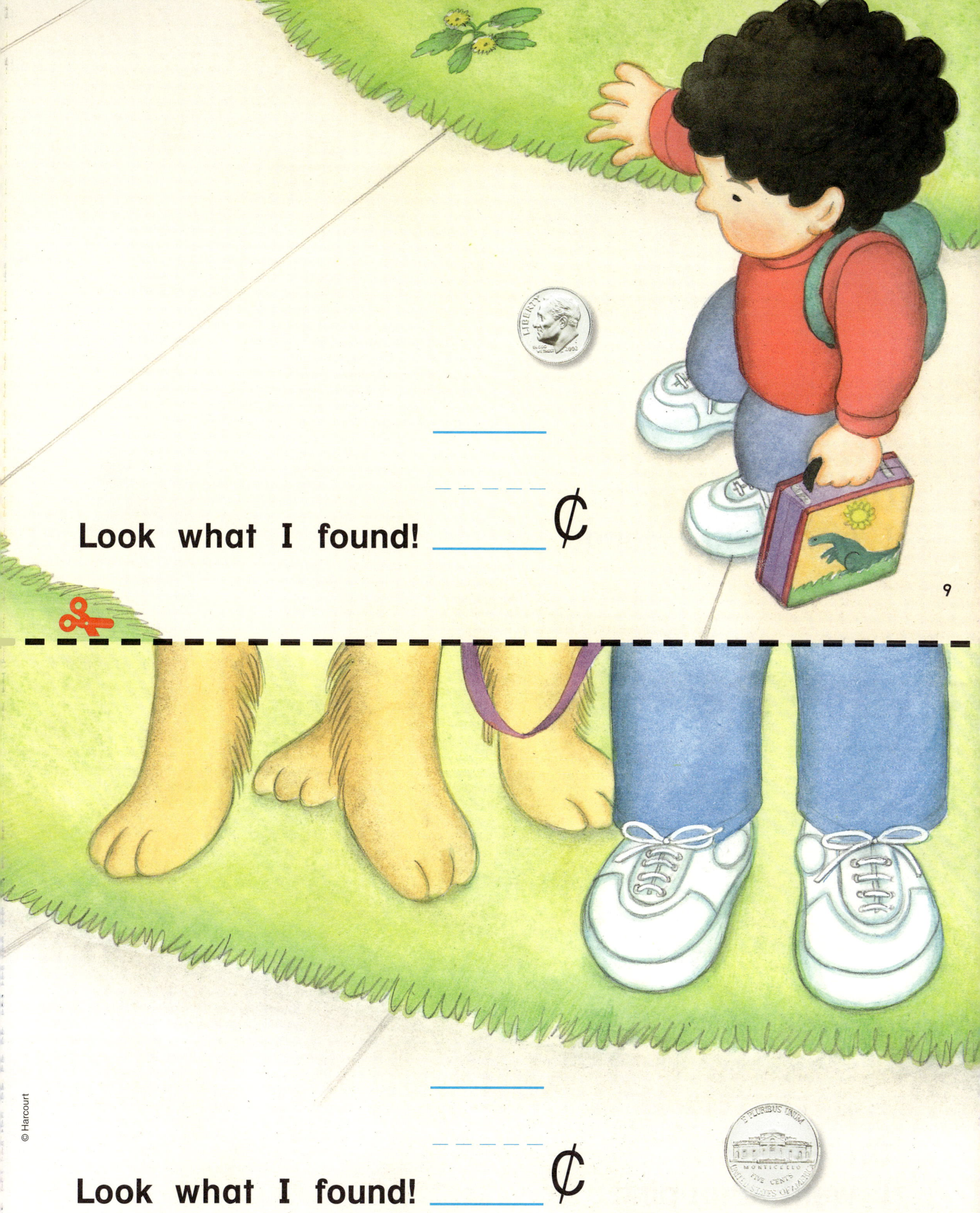

Look what I found! ______ ¢

Look what I found! ______ ¢

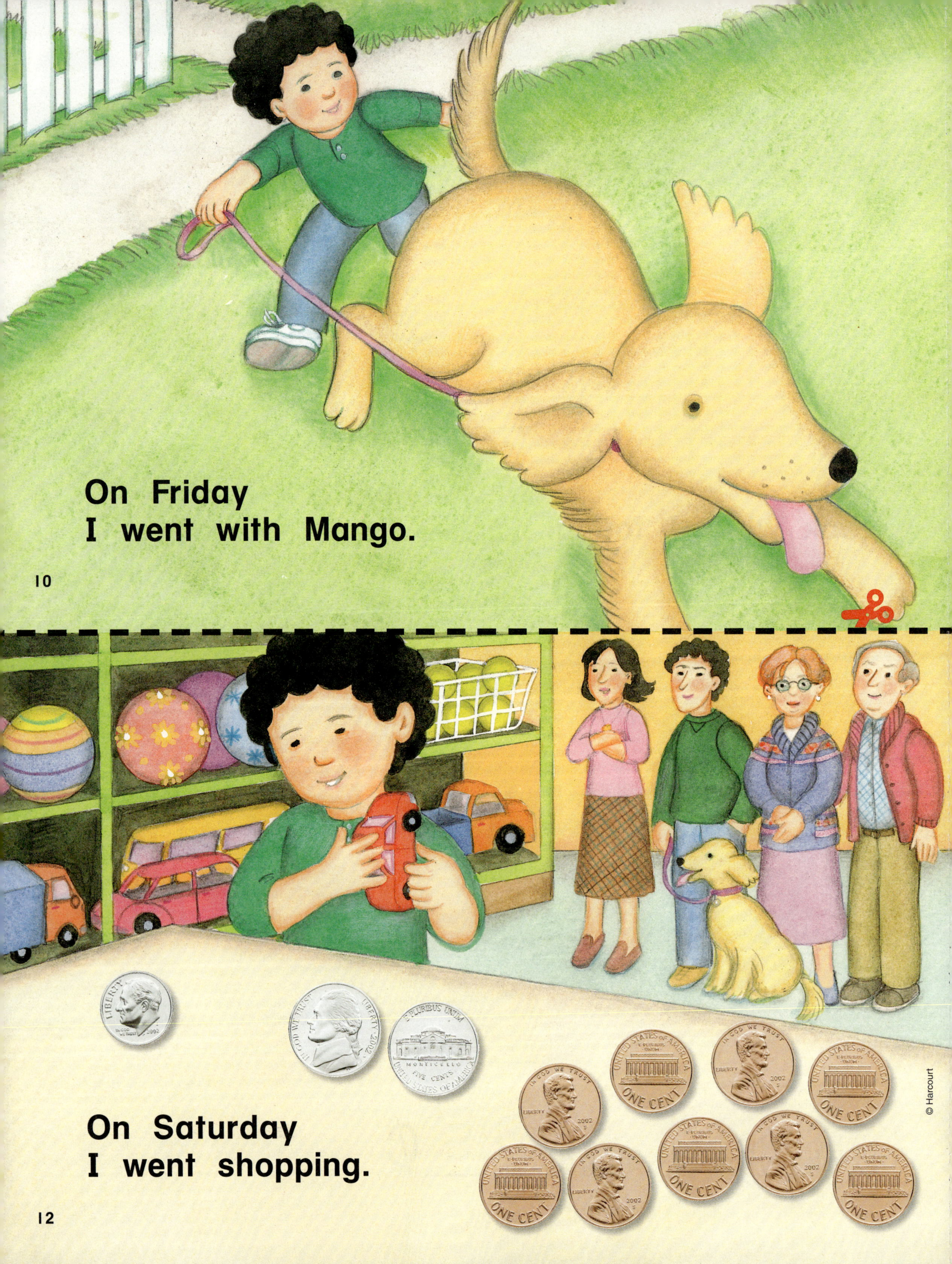

On Friday
I went with Mango.

On Saturday
I went shopping.

Name ______________________________

Review

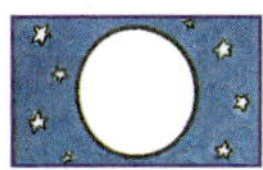

March

Sunday	Monday	Tuesday	Wednesday	Thursday	Friday	Saturday
	1	2	3	4	5	6
7	8	9	10	11	12	13
14	15	16	17	18	19	20
21	22	23	24	25	26	27
28	29	30	31			

______ **Wednesdays**

______ **Fridays**

What times of day do the pictures show? Circle the time of day that is missing.

Count the Wednesdays. Write how many.

Count the Fridays. Write how many.

Circle the activity that takes more time.

CHAPTER 8 • REVIEW

Cumulative Review

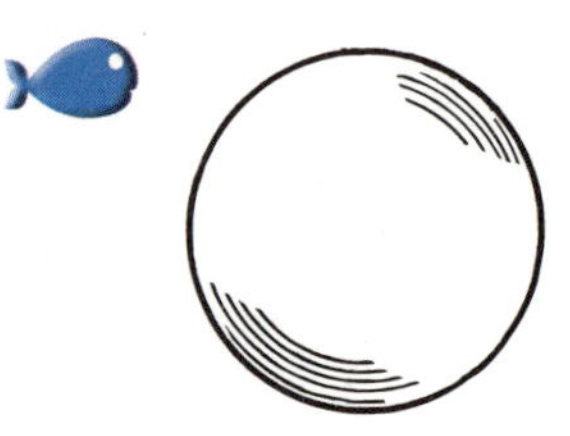
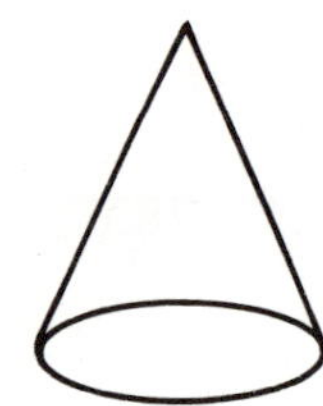
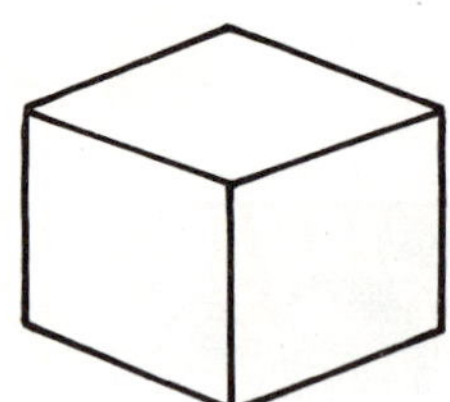
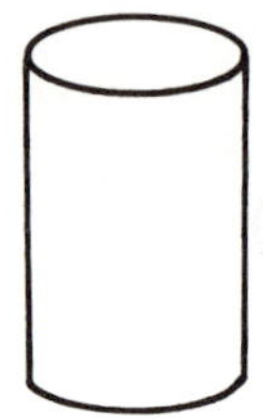

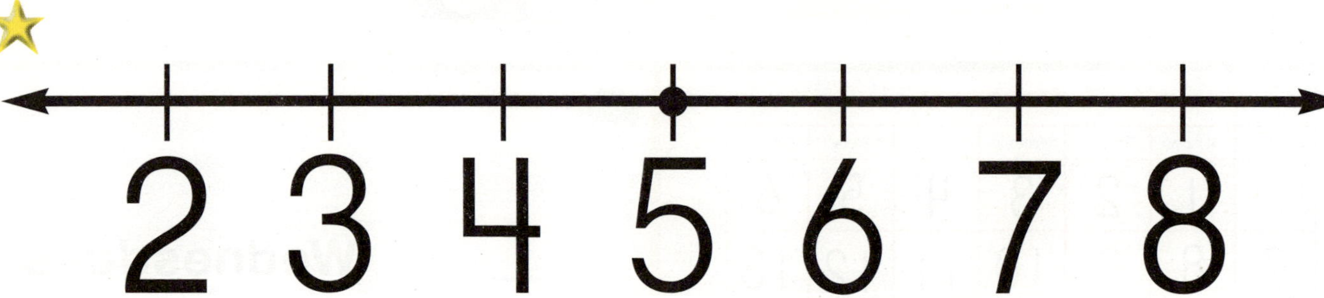

Use blue to color the cylinder. Use red to color the sphere. Use yellow to color the cube. Use green to color the cone.

Use green to circle the shape with curves. Use purple to circle the shapes with four sides. Use orange to circle the shape with three corners.

Put your finger on 5. Count up 2. What number are you on? Circle the number.

Write how many cents. Circle the coins that show 5¢.

Circle the activity that takes more time.

Name ______________________________

Test

_____ ¢

_____ ¢

March

Sunday	Monday	Tuesday	Wednesday	Thursday	Friday	Saturday
	1	2	3	4	5	6
7	8	9	10	11	12	13
14	15	16	17	18	19	20
21	22	23	24	25	26	27
28	29	30	31			

_____ **Saturdays**

_____ **Days in March**

- Write how many cents.
- What times of day do the pictures show? Circle the time of day that is missing.
- Count the Saturdays. Write how many.
- Write how many days in March.
- Circle the activity that takes less time.

CHALLENGE

Dimes and Nickels

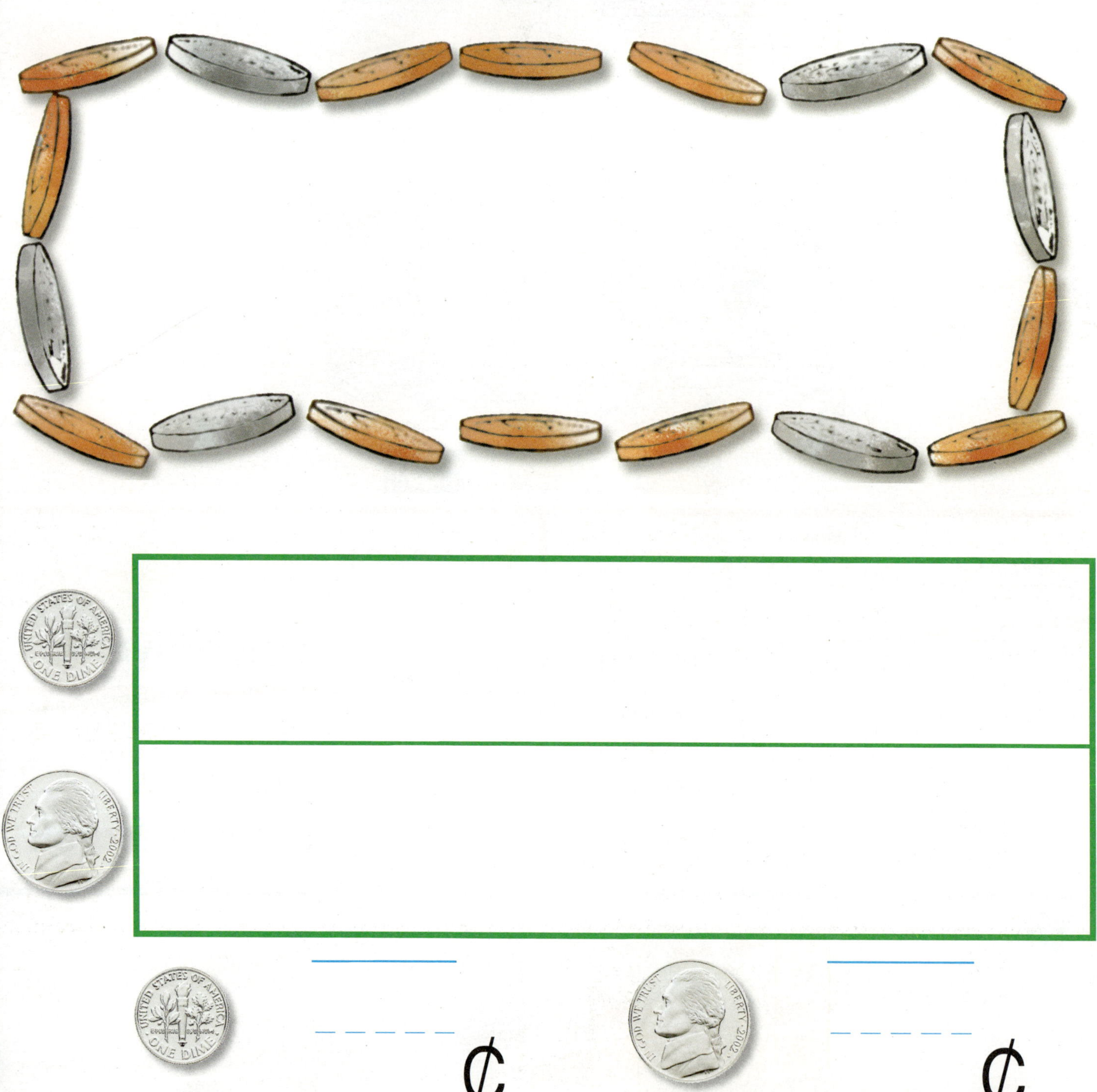

___ ¢ ___ ¢

Place a handful of dimes and nickels on the workspace. Sort the coins by kind. Move the coins to the box. Count the dimes by tens, write how many cents. Count the nickels by fives. Write how many cents. Circle the amount that shows the greater value.

CHAPTER
9
Measurement
HARCOURT
Math
Carrot
Beets
Pumpkin
Beans
© Harcourt
Harcourt

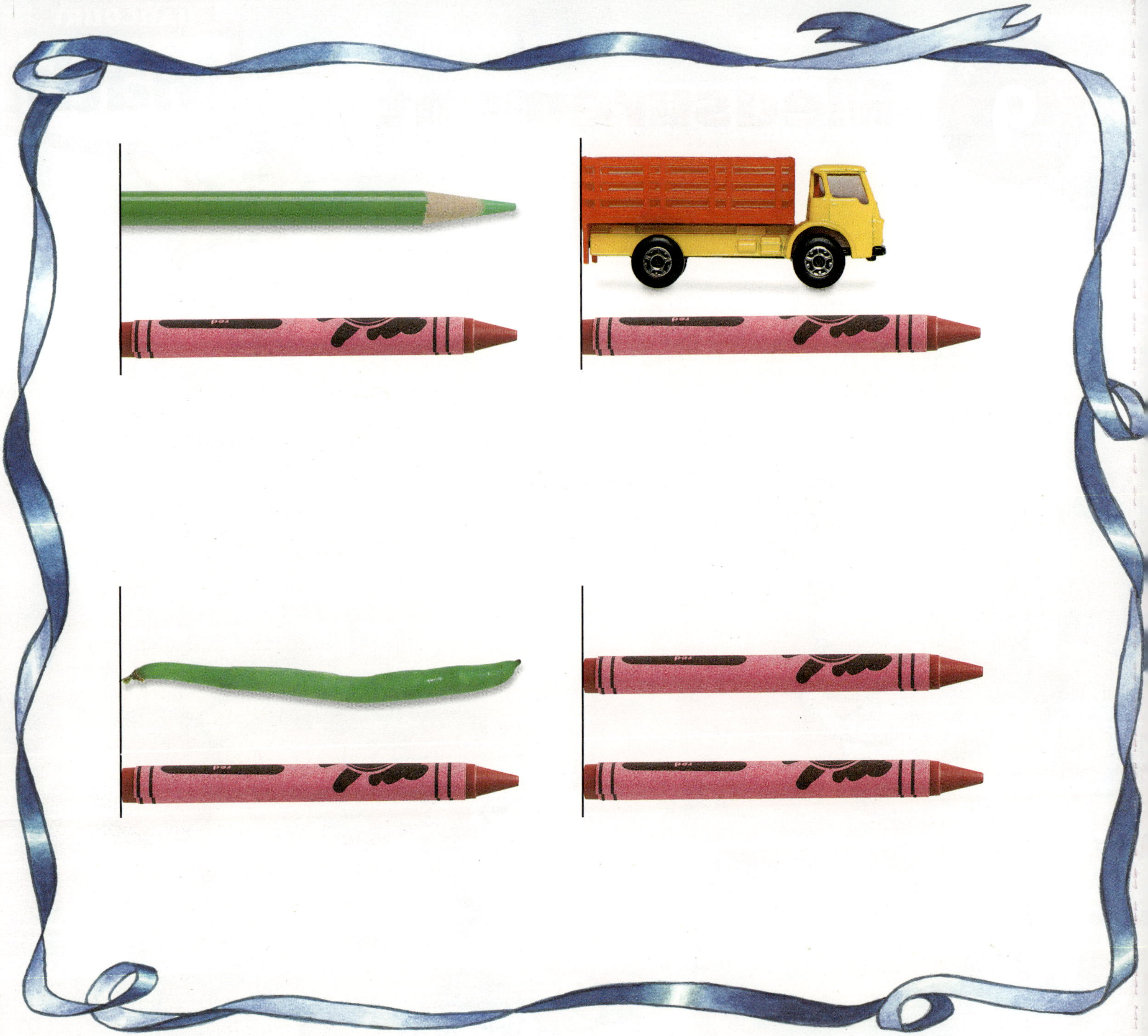

Circle the objects that are about as long as one red crayon.

Grateful acknowledgment is made to Troll Communications L. L. C. for permission to reprint the cover illustration by Cheryl Nathan from *The Long and Short of It* by Cheryl Nathan and Lisa McCourt. Illustration copyright © 1998 by Cheryl Nathan.

Printed in the United States of America

Photography Credits:

All photography by Harcourt photographers listed, © Harcourt: Weronica Ankarorn, Victoria Bowen, Ken Kinzie, Sheri O'Neal, Quebecor Imaging, and Terry Sinclair.

Illustration Credits:

Shirley Beckes: 221, 222; **Rose Mary Berlin:** 215, 218; **Nan Brooks:** 235, 236; **Shelley Dieterichs:** 223, 224, storybook; **Judy Love:** 231, 232; **Stephanie Peterson:** 225, 226.

15 16 17 18 19 20 1678 16 15 14 13 12 11
4500311726

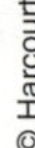

SCHOOL HOME CONNECTION

Dear Family,

Today we started a new chapter, Measurement. We will learn to measure how long objects are. We will also compare how much different containers hold and how heavy different objects are.

Love,

____

Vocabulary Power

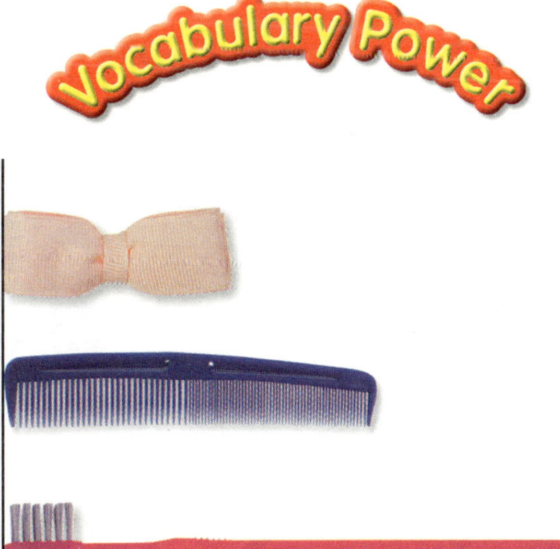

shortest, longest

The bow is the shortest. The toothbrush is the longest.

ACTIVITY

- Help your child compare an earlier height measurement with his or her height today.
- Have your child compare the amounts of water two different plastic containers hold.

BOOKS TO SHARE

To read about measurement with your child, look for these books at your local library.

The Long and Short of It, by Cheryl Nathan and Lisa McCourt. Bridgewater Books, 1998.

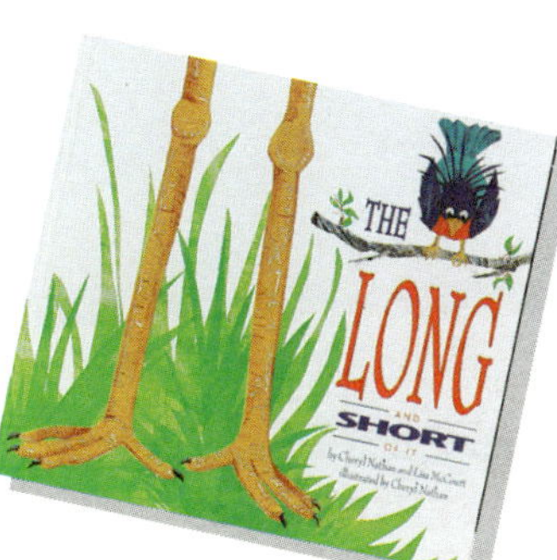

Inch by Inch, by Leo Lionni. Morrow, 1995.

Twice My Size, by Adrian Mitchell. Millbrook, 1999.

Visit *The Learning Site* for additional ideas and activities. www.harcourtschool.com

MATH GAME

MY HOME

longer than
shorter than
wider than
taller than
thicker than
thinner than

MATERIALS: classroom book, paper clip, pencil
DIRECTIONS: Play with a partner and decide who goes first. Players take turns spinning the spinner and finding objects that are longer than, shorter than, wider than, taller than, thicker than, or thinner than a book. The first player to use all sections of the spinner wins.

Name ______________________________

Compare Lengths

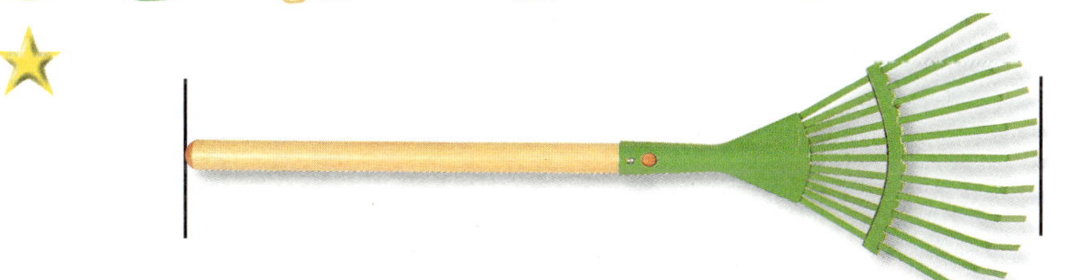

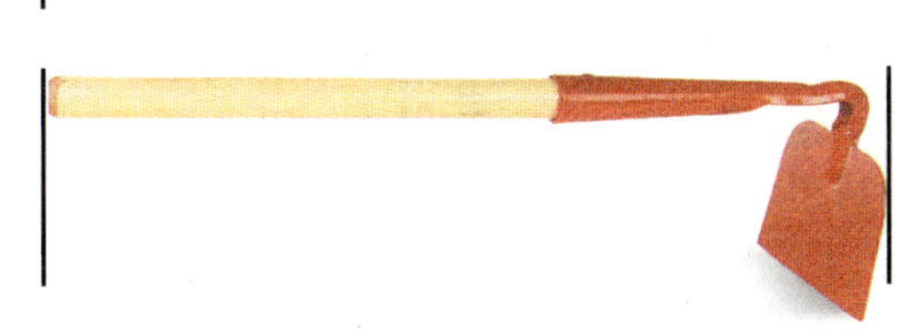

Circle the longer object. Draw a line under the shorter object.

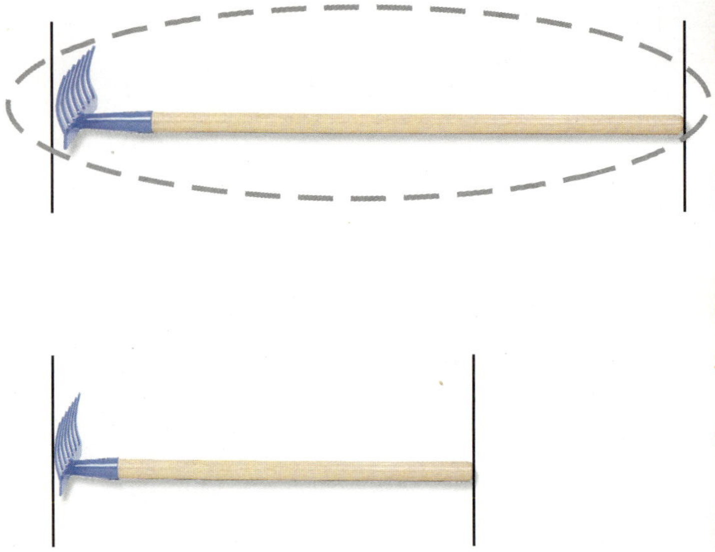

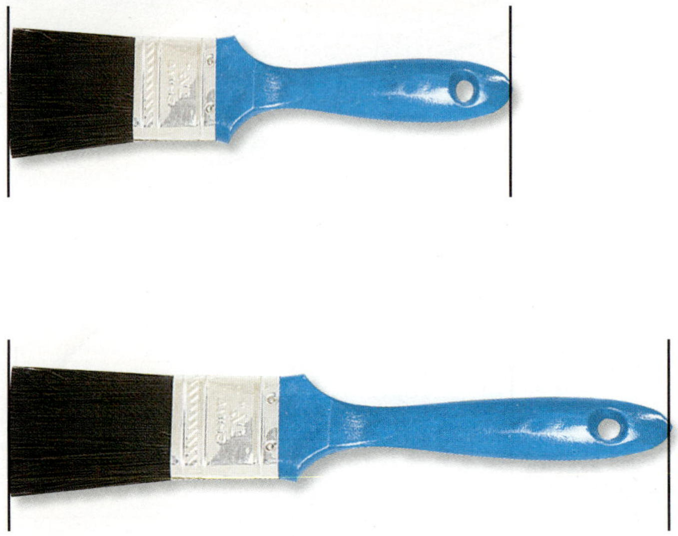

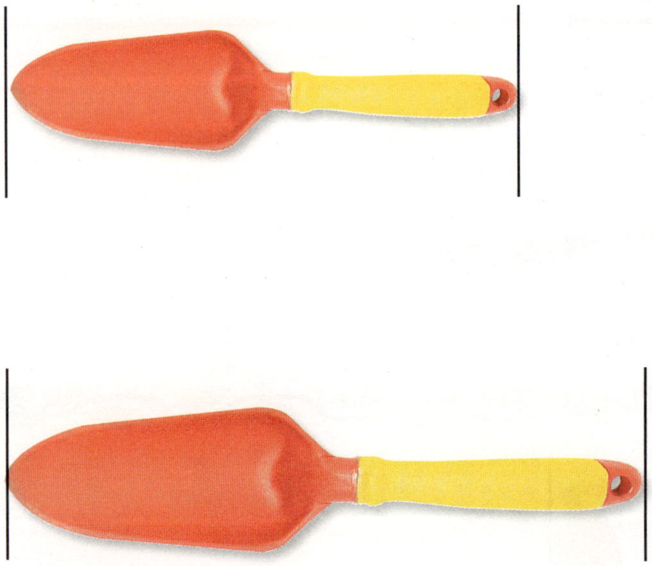

Circle the longer object. Draw a line under the shorter object.

HOME ACTIVITY • Have your child compare the lengths of a fork and a spoon and tell which is longer.

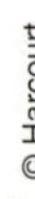

Name ____________________

Order Lengths

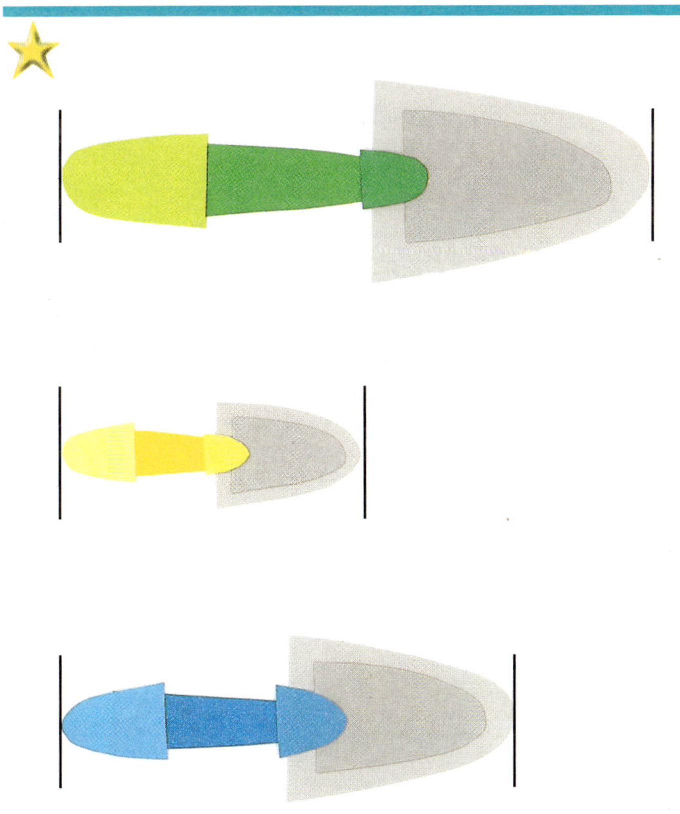

Circle the groups of objects that are in order from shortest to longest, starting at the top.

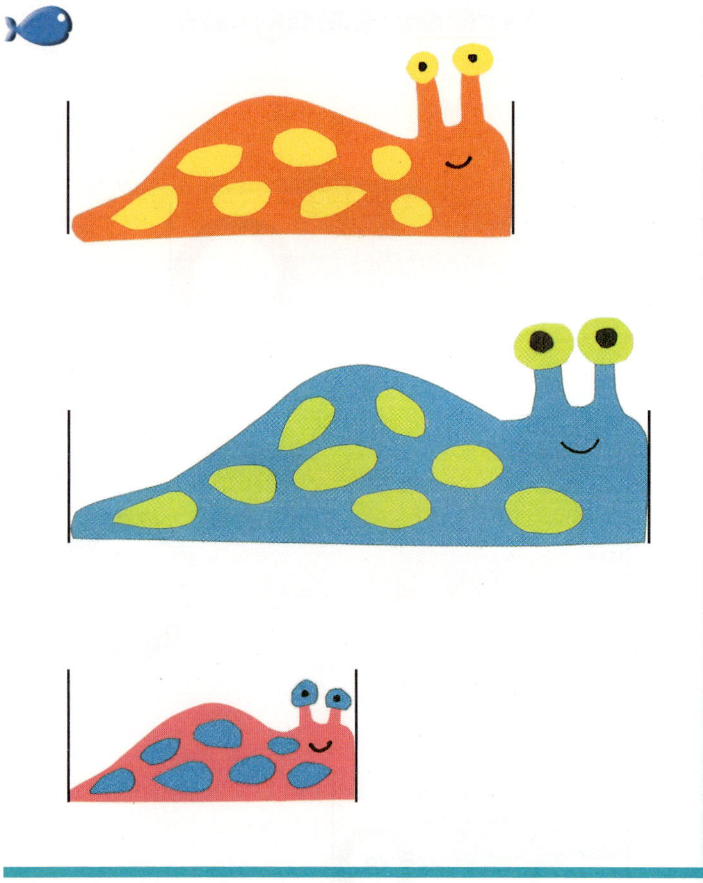

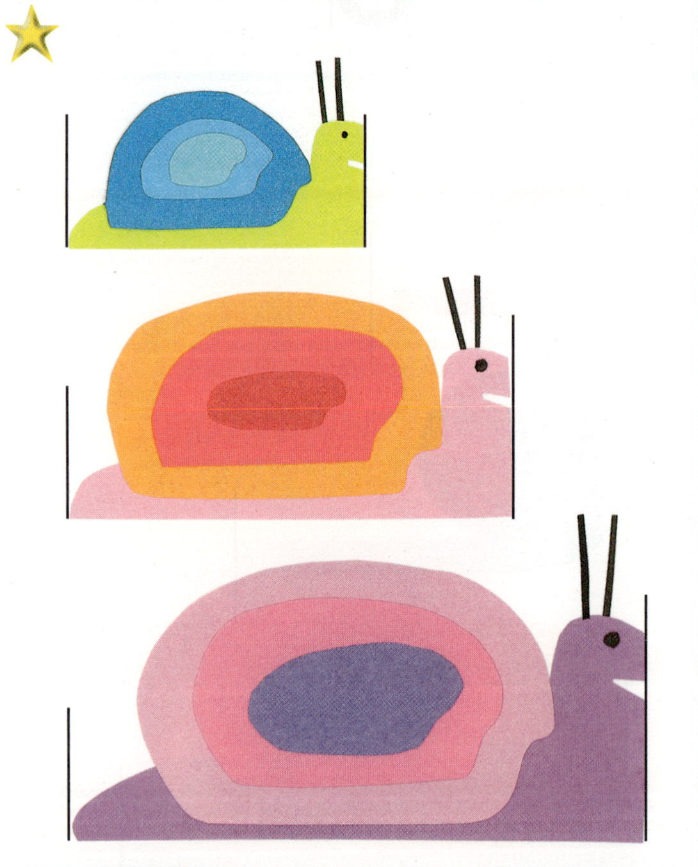

Circle the groups of objects that are in order from shortest to longest, starting at the top.

HOME ACTIVITY • Have your child put a teaspoon, a tablespoon, and a serving spoon in order from shortest to longest.

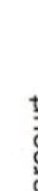

Name ____________________

Indirect Comparison

Go on a measurement walk. Use yarn of different colors to measure the counter and the door. Cut the yarn and compare the two pieces. Circle the picture of the place where you used the longer piece.

Use yarn of different colors to measure the desk and the shelves. Cut the yarn and compare the two pieces. Circle the picture of the place where you used the longer piece.

Go on a measurement walk. Use yarn of different colors to measure the table and the bulletin board. Cut the yarn and compare the two pieces. Circle the picture of the place where you used the shorter piece.

Use yarn of different colors to measure the easel and the chair. Cut the yarn and compare the two pieces. Circle the picture of the place where you used the shorter piece.

HOME ACTIVITY • Have your child explain how he or she used yarn of different colors to compare the lengths of large classroom objects.

Name ____________________

Measure Lengths with Nonstandard Units

cubes

cubes

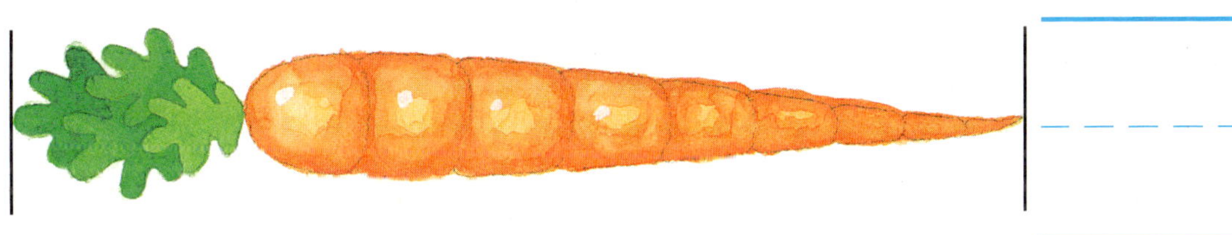

cubes

cubes

Use cubes to measure the vegetable. About how many cubes long is it? Write the number.

cubes

cubes

cubes

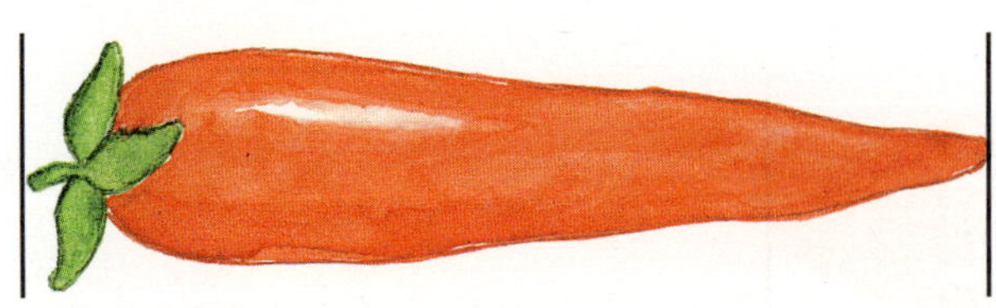

cubes

Use cubes to measure the vegetable. About how many cubes long is it? Write the number.

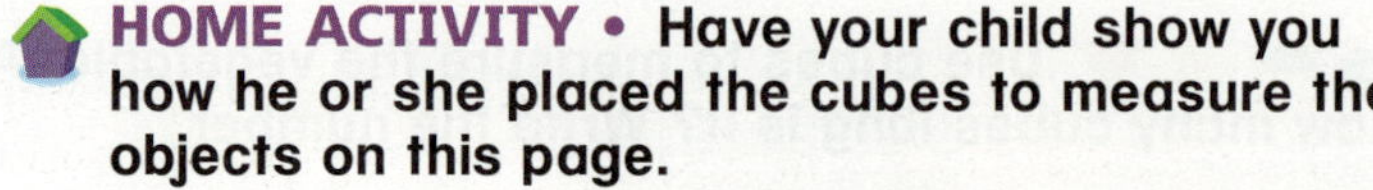

HOME ACTIVITY • Have your child show you how he or she placed the cubes to measure the objects on this page.

Name ______________________

Estimate and Measure

Estimate ______ paper clips

Measure 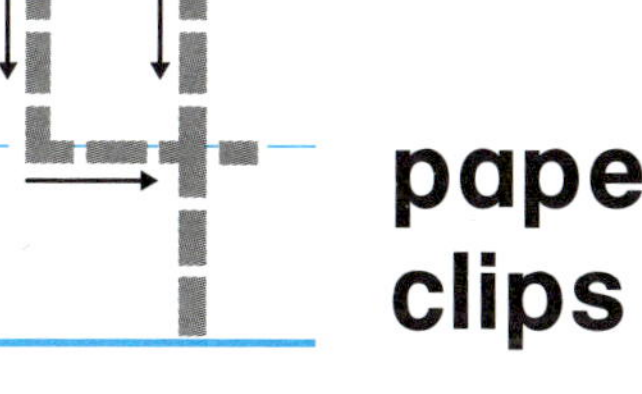 paper clips

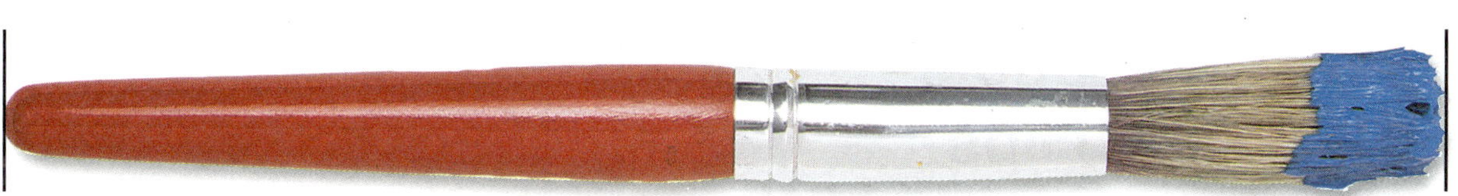

Estimate ______ paper clips

Measure ______ paper clips

Estimate ______ paper clips

Measure ______ paper clips

Estimate about how many paper clips long the object is. Then measure. Write about how many paper clips long it is.

Estimate ______ paper clips   Measure ______ paper clips

Estimate ______ paper clips   Measure ______ paper clips

Estimate ______ paper clips   Measure ______ paper clips

Estimate about how many paper clips long the object is. Then measure. Write about how many paper clips long it is.

HOME ACTIVITY • Have your child estimate the lengths of objects in paper clips and then measure them to check.

Name ______

Review

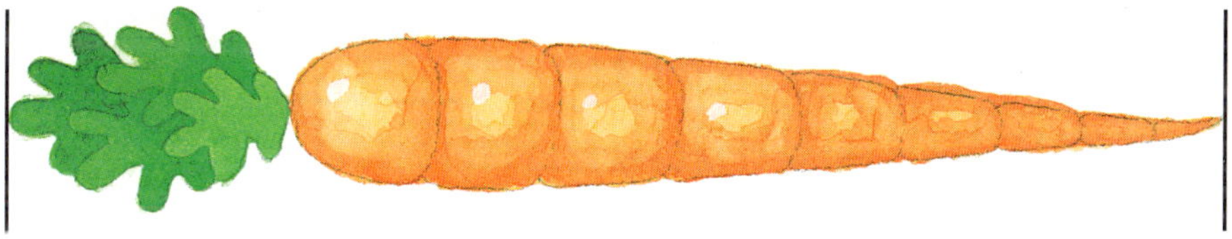

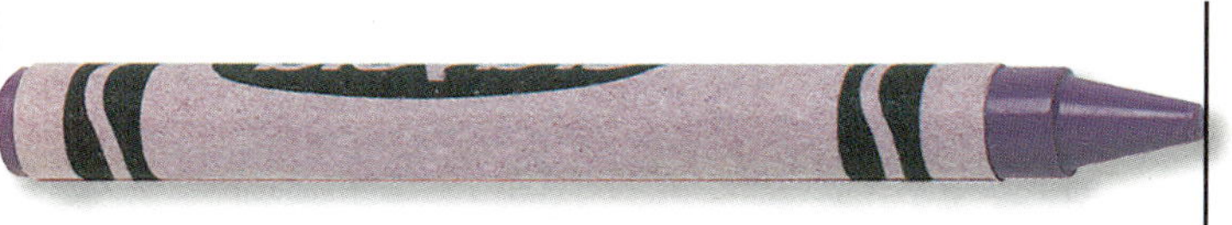

cubes

Estimate ______ paper clips

Measure ______ paper clips

Circle the longer object. Underline the shorter object.

Use yarn in different colors to measure the teacher's desk and your table. Cut the yarn and compare the two pieces. Circle the picture of the place where you used the longer piece.

Use cubes to measure the carrot. Write the number that tells about how many cubes long it is.

Estimate about how many paper clips long the crayon is. Then measure. Write about how many paper clips long it is.

Cumulative Review

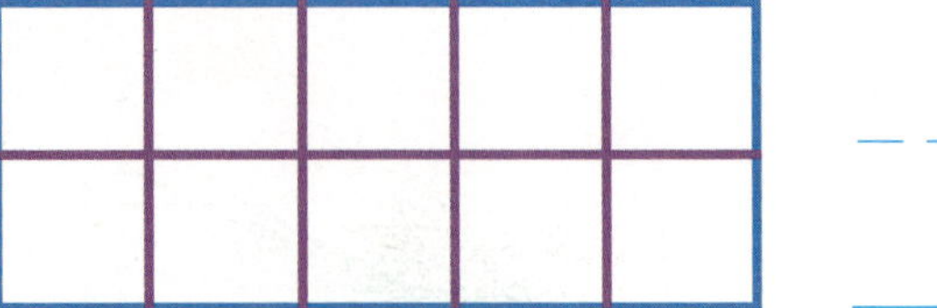

March

Sunday	Monday	Tuesday	Wednesday	Thursday	Friday	Saturday
	1	2	3	4	5	6
7	8	9	10	11	12	13
14	15	16	17	18	19	20
21	22	23	24	25	26	27
28	29	30	31			

Days in March

Draw more Xs to show the number. Write the number.
Count the pennies. Write how many cents.
Look at the calendar. Write how many days in March.
Circle the group of objects that are in order from shortest to longest, starting at the top.

Name ______________________

Compare Capacity

Circle the container that holds more. Mark an X on the container that holds less.

Circle the container that holds more. Mark an X on the container that holds less.

HOME ACTIVITY • Set out several small food items, such as marshmallows, or larger ones, such as apples. Ask your child to find a container that is just the right size to hold them.

Name ______________________________

Compare Weight

Left

Right

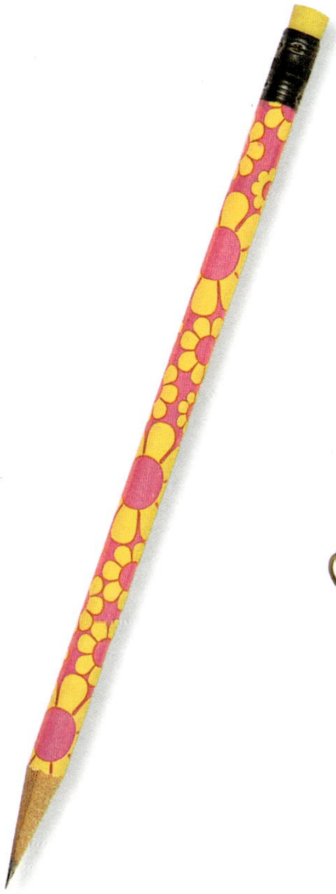

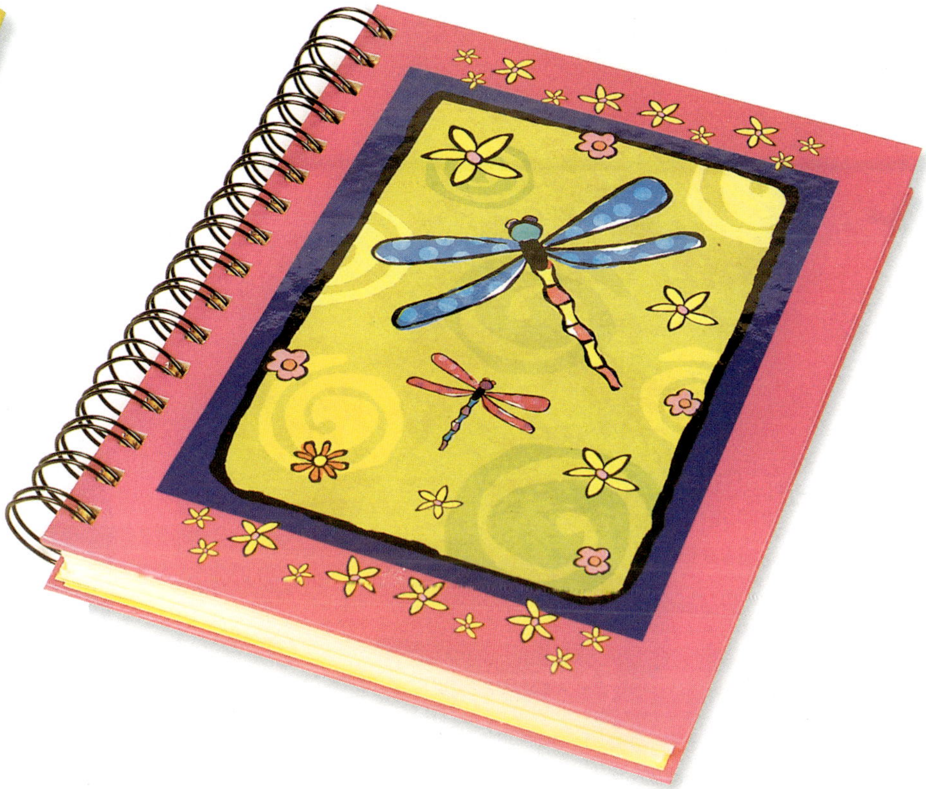

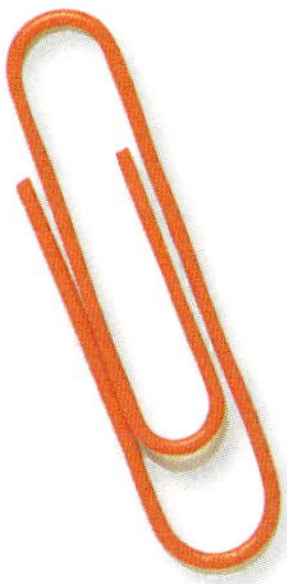

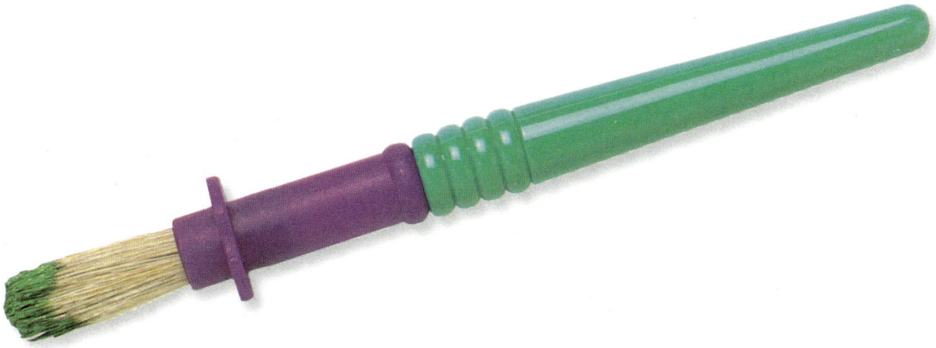

Hold one object in your left hand and one object in your right hand. Circle the picture of the object that feels heavier.

Left

Right

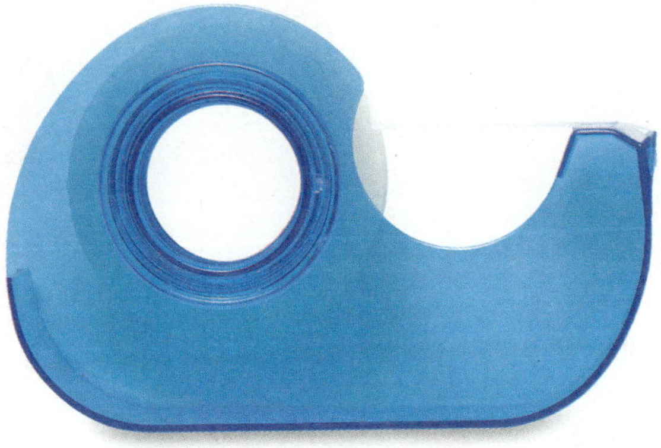

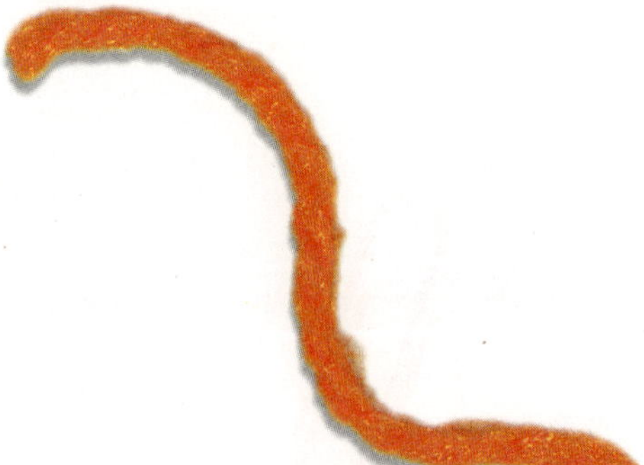

Hold one object in your left hand and one object in your right hand. Mark an X on the picture of the object that feels lighter.

HOME ACTIVITY • Give your child two objects of clearly different weights. Have him or her hold one in each hand and tell which feels heavier.

Name ______________________________

Problem Solving Skill
Use a Picture

What is wrong in this picture? Circle the things that are unlikely to happen when the weather is hot.
What is wrong in this picture? Circle the things that are unlikely to happen when the weather is cold.

Use red to circle the pictures that most likely show hot weather. Use blue to circle the pictures that most likely show cold weather.

HOME ACTIVITY • Have your child describe what he or she would wear when the weather is hot and when it is cold.

Look in the Garden

By ______________________________

HOME ACTIVITY • This book will help review measurement. Invite your child to share this book with you.

Circle the shorter worm.

Circle the longer caterpillar.

Circle the longest cricket.

Circle the shortest lizard.

Circle the lighter object.

Circle the heavier object.

© Harcourt

Circle the basket that holds more.

Circle the bucket that holds less.

Is it hot or cold? How do you know?

Is it hot or cold?
How do you know?

Look in the garden.
What do you see?

Name ____________________

Review

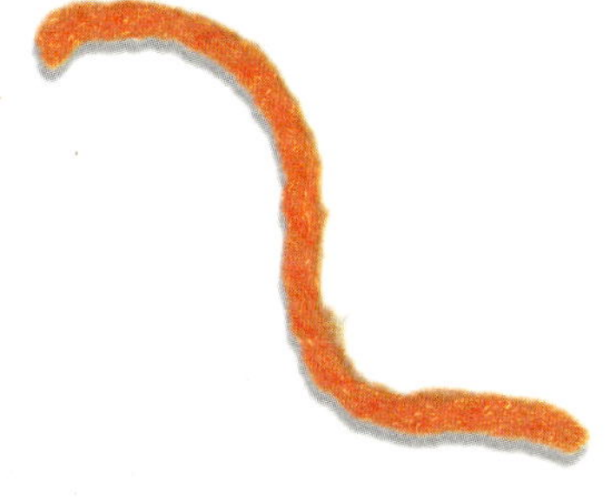

Circle the container that holds more. Mark an X on the container that holds less.

Hold one object in your left hand and one object in your right hand. Mark an X on the object that feels heavier.

Use red to circle the picture that most likely shows hot weather. Use blue to circle the picture that most likely shows cold weather.

Cumulative Review

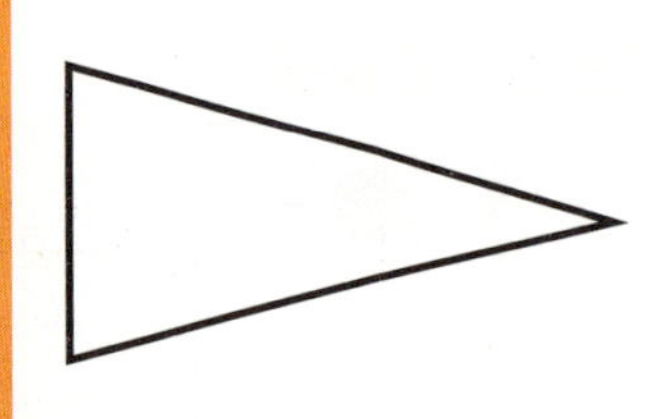

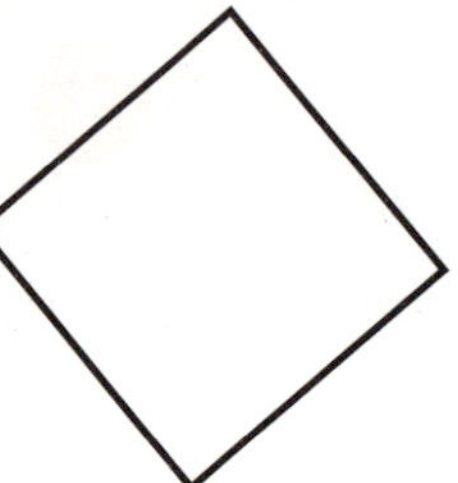

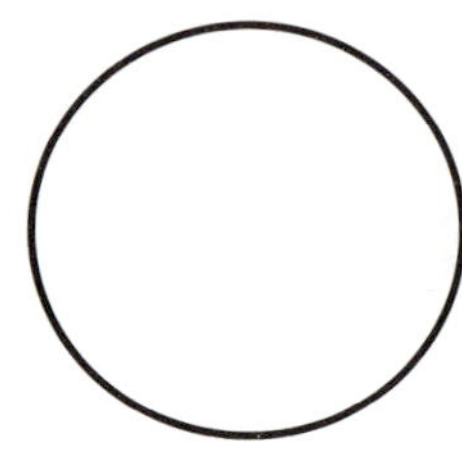

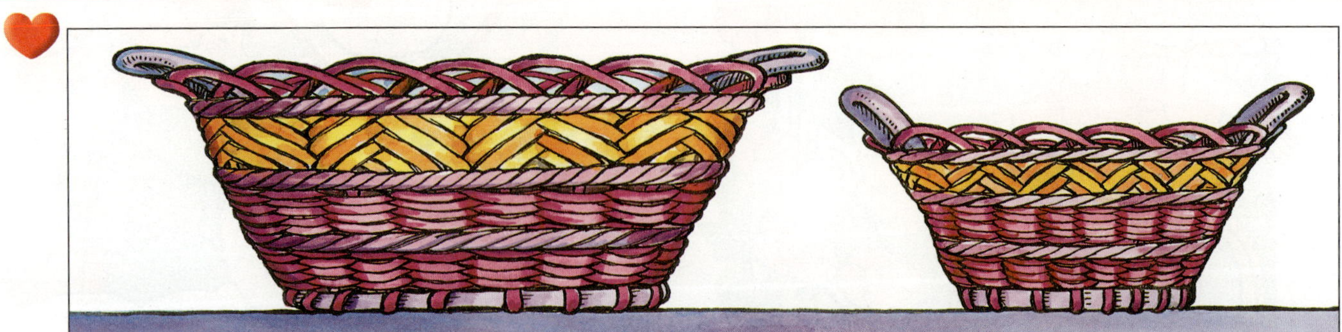

Look at the object at the beginning of the row. Color in the outline that matches the shape of the object.

Use yellow to color the numbers you say when you count by fives. Use blue to circle the numbers you say when you count by tens. What patterns do you see?

Go on a measurement walk. Use yarn of different colors to measure the desk and the shelves. Cut the yarn and compare the two pieces. Circle the picture of the place where you used the longer piece.

Circle the container that holds more. Mark an X on the container that holds less.

Name ______________________________

Test

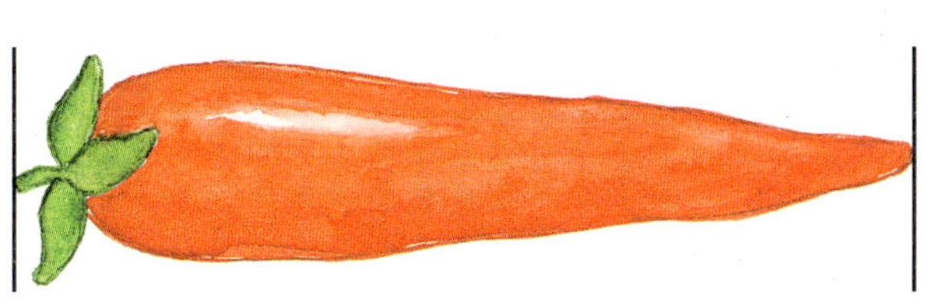

______ cubes

Circle the group of objects that are in order from shortest to longest, starting at the top.

Use cubes to measure the vegetable. About how many cubes long is it? Write the number.

Circle the container that holds more. Mark an X on the container that holds less.

Hold one object in your left hand and one object in your right hand. Mark an X on the object that feels lighter.

CHALLENGE

How Far?

short steps

LONG STEPS

short steps

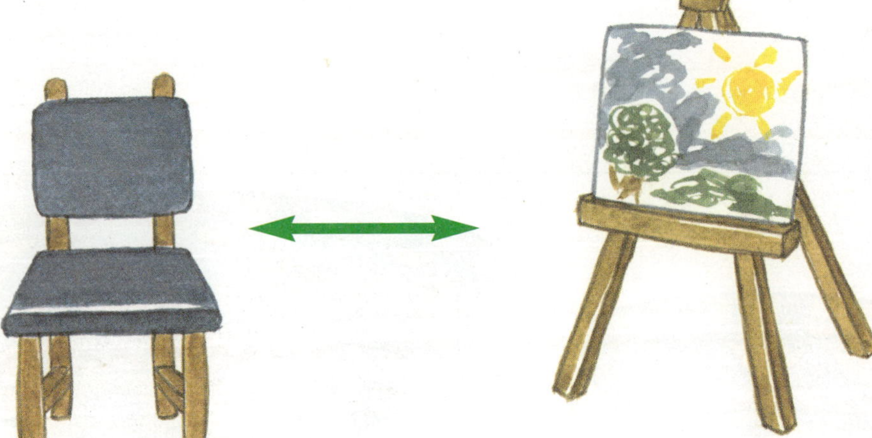

LONG STEPS

short steps

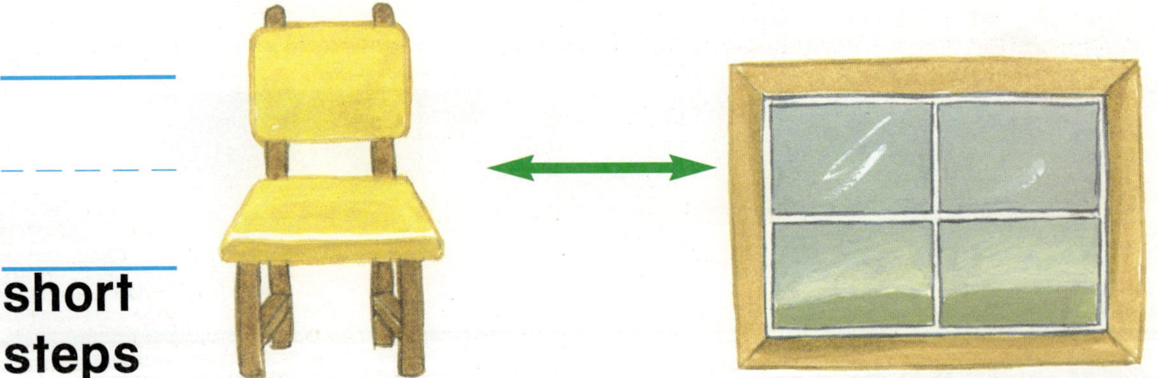

LONG STEPS

Use short steps to measure how far it is from you
place. Write the number of short steps you walke
Use LONG STEPS to measure how far it is from y
place. Write the number of LONG STEPS you walk

9780153527111
TP
APEX

HARCOURT Math

CHAPTER 10 Data, Graphing, and Probability

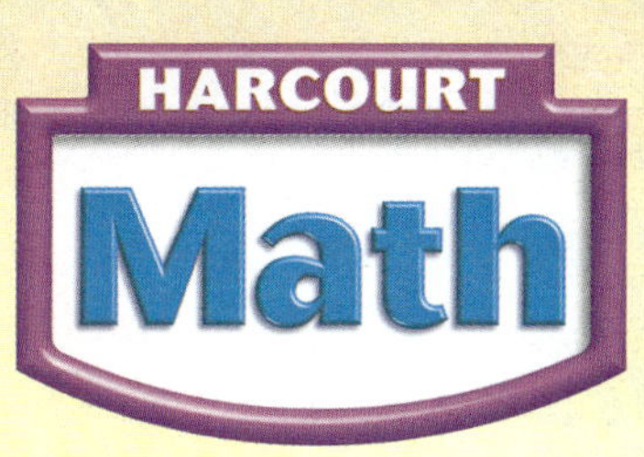

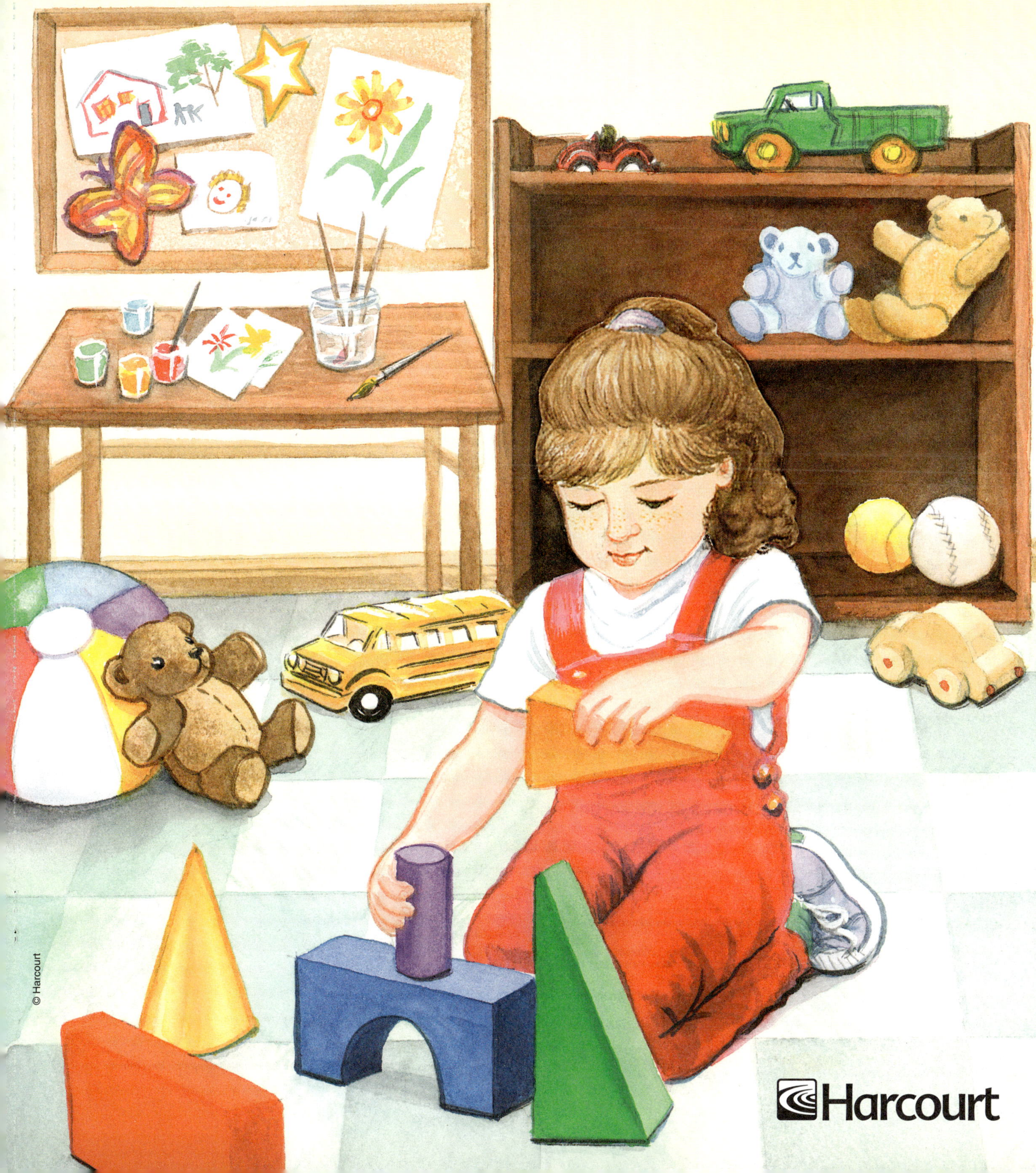

Harcourt

Sort the shapes. Draw your groups in the sorting rings.

For permission to reprint copyrighted material, grateful acknowledgment is made to the following sources:

Barefoot Books Ltd.: Cover illustration by Debbie Harter from *Bear in a Square* by Stella Blackstone. Illustration copyright © 1998 by Debbie Harter.

Margaret K. McElderry Books, Simon & Schuster Children's Publishing Division: Cover illustration by Keiko Narahashi from *What's what?* by Mary Serfozo. Illustration copyright © 1996 by Keiko Narahashi.

Random House Children's Books, a division of Random House, Inc.: Cover illustration by Jose Aruego and Ariane Dewey from *Five Little Ducks* by Raffi. Illustration copyright © 1989 by Jose Aruego and Ariane Dewey.

Printed in the United States of America

Photography Credits:

All photography by Harcourt photographers listed, © Harcourt: Weronica Ankarorn, Victoria Bowen, Ken Kinzie, Sheri O'Neal, Quebecor Imaging, and Terry Sinclair.

Illustration Credits:

Joe Boddy: 245, 246, 251, 252, 255, 256, 259, 260, 263, 264; **Sharon Holm:** 247, 248, 249, 250; **Richard Kolding:** 261, 262; **Kurt Nagahori:** 244; **Ken Spengler:** storybook; **Matt Straub:** 242, 243; **Stan Tusan:** 257, 258; **Mary O'Keefe Young:** cover.

15 16 17 18 19 20 1678 16 15 14 13 12 11
4500311726

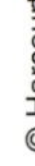

SCHOOL HOME CONNECTION

Dear Family,

Today we started a new chapter, Data, Graphing, and Probability. In this chapter we will learn more about graphs and about tally tables. We will also learn when something is more likely or less likely to happen.

Love,

____

Vocabulary Power

tally marks

Lunch

tally table

Visit *The Learning Site* for additional ideas and activities. www.harcourtschool.com

- Give your child several buttons, some with two holes and some with four holes. Have him or her sort the buttons. Then ask your child to make a tally table showing how he or she sorted.

BOOKS TO SHARE

To read more about data and graphing with your child, look for these books in your local library.

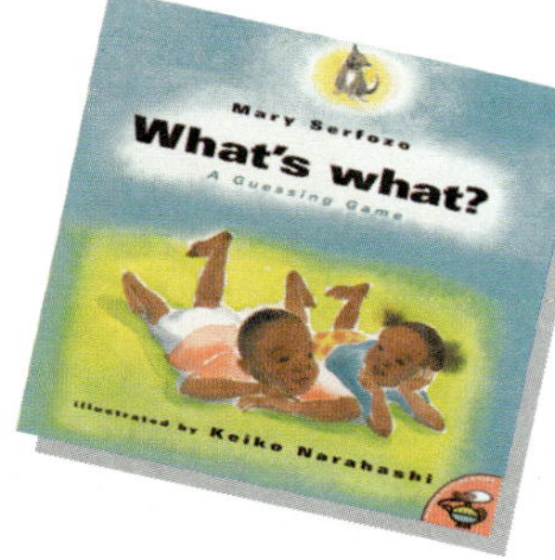

What's what?
by Mary Serfozo. Simon & Schuster, 1996.

Is It Rough? Is It Smooth? Is It Shiny?
by Tana Hoban. Greenwillow, 1984.

Who Hops?
by Katie Davis. Harcourt, 1998.

MATERIALS: crayons, paper clip, pencils
DIRECTIONS: Play with a partner and decide who goes first. The first player spins the spinner and draws that shape in the correct column of his or her graph. Take turns. The first player to fill a column wins.

Name ____________________ **Make Concrete Graphs**

How Many Pennies and Nickels?

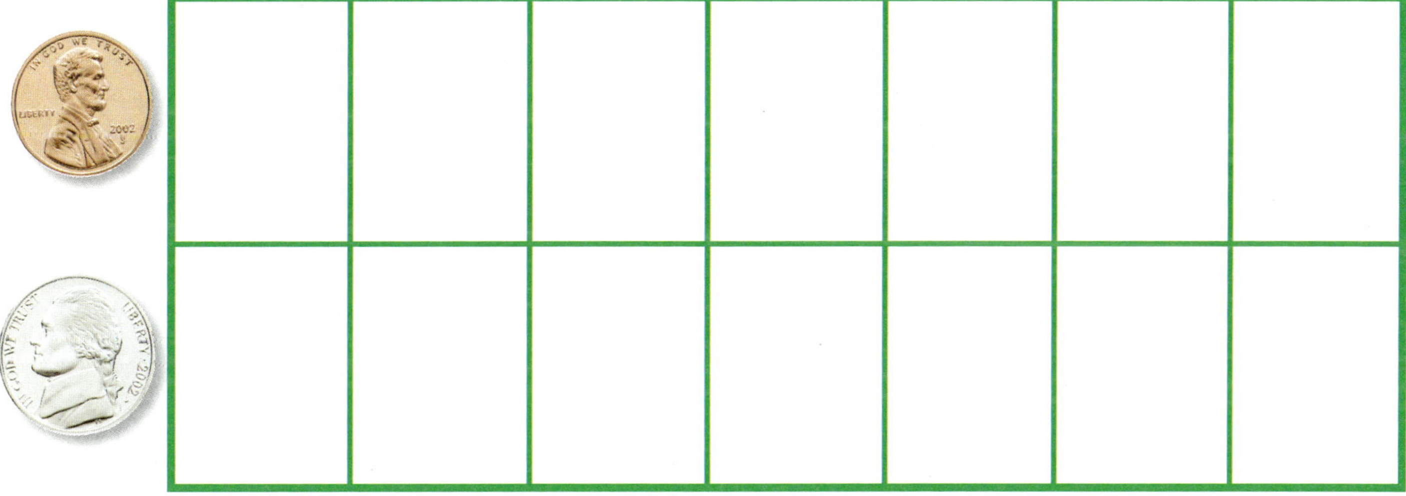

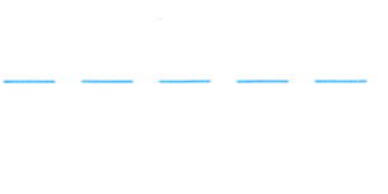

penny nickel

Place a handful of coins on the workspace. Sort your coins.
Make a graph with your coins.
Write how many of each coin. Circle the number that shows more coins. Mark an X on the number that shows fewer coins.

How Many Coins?

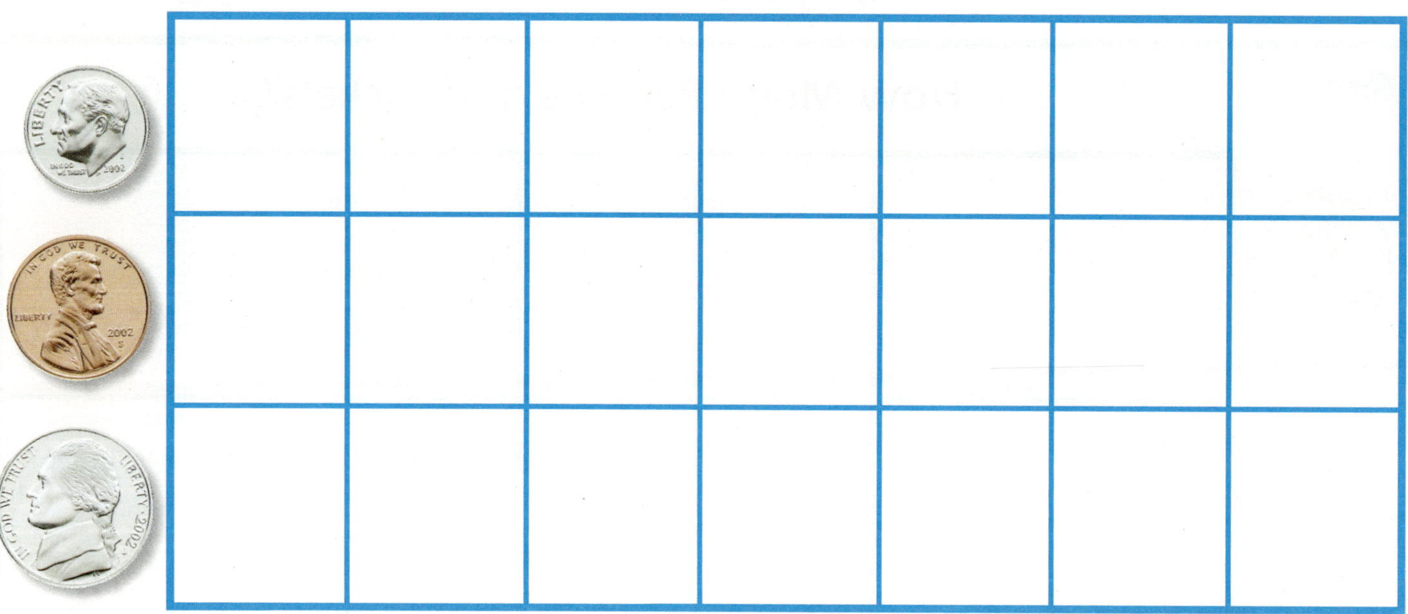

dime **penny** **nickel**

Place a handful of coins on the workspace. Sort your coins.
Make a graph with your coins.
Write how many of each coin. Circle the number that shows the most coins. Mark an X on the number that shows the fewest coins.

HOME ACTIVITY • Have your child explain to you how he or she made the coin graph on this page.

Name ________________________

Read Picture Graphs

Where We Played

Use the graph. Write how many in each group.
Circle the place where more children played.

Books We Read

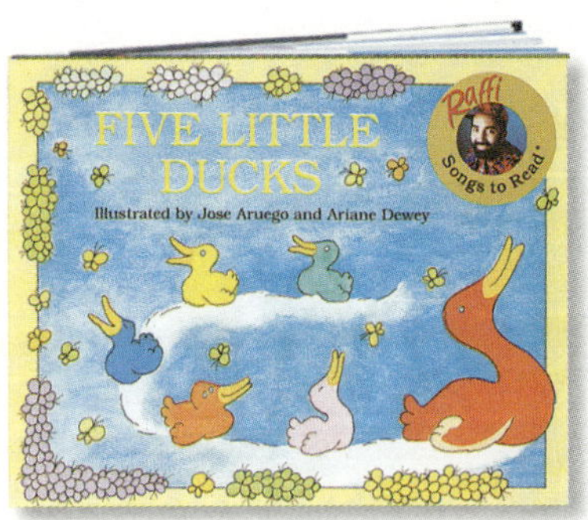

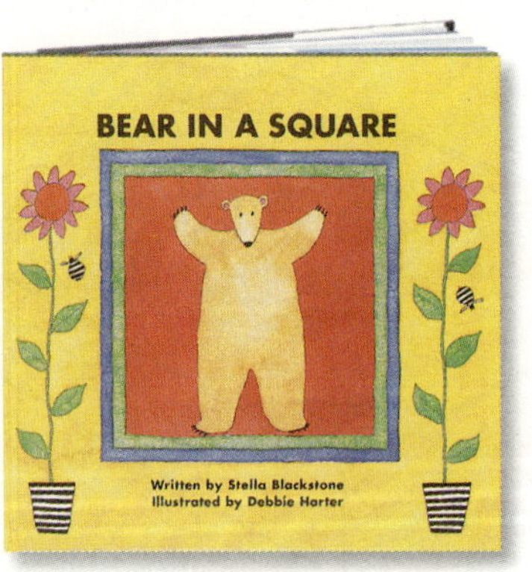

Use the graph. Write how many in each group.
Circle the book that fewer children read.

HOME ACTIVITY • Ask your child to explain how the graph on this page shows which book more children read.

Name ______________________________

Make Picture Graphs

Shirts

Look at the picture. Make a picture graph about plain shirts and striped shirts.

Write how many of each kind of shirt. Circle the number that shows more.

Girls and Boys in the Library

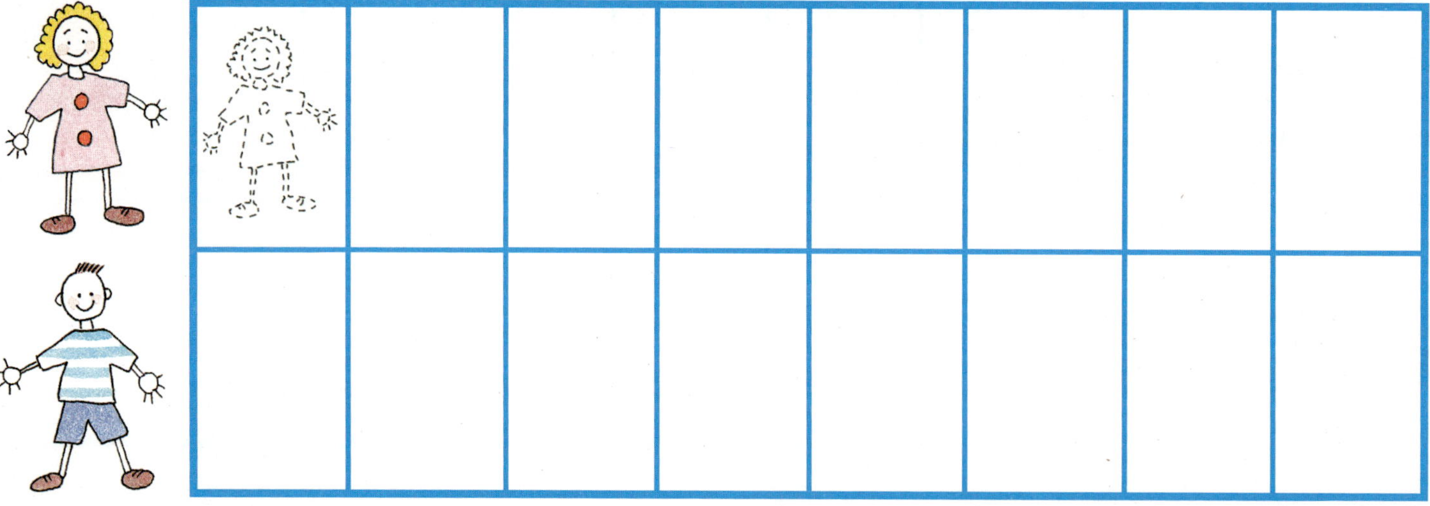

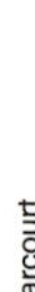

Look at the picture. Make a graph about girls and boys.
Write how many girls and how many boys. Circle the number that shows fewer.

HOME ACTIVITY • Have your child explain the graph he or she made on this page.

Name ___________________________

Problem Solving Skill
Use Data from a Graph

Party Balloons

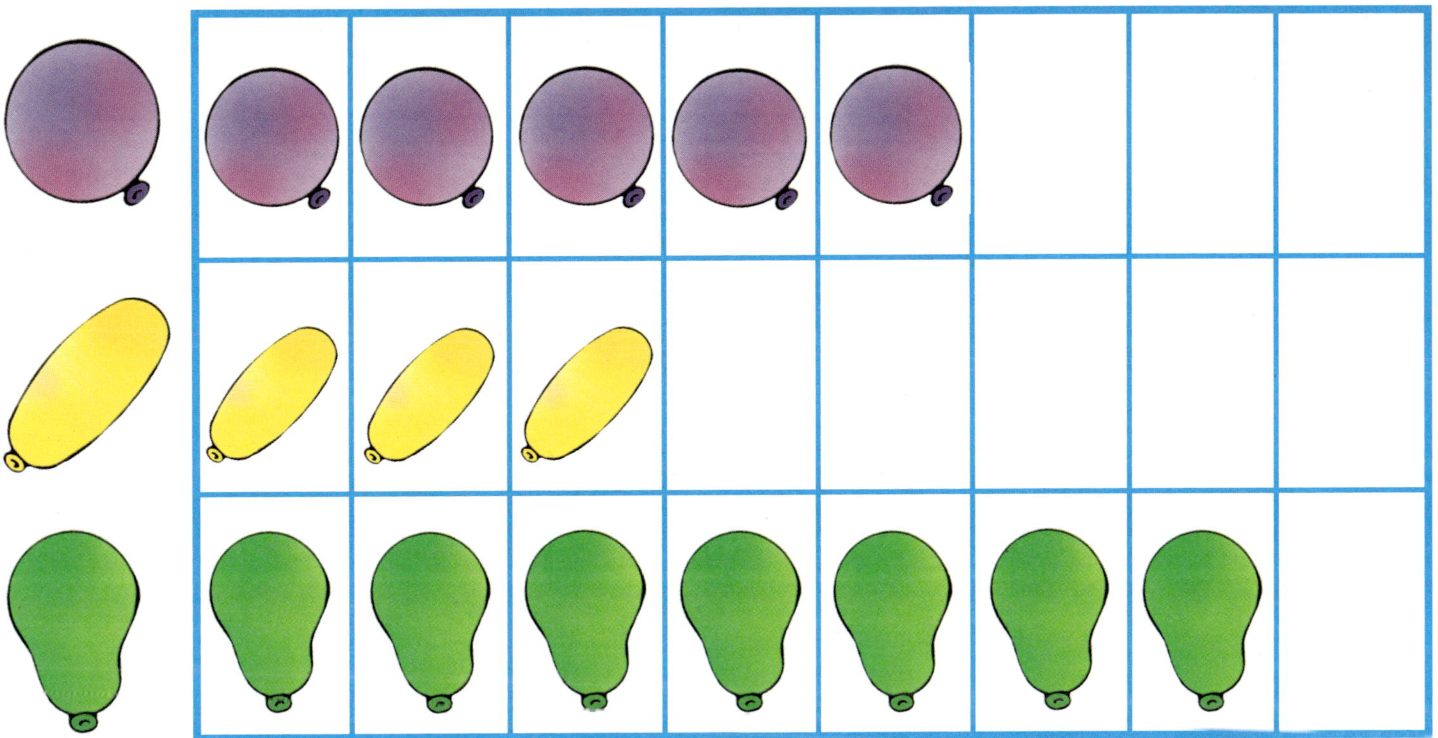

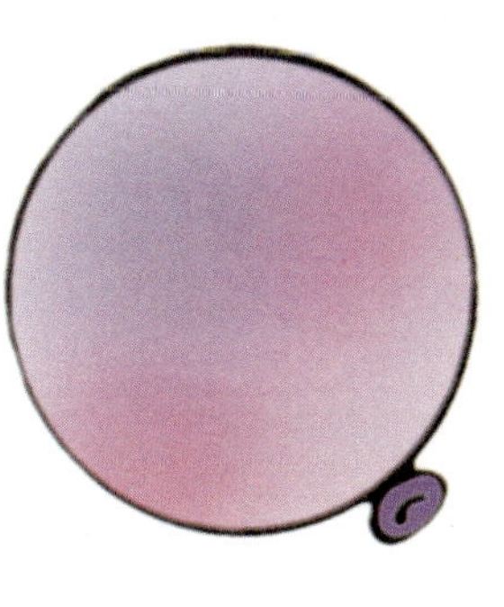

Look at the graph. Write how many of each kind of balloon. Circle the number that shows the most balloons. Mark an X on the number that shows the fewest balloons.

PROBLEM SOLVING

Party Gifts

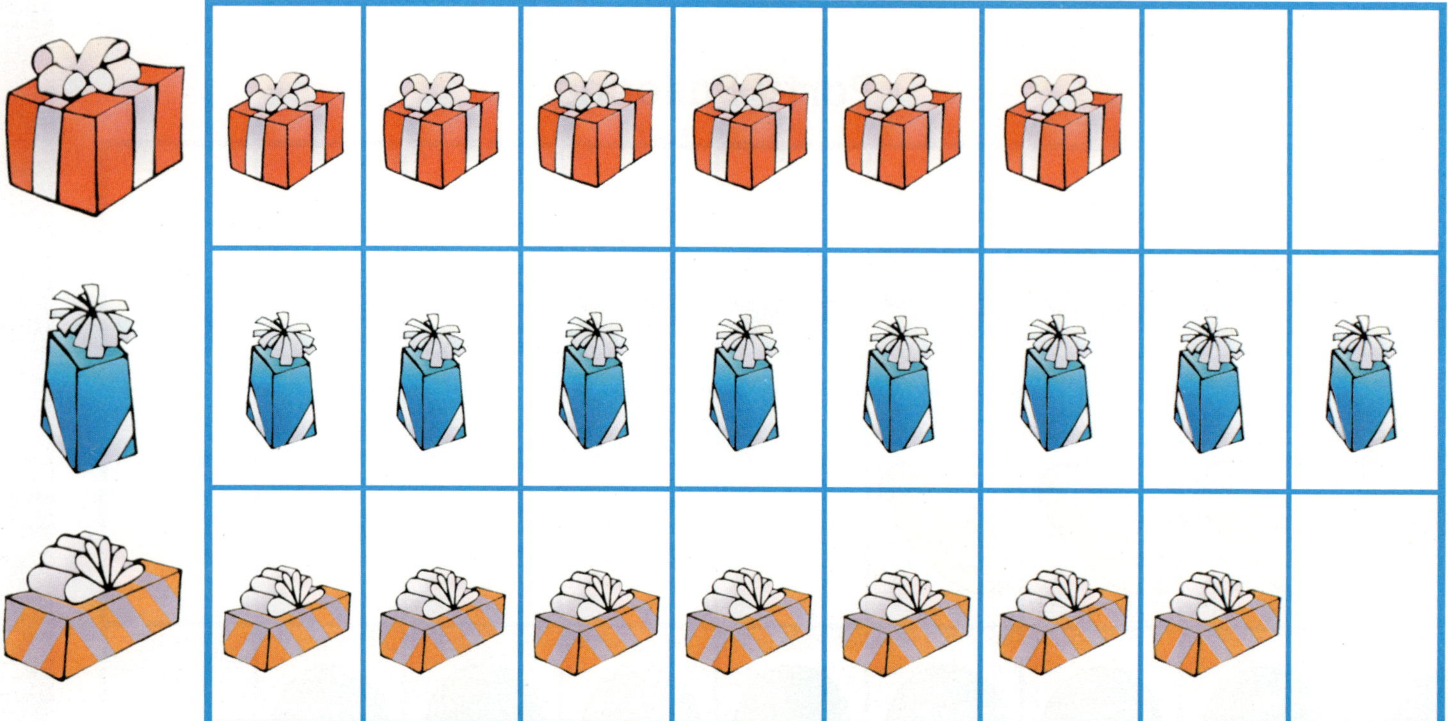

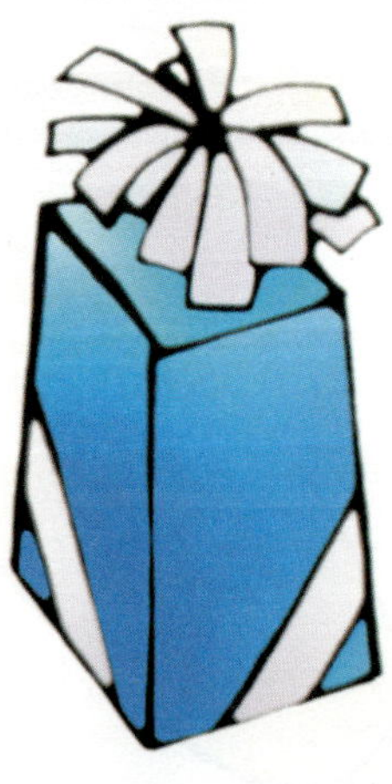

Look at the graph. Write how many of each kind of gift. Which number shows the kind there were the most of at the party? How do you know? Circle the number.

HOME ACTIVITY • Have your child ask family members about their favorite color and then make a graph to show the information he or she gathered.

Name ______________________________

Review

Shapes

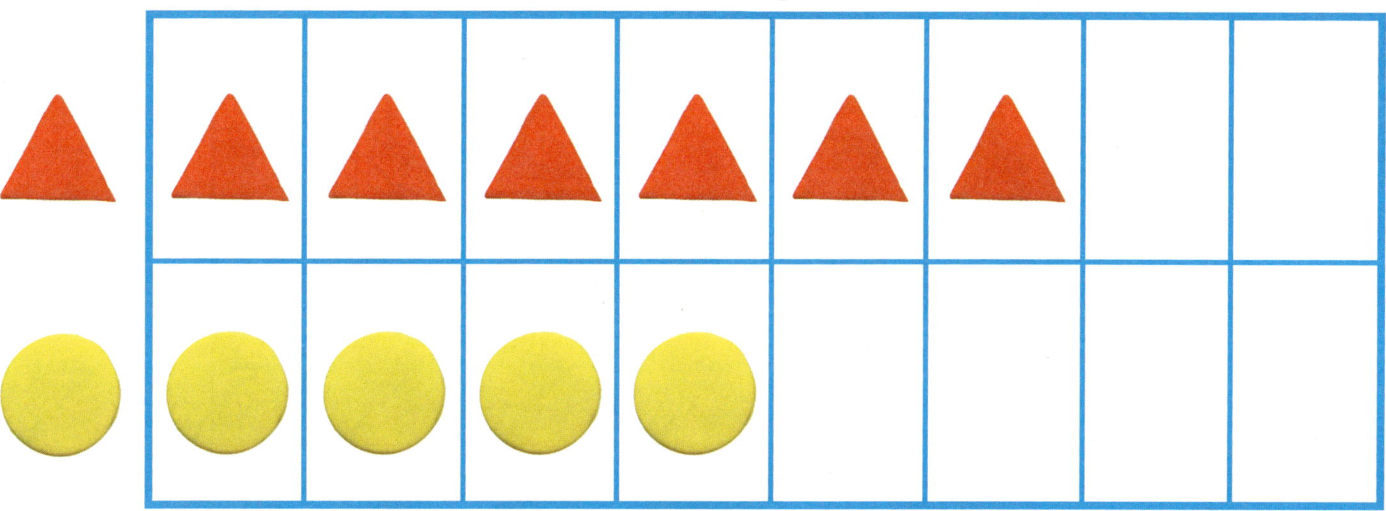

Use the graph. Write how many in each group.
Circle the picture that shows which group has more shapes.

Cumulative Review

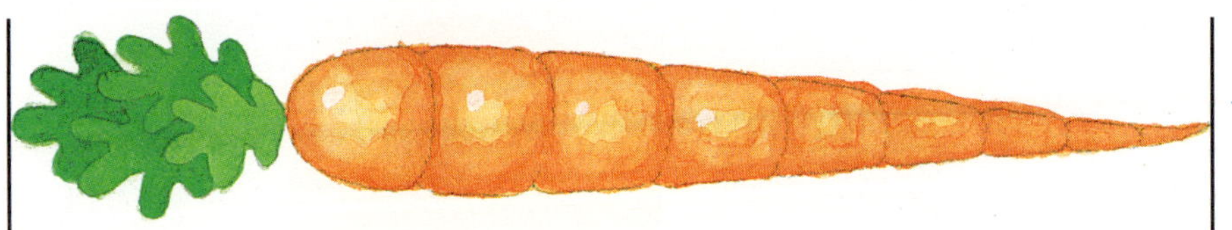

_____ cubes

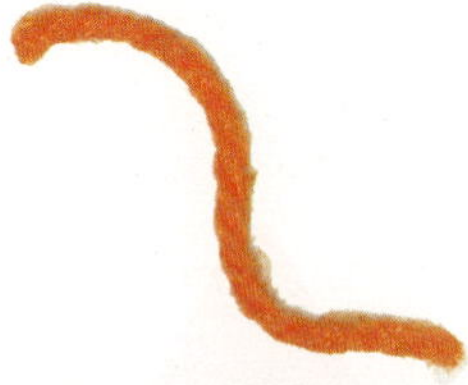

Build the cube train. Take one cube from each end of the train and snap these cubes together. Do this as many times as you can. If you have only pairs, the number is even. Circle the number. If you have one cube left over, the number is odd. Mark an X on the number.

What times of day do the pictures show? Circle the time of day that is missing.

Use cubes to measure the carrot. Write the number that tells about how many cubes long.

Hold one object in your left hand and one object in your right hand. Mark an X on the object that feels lighter.

Name ______________________

Read a Tally Table

Ways We Go To School

Look at the table. Write how many for each way.
Circle the picture that shows the way more children go to school.

Sports We Played

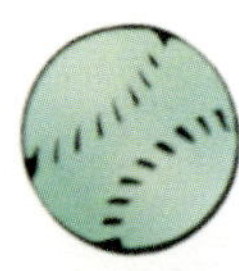

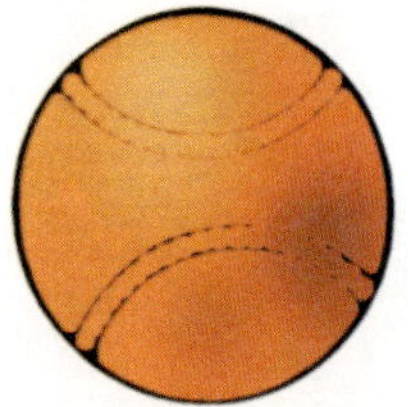
III

卌 II

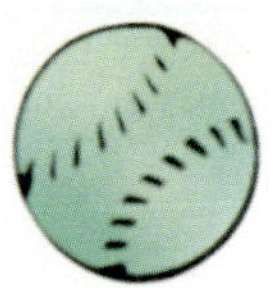
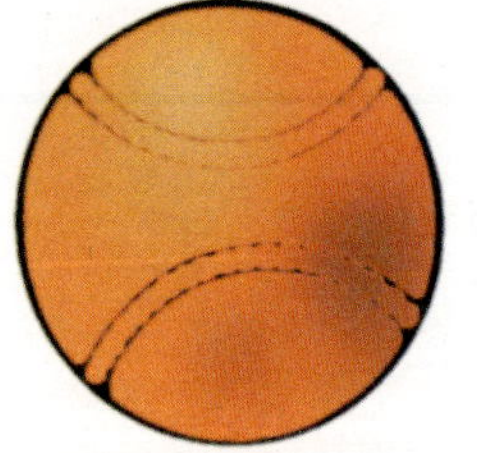

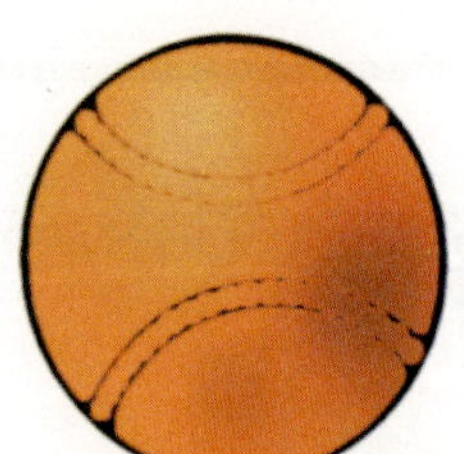

★

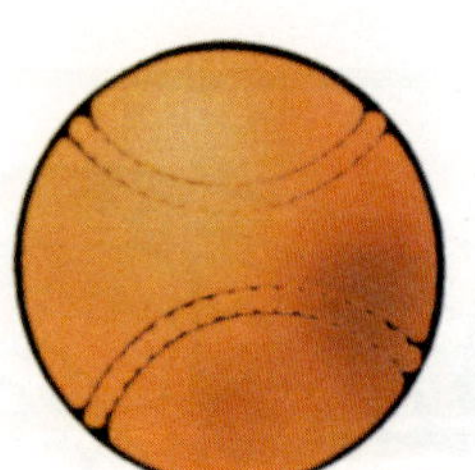

Look at the table. Write how many for each sport.
Circle the ball that shows which sport the most children played.
★ Circle the ball that shows which sport the fewest children played.

HOME ACTIVITY • Ask your child to explain what each mark on the table stands for.

Name ______________________

Do You Have a Pet?

Yes	
No	

Yes ______

No ______

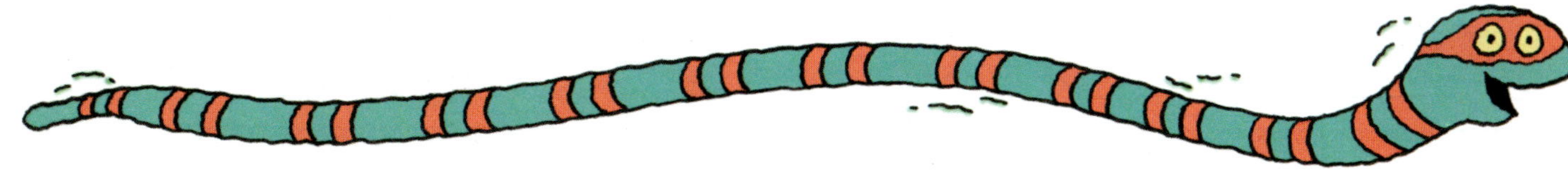

Ask five classmates if they have a pet. Make a tally table.
Write how many for each answer. Circle the number that is greater. Do more of the children you asked have a pet or not have a pet? How do you know?

Are You Wearing Yellow?

Yes	
No	

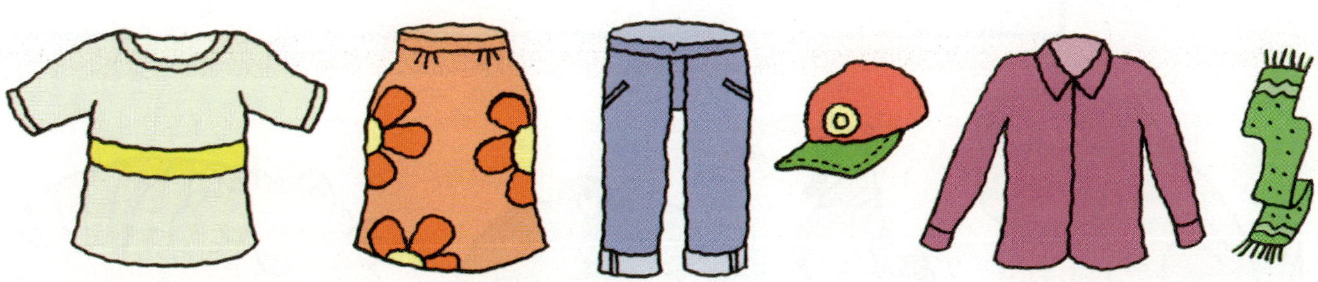

Yes ______

No ______

Ask five classmates if they are wearing yellow. Make a tally table.

Write how many for each answer. Circle the number that is less. Are fewer of the children you asked wearing yellow or not wearing yellow? How do you know?

HOME ACTIVITY • Have your child ask family members if they like pizza. Help him or her make a tally table to show the results.

Name ______________________________

Chance

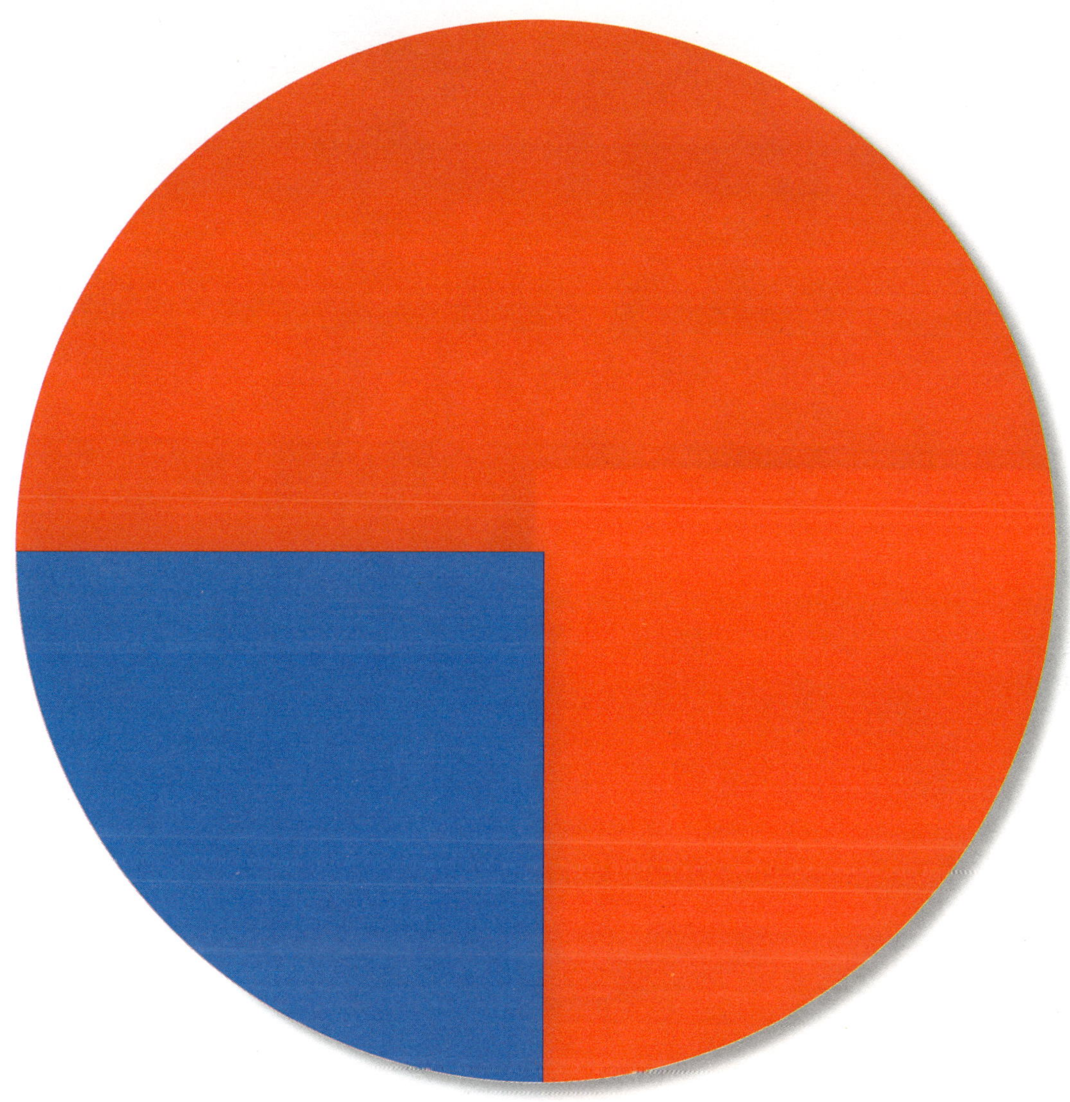

Red and Blue

Use a paper clip and a pencil to make a spinner. Spin ten times. Make a tally mark in the table after each spin. Which color did the paper clip land on more often? Why did this happen? Circle the row with more tally marks.

Blue and Red

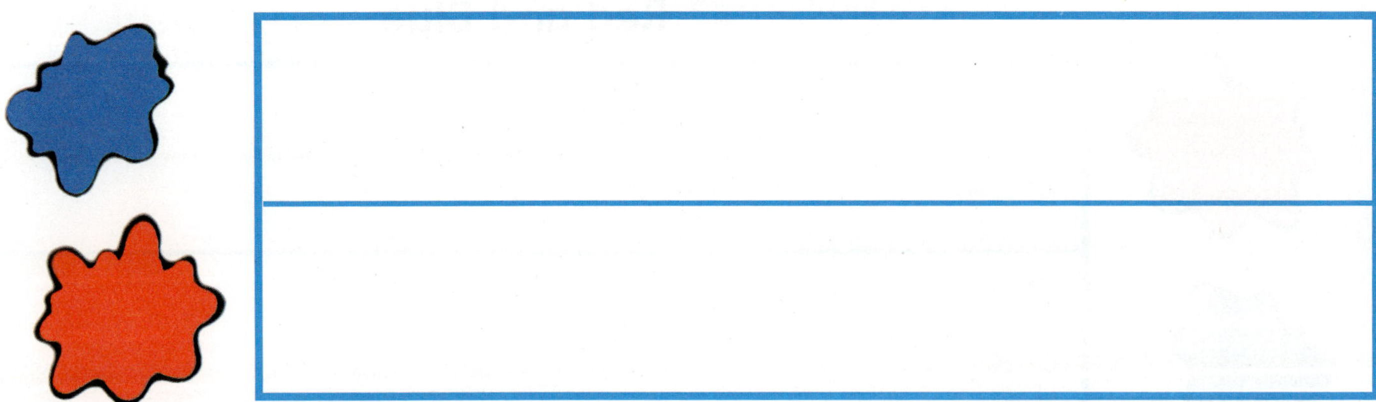

Use a paper clip and a pencil to make a spinner. Spin ten times. Make a tally mark in the table after each spin. Which color did the paper clip land on more often? Why did this happen? Circle the row with more tally marks.

HOME ACTIVITY • Ask your child to spin the spinner on this page more than ten times. Help him or her tally the results.

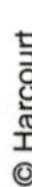

Name ______________________

Explore Probability

Circle the picture that shows which is more likely to happen.

Circle the picture that shows which is less likely to happen.

HOME ACTIVITY • Use phrases such as "Could that really happen?" or "Is that likely to happen?" with your child to help him or her explore probability.

Name ______________________

Problem Solving Skill
Make a Prediction

______

- - - - -

______

Ask two classmates how many pockets they have. Draw a picture to show how many pockets in all. Write how many pockets the two classmates have. Do you think four classmates will have more or fewer pockets?

PROBLEM SOLVING

Ask four classmates how many pockets they have. Draw a picture to show how many pockets in all. Write how many pockets the four classmates have. What did you learn?

HOME ACTIVITY • Have your child explain to you how he or she predicted whether four children would have more or fewer pockets than two children.

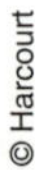

What's for Lunch?

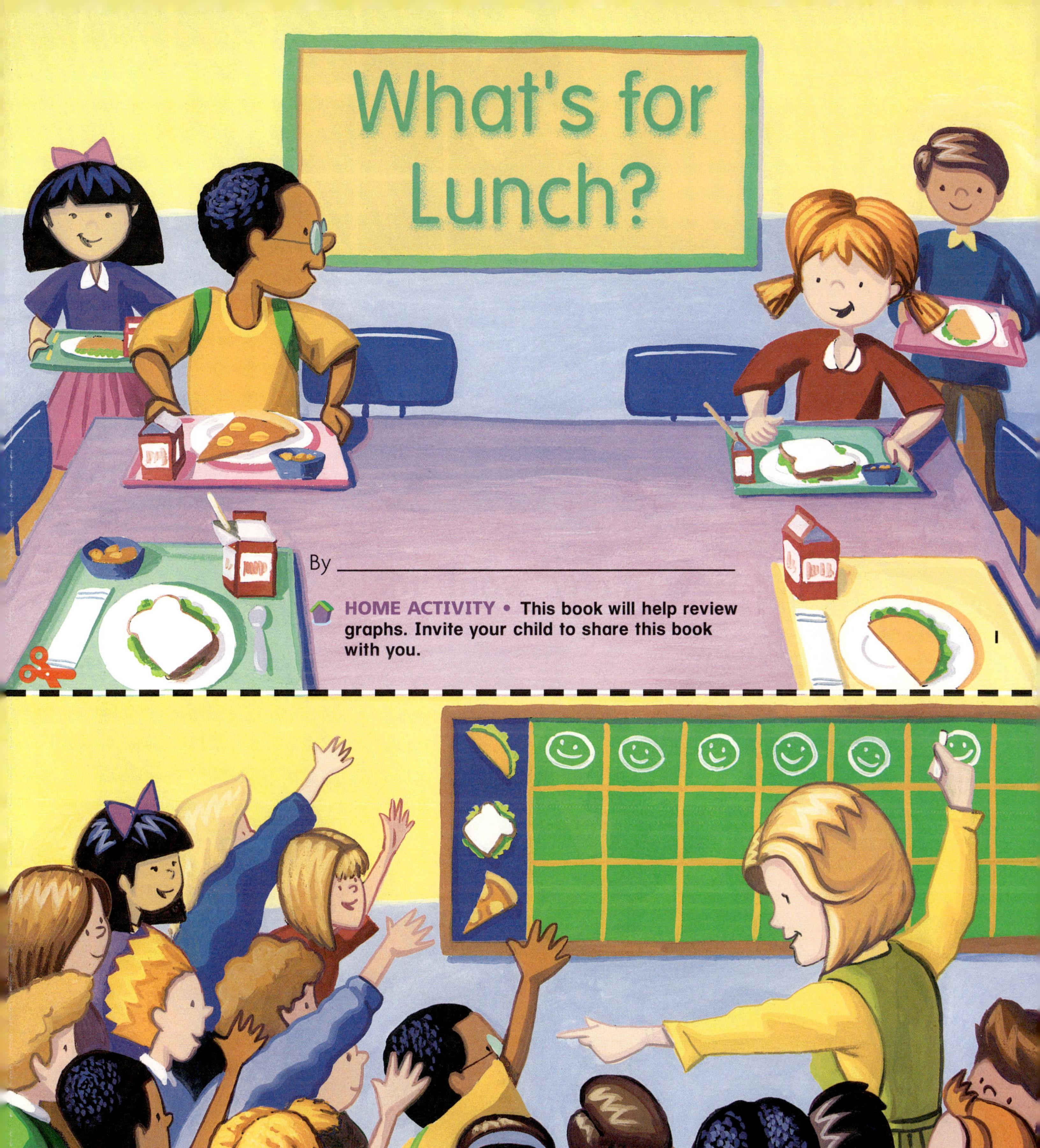

By ______________________________

HOME ACTIVITY • **This book will help review graphs. Invite your child to share this book with you.**

We want tacos!

How many want tacos?
2
How many want sandwiches?
4
© Harcourt

We want sandwiches!
5
We want pizza!
7
© Harcourt

How many want pizza?
Time for lunch!
© Harcourt

Name ____________________

Review

Ways We Go To School

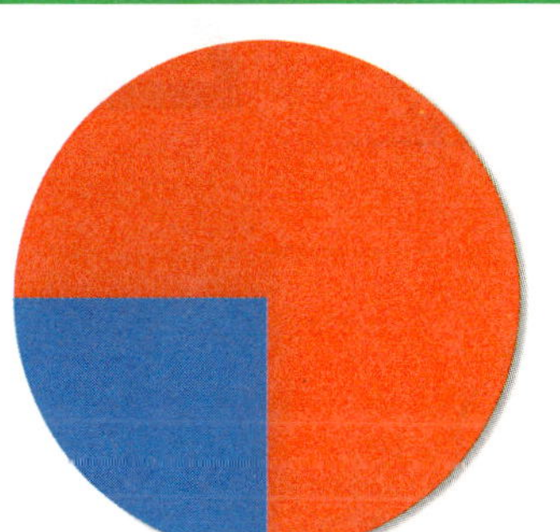

Red and Blue

Look at the tally table. Write how many. Circle the picture that shows how more children go to school.

Use a paper clip and a pencil to make a spinner. Spin ten times. Make a tally mark in the table after each spin. Circle the row with more tally marks.

Circle the picture that shows which is more likely to happen.

Circle the picture that shows which is less likely to happen.

Cumulative Review

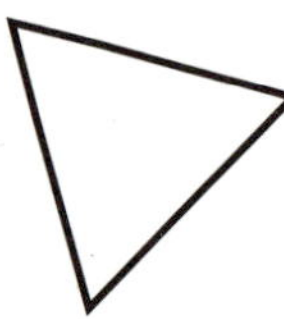
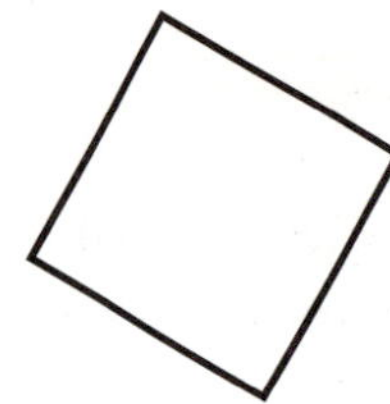
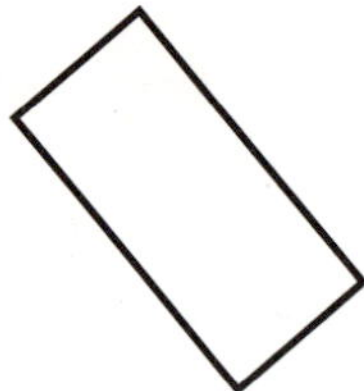
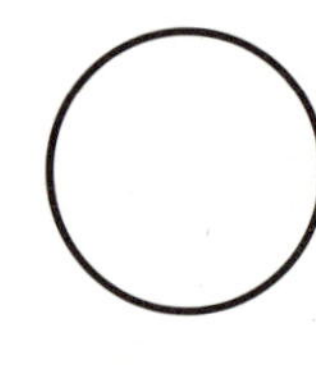

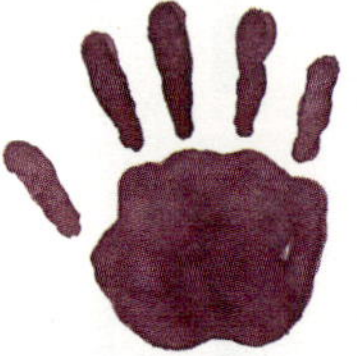

5 10 15 20 25

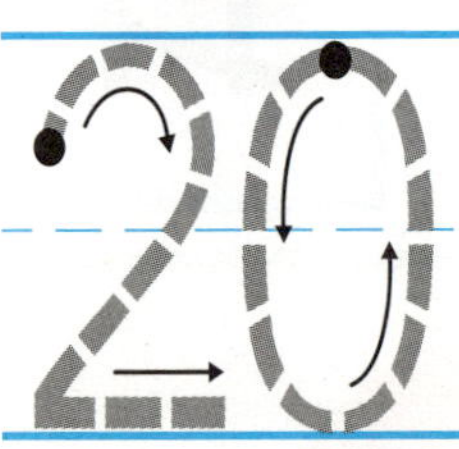

Where We Played

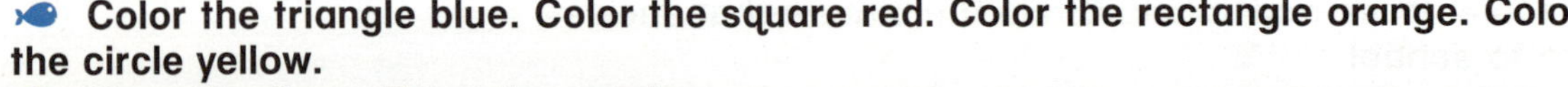

Color the triangle blue. Color the square red. Color the rectangle orange. Color the circle yellow.

Count by fives. Trace the number.

Circle the container that holds more. Mark an X on the container that holds less.

Use the graph. Write how many in each group. Circle the number that shows where more children played.

Name ________________________________

Test

Books We Read

Red and Blue

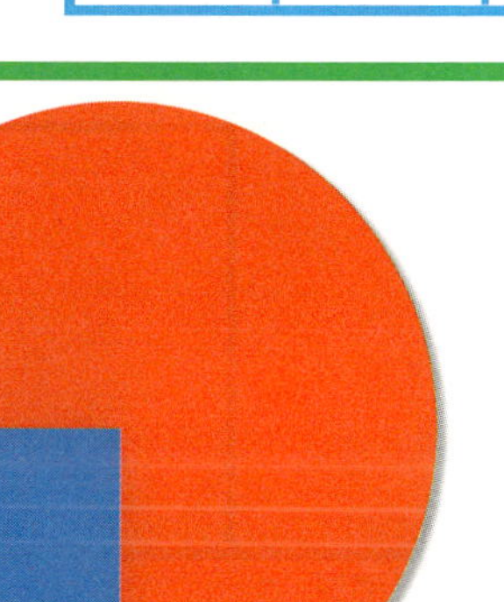

Use the graph. Write how many in each group. Circle the number that shows which book fewer children read.
Use a paper clip and a pencil to make a spinner. Spin ten times. Make a tally mark in the table after each spin. Circle the row with more tally marks.
Circle the picture that shows which is more likely to happen.
Circle the picture that shows which is less likely to happen.

CHALLENGE

Penny Graphs

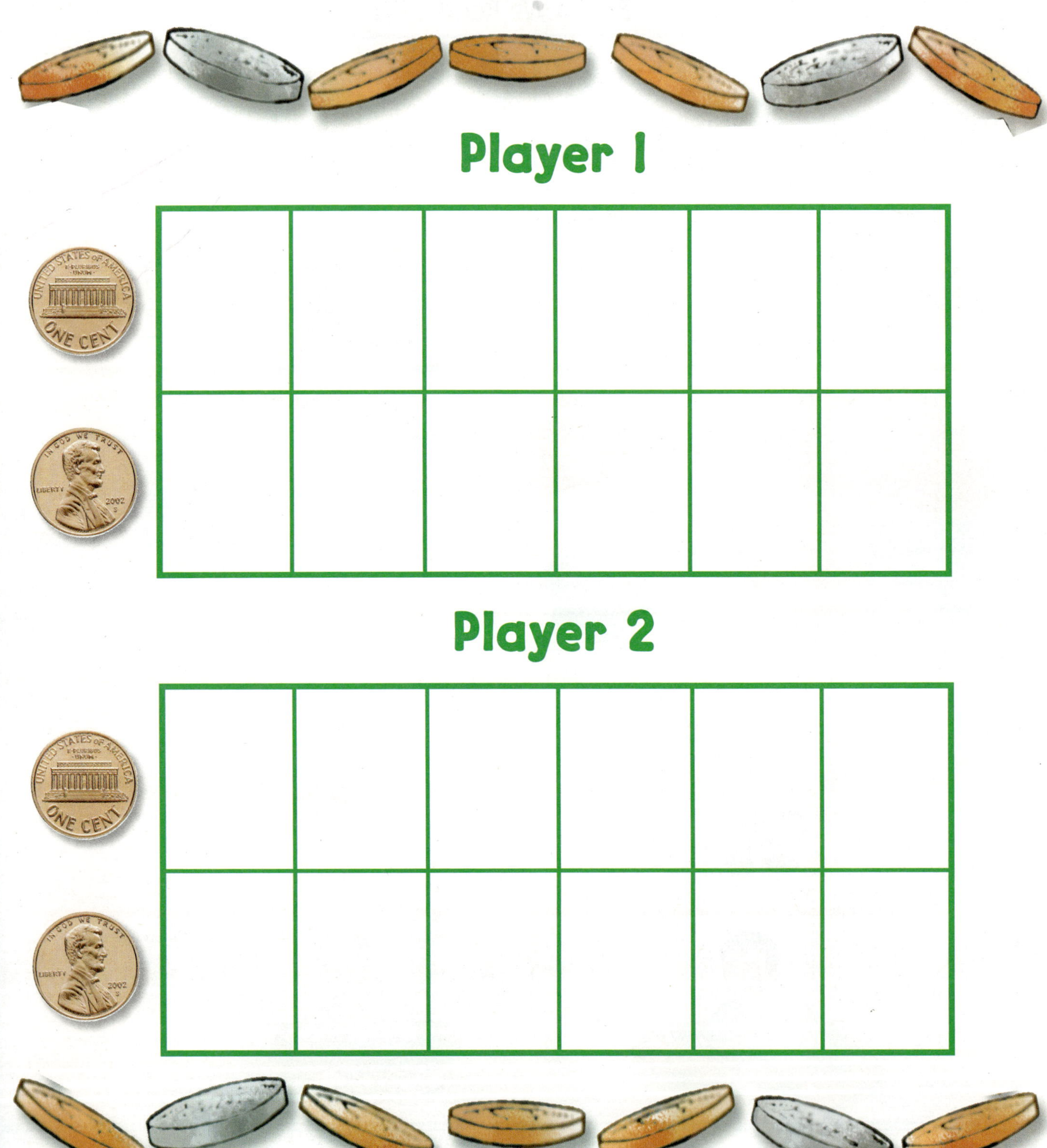

Play with a partner. Flip a penny. Color a square in the graph to show if it landed on heads or tails. When one player has filled a row, compare graphs.

CHAPTER
11
Addition
HARCOURT
Math
© Harcourt
Harcourt

Circle the group that has more pennies.

Grateful acknowledgment is made to Charlesbridge Publishing for permission to reprint the cover illustration by Frank Mazzola, Jr. from *The Crayon Counting Book* by Pam Muñoz Ryan and Jerry Pallotta. Illustration copyright © 1996 by Frank Mazzola, Jr.

Printed in the United States of America

Photography Credits:

All photography by Harcourt photographers listed, © Harcourt: Weronica Ankarorn, Victoria Bowen, Ken Kinzie, Sheri O'Neal, Quebecor Imaging, and Terry Sinclair.

Illustration Credits:

Liz Allen: 285, 286; **Tuko Fujisaki:** 271; **Obadinah Heavner:** Storybook; **Betsey James:** 273, 274; **Chris Lensch:** 283, 284; **Claude Martinot:** 277, 278; **Dan McGeehan:** 279, 280; **Jill Meyerhoff:** 275, 276, 289, 290; **Pamela Thompson:** cover; **Greg Valley:** 272; **Kathy Wilburn:** 287, 288; **James Williamson:** 270.

15 16 17 18 19 20 1678 16 15 14 13 12 11
4500311726

SCHOOL HOME CONNECTION

Dear Family,

Today we started a new chapter, Addition. We will learn to join two groups to find out how many in all. We will also read and complete addition sentences.

Love,

____

Vocabulary Power

in all

5 bugs and 3 bugs is 8 bugs in all

addition sentence

$5 + 3 = 8$

5 plus 3 equals 8

Visit *The Learning Site* for additional ideas and activities. www.harcourtschool.com

ACTIVITY

- Play a shopping game. Tag some small objects with prices from 1¢ to 5¢. Have your child use pennies to "buy" two objects.

To read about addition with your child, look for these books in your local library.

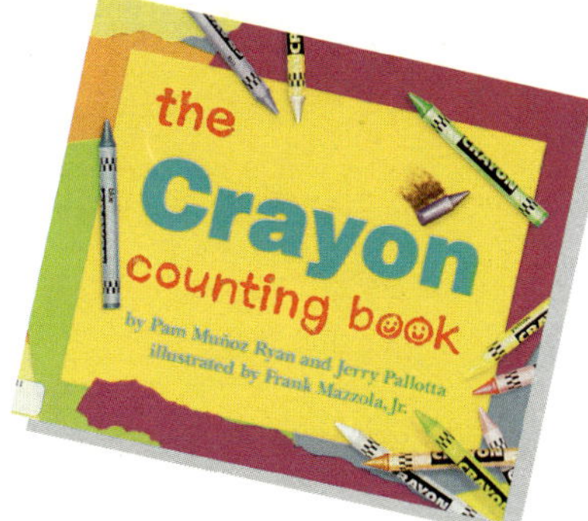

The Crayon Counting Book, by Pam Muñoz Ryan and Jerry Pallotta. Charlesbridge Publishing, 1996.

What! Cried Granny, by Kate Lum. Penguin Putnam, 1999.

Math Game

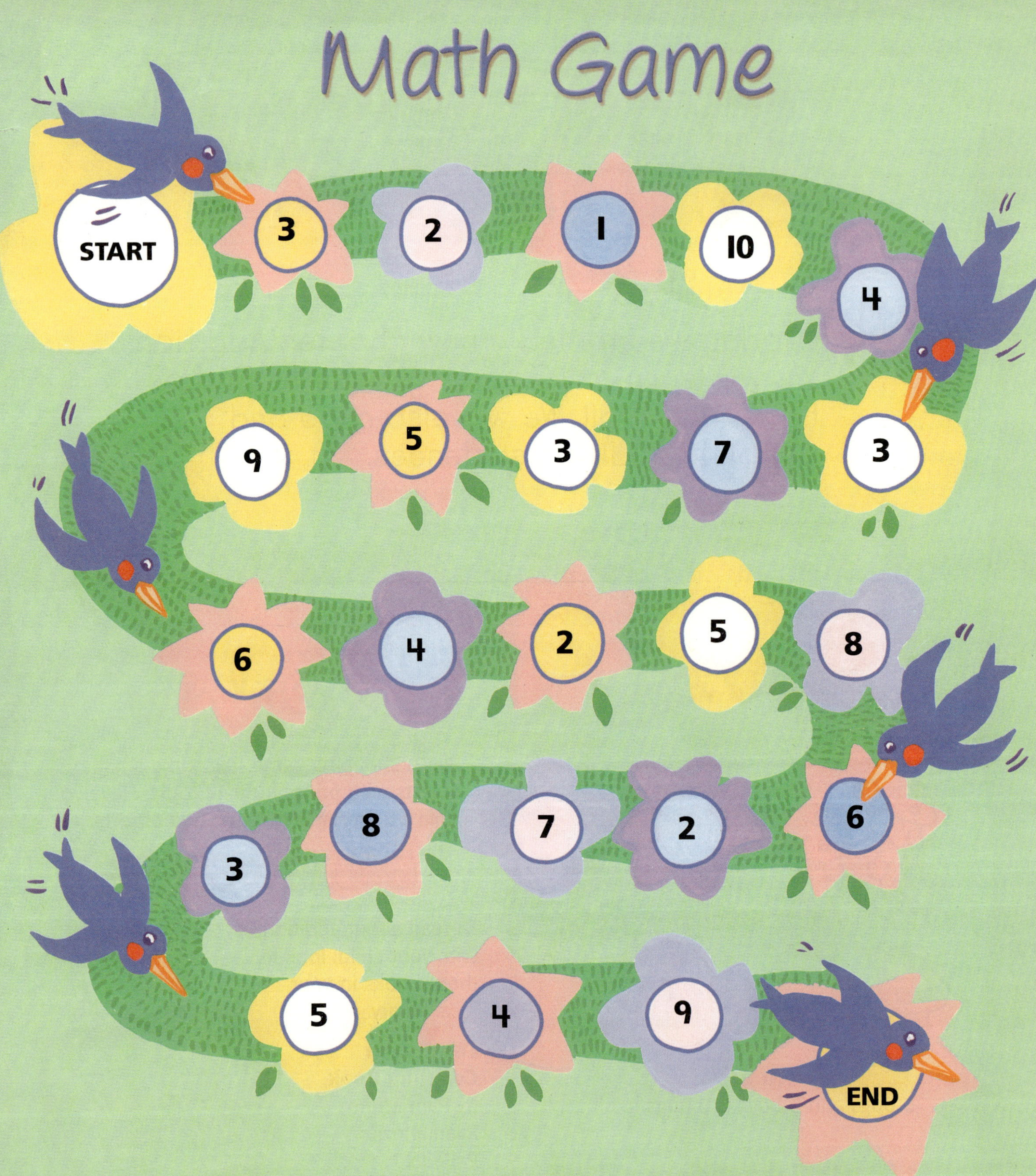

MATERIALS: game marker for each player, number cube (1–6)
DIRECTIONS: Players take turns tossing the number cube and moving that many spaces. Each player adds 1 to the number on which he or she lands. If the player adds correctly, the marker stays on that space. If not, the marker goes back to where it was. The first player to reach END wins.

Name ______________________

Problem Solving Strategy
Act It Out

Listen to and act out the story. One more child is joining the group. Write the number that tells how many children in all.

Listen to and act out the story. More children come to play. Write the number that tells how many children in all.

HOME ACTIVITY • Make two stacks of books. Ask your child to count the books in each stack and then find how many books in all.

Name ___________________________

Model Addition

2 1 3

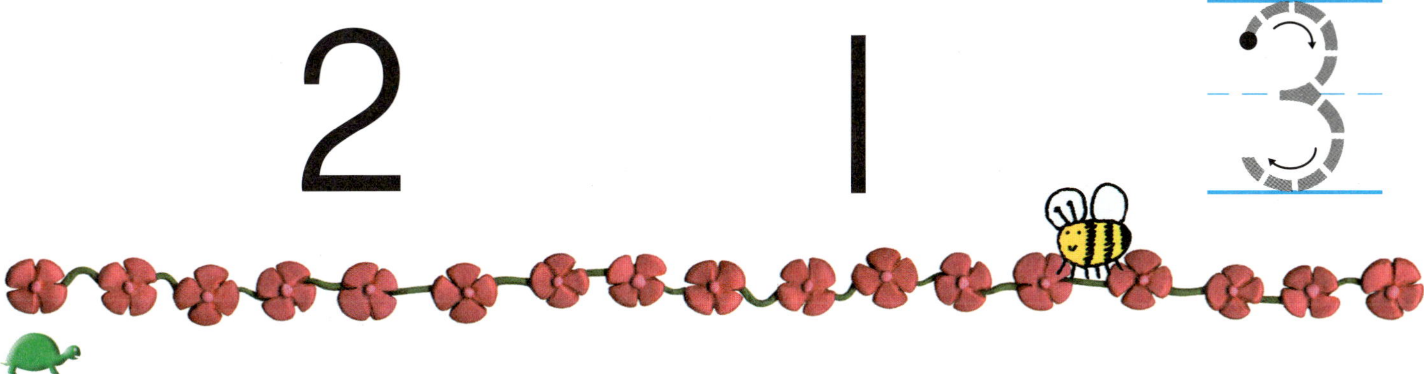

7 3

5 4

Listen to the story. Model the story with connecting cubes. Write the number that tells how many in all.

2 2 4

4 3

6 2

Listen to the story. Model the story with connecting cubes. Write the number that tells how many in all.

HOME ACTIVITY • Tell your child a very short story about adding 1 object to a group of 4 objects. Have your child model the story with small objects and write the number that tells how many objects in all.

Name ________________________________

Addition Patterns

1  1 = 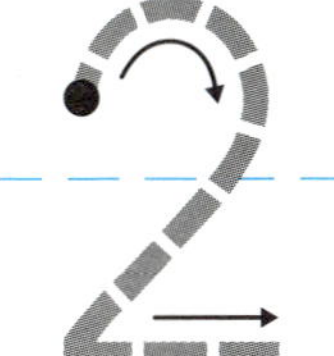

2  1 = ____

3  1 = ____

4 + 1 = ____

Count the birds on the branch. Then draw one more bird coming. Write the number that tells how many birds in all.

5 + 1 =

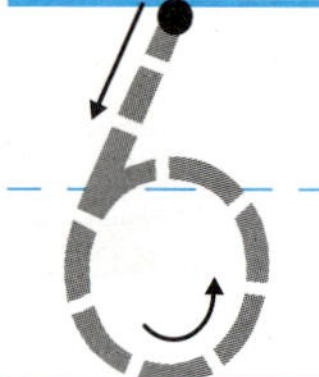

6 + 1 =

7 + 1 =

8 + 1 =

9 + 1 =

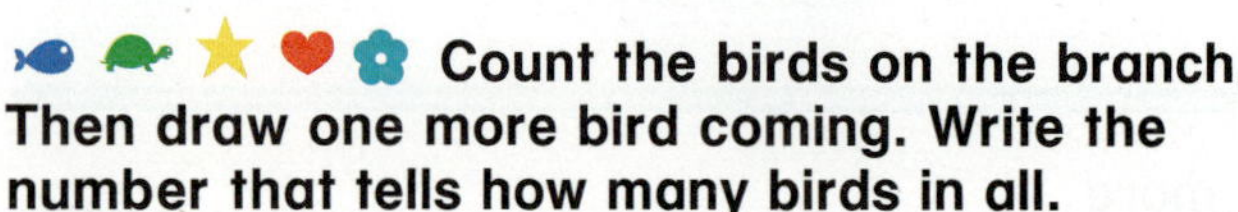

Count the birds on the branch. Then draw one more bird coming. Write the number that tells how many birds in all.

HOME ACTIVITY • Tell your child an addition story that adds one more. Encourage your child to use objects or drawings to act out the story.

Name ______________________

Use Pictures to Add

 + 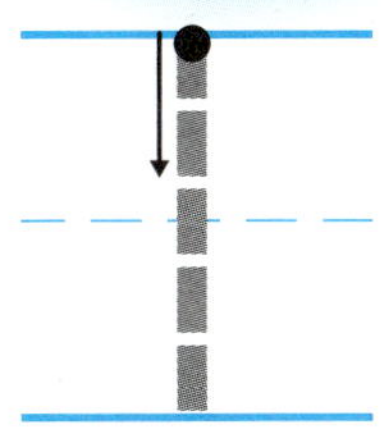  

Tell a story about the pictures. Complete the addition sentence.

___ + ___ = ___

___ + ___ = ___

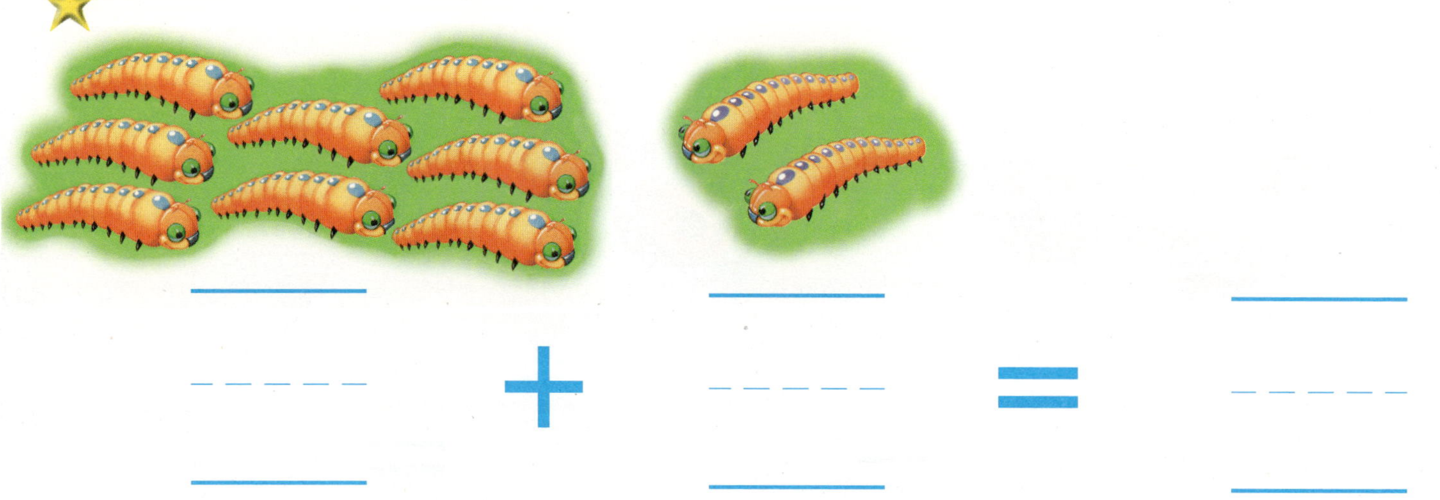

___ + ___ = ___

Tell a story about the pictures. Complete the addition sentence.

HOME ACTIVITY • Ask your child to draw a picture that shows the adding of two groups.

Name ______________________

Review

4 3 ___

6 + 1 = ___

___ + ___ = ___

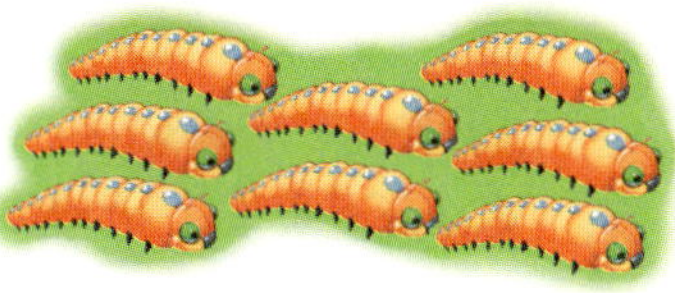

___ + ___ = ___

Listen to the story. Model the story with connecting cubes. Write the number that tells how many in all.

Count the birds on the branch. Then draw one more bird coming. Write the number that tells how many birds in all.

Tell a story about the pictures. Complete the addition sentence.

Cumulative Review

___ + ___ = ___

Ways We Go To School

Tell a story about the pictures. Complete the addition sentence.
Circle the longer object. Underline the shorter object.
Look at the tally table. Write how many for each way. Circle the picture that shows how more children go to school.
Circle the picture that shows which is more likely to happen.

Name ___________________________

Add with Money

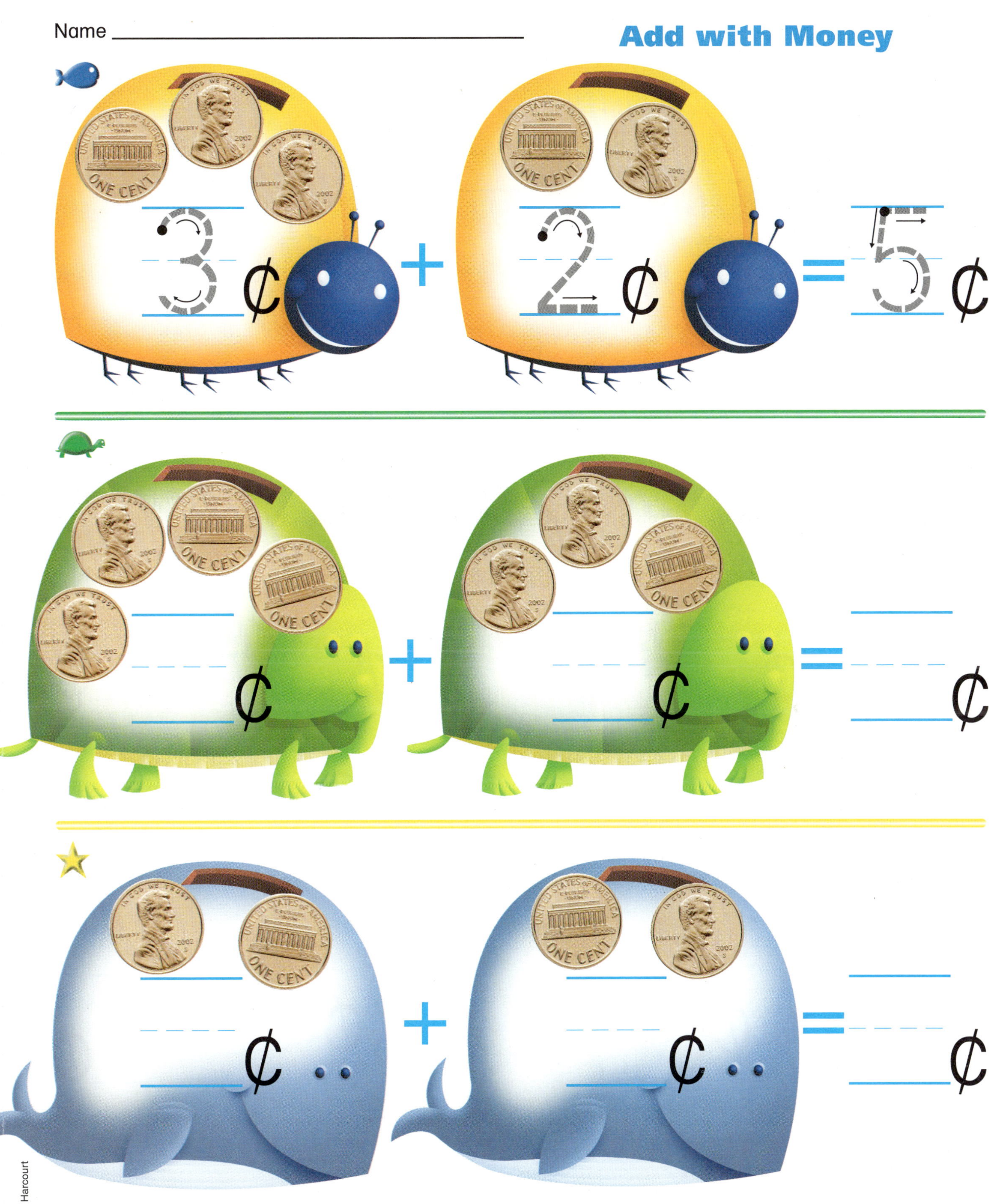

Count the pennies in each bank. Write how many cents. Add. Write how many cents in all.

¢ + ¢ = 4 ¢

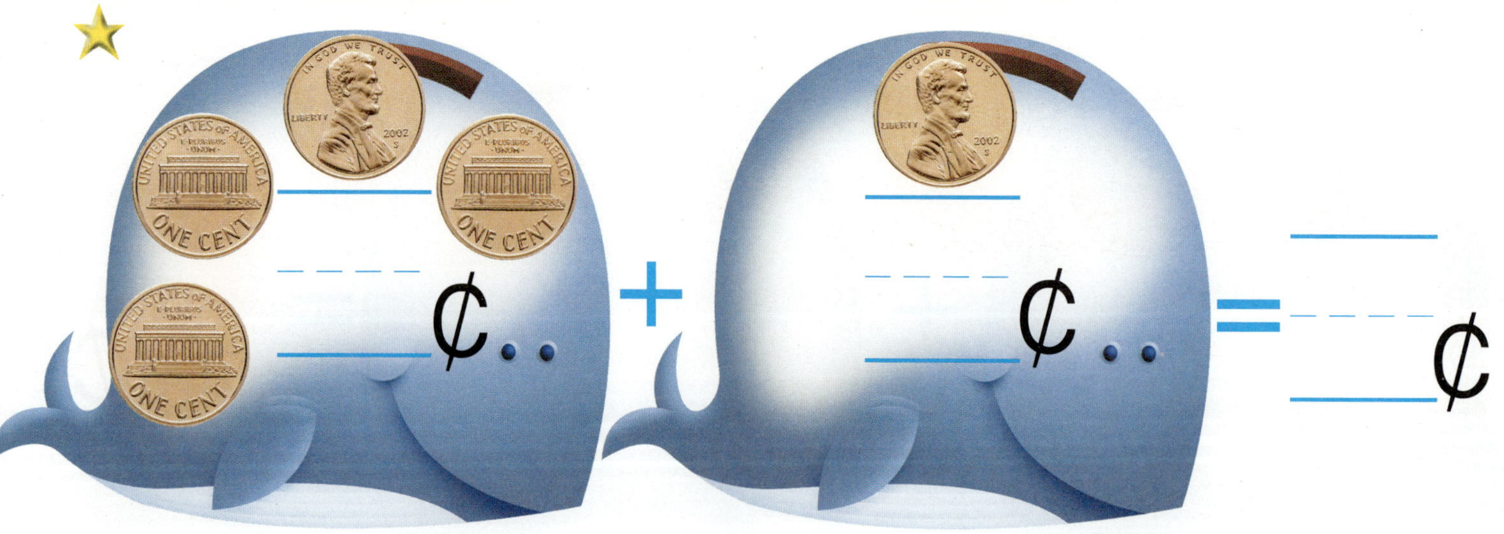

Count the pennies in each bank. Write how many cents. Add. Write how many cents in all.

HOME ACTIVITY • Have your child use real pennies to model these addition problems.

Name ______________________

Addition Problems

 +  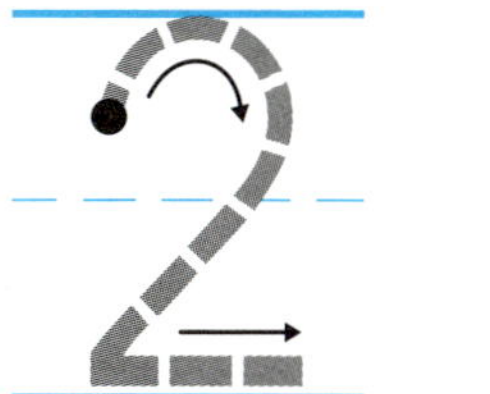 =  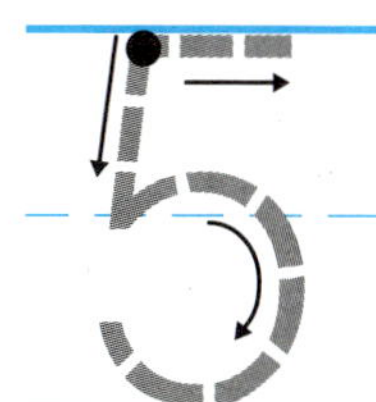

___ + ___ = ___

  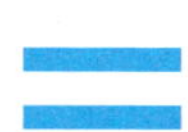

___ + ___ = ___

Tell a story about the animals. Complete the addition sentence.

Tell a story about the animals in the picture. Write the addition sentence.

HOME ACTIVITY • Have your child draw simple animals to show adding groups. Then help him or her write the addition sentence.

Name ___________________________

5 + 3 = 8

___ + ___ = ___

Tell an addition story. Act out your story with objects. Draw the objects. Then complete the addition sentence.

+ =

+ =

Tell an addition story. Act out your story with objects. Draw the objects. Then complete the addition sentence.

HOME ACTIVITY • Have your child create and act out an addition story using objects.

Name ______________________________

Problem Solving Strategy
Make a Model

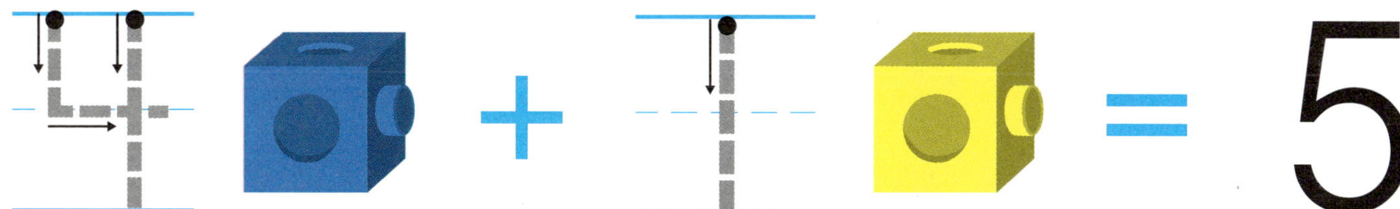

4 + 1 = 5

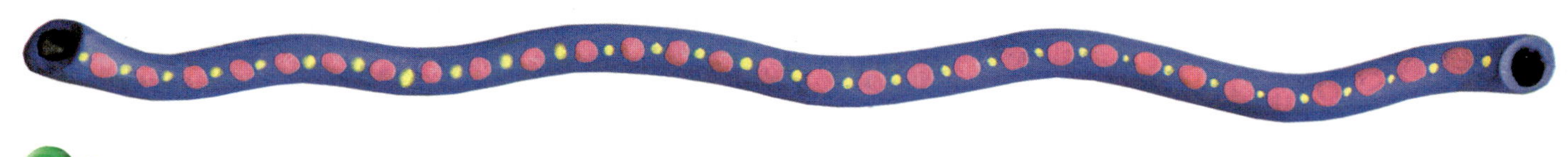

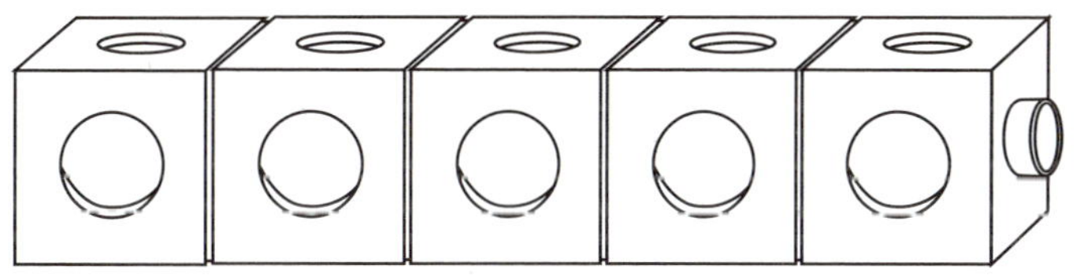

___ + ___ = 5

Use blue and yellow connecting cubes to show different ways to make 5. Color the cubes. Write the numbers for each color to complete the addition sentence.

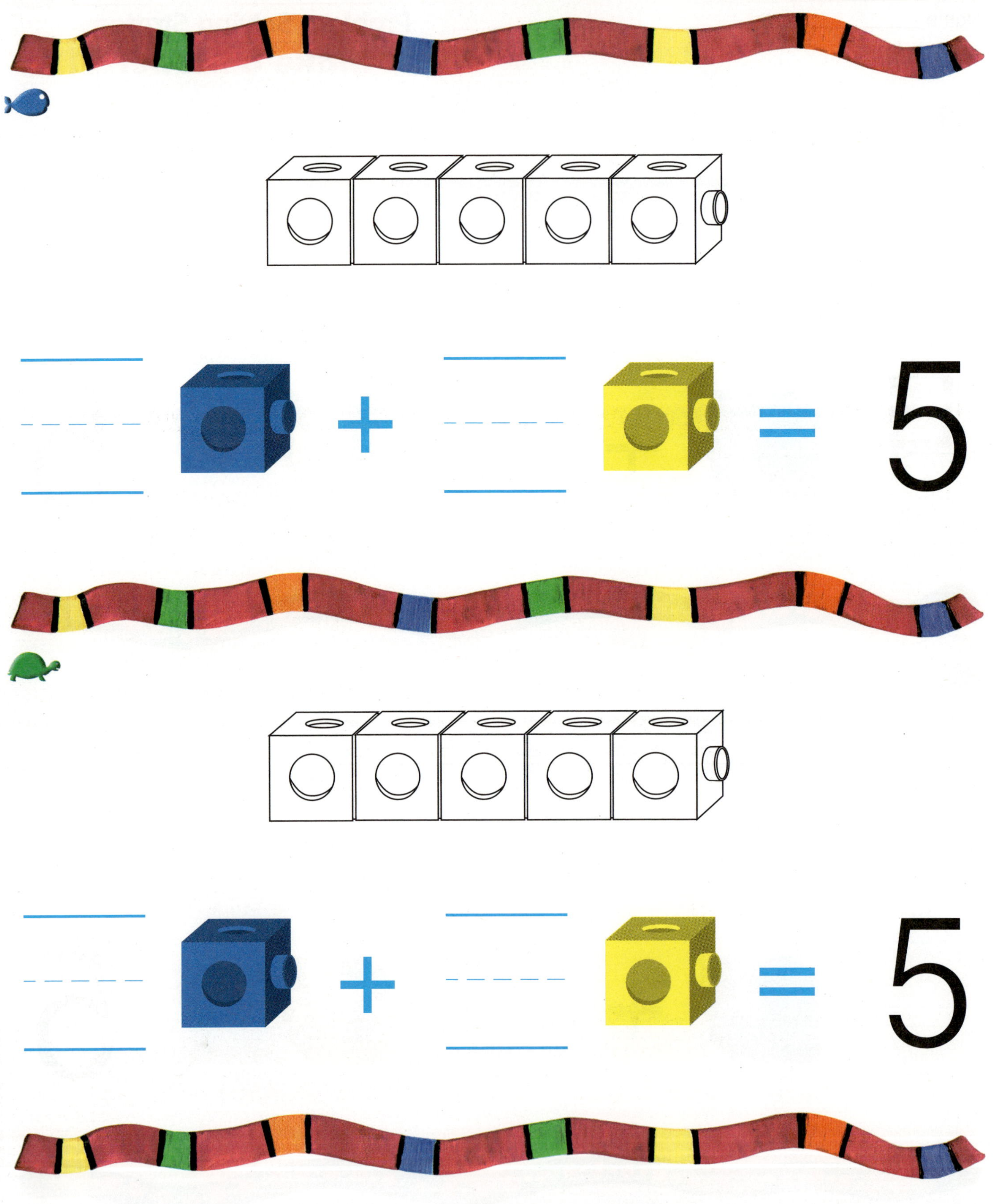

Use blue and yellow connecting cubes to show different ways to make 5. Color the cubes. Write the numbers for each color to complete the addition sentence.

HOME ACTIVITY • Write three addition problems that each add up to 5. Give your child 5 pennies to use to model the problems, using heads for the first number and tails for the second number.

Our Home

By ______________________

HOME ACTIVITY • **This book will help review addition. Invite your child to share this book with you.**

2 + 1 = ____

2 bees

3 caterpillars

3 + 2 = ____

4 + 4 = ____

4 baby birds

5 squirrels

$5 + 4 =$ ____

9

$8 + 2 =$ ____

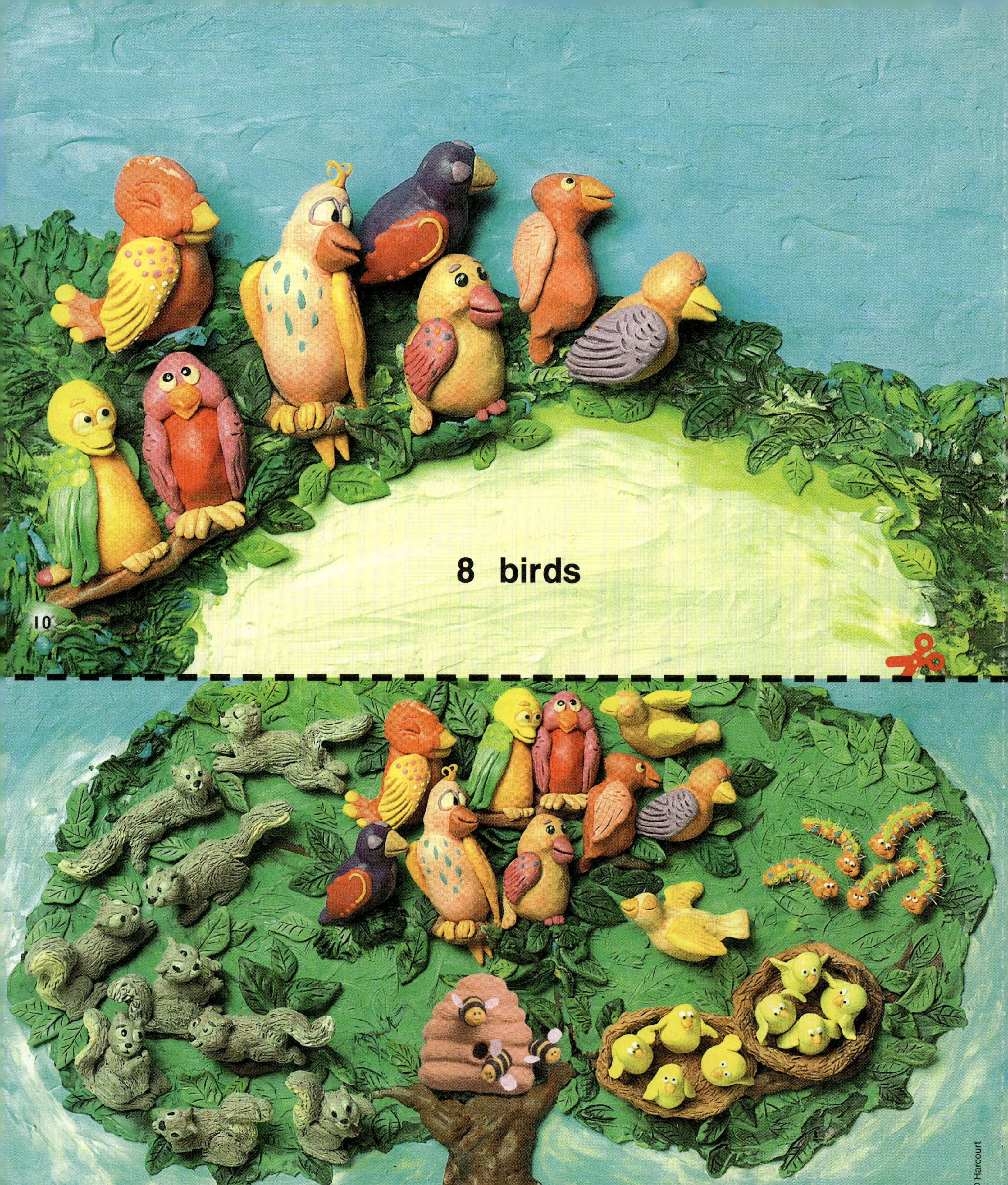

8 birds

Welcome to our home!

Name ___

Review

___ + ___ = ___

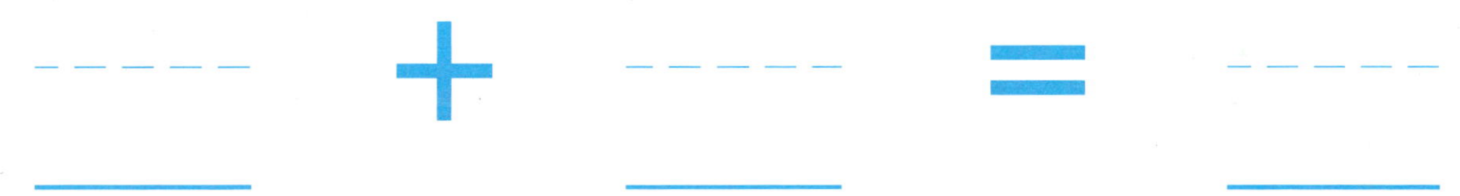

___ + ___ = ___

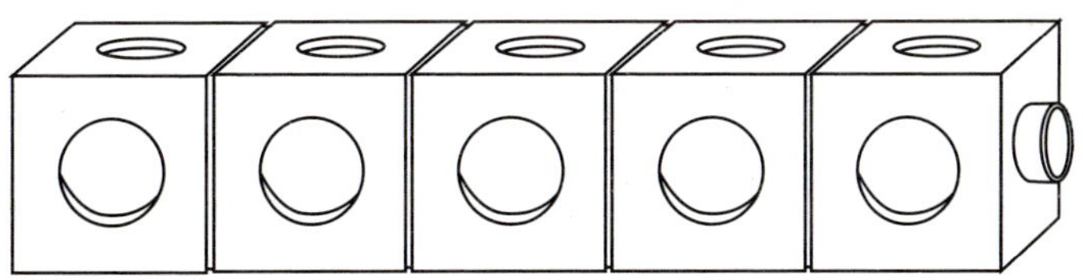

___ + ___ = 5

Tell a story about the ducks in the picture. Complete the addition sentence.

Tell an addition story. Act out your story with objects. Draw the objects and complete the addition sentence.

Use blue and yellow connecting cubes to show different ways to make five. Color the cubes. Write the numbers that tell how many of each color.

Cumulative Review

4 5 6 ■ 8

2
7

1	2	3	4	5	6	7	8	9	10
11	12	13	14	15	16	17	18	19	20
21	22	23	24	25	26	27	28	29	30

Circle the missing number.
Color to finish the pattern. Touch and count by twos.
Use red to circle the picture that most likely shows hot weather.
Use blue to circle the picture that mostly likely shows cold weather.
Count the pennies in each bank. Write how many. Add. Write how many in all.

Name ______________________________

Test

5  1 = ____

____   ____  ____

____ + ____ = ____

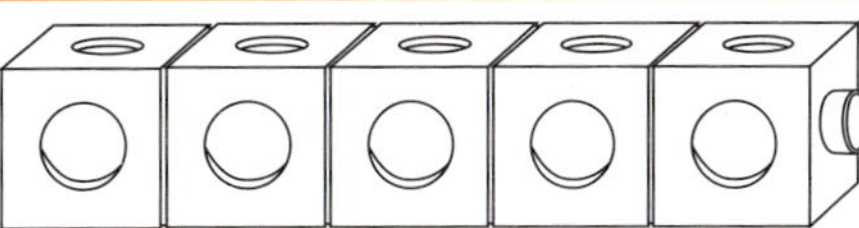

____   ____    5

Count the birds on the branch. Then draw one more bird coming. Write the number that tells how many birds in all.

Tell a story about the frogs in the picture. Complete the addition sentence.

Tell an addition story. Act out your story with objects. Draw the objects and complete the addition sentence.

Use blue and yellow connecting cubes to show different ways to make five. Color the cubes. Write the numbers that tell how many of each color.

CHALLENGE

Dimes and Pennies

10¢ + ___¢ = ___¢

___¢ + ___¢ = 12¢

___¢ + 3¢ = ___¢

10¢ + ___¢ = ___¢

Complete the addition sentence.

HARCOURT
Math
CHAPTER
12
Subtraction
© Harcourt
Harcourt

Count the turtles. Draw a group that has one fewer.

Printed in the United States of America

Photography Credits:

All photography by Harcourt photographers listed, © Harcourt: Weronica Ankarorn, Victoria Bowen, Ken Kinzie, Sheri O'Neal, Quebecor Imaging, and Terry Sinclair.

Illustration Credits:

Ken Bowser: 305, 306, 309, 310, 311, 312; **Priscilla Burris:** storybook; **Susan Calitri:** 315, 316; **Daniel Del Valle:** 242; **Kathy Ember:** cover; **Tim Haggerty:** 298; **Obadinah Heavner:** 313, 314; **Betsey James:** 299, 300; **Heidi King:** 242; **Dan McGeehan:** 242; **Stan Tusan:** 297; **Sally Vitsky:** 301, 302.

15 16 17 18 19 20 1678 16 15 14 13 12 11
4500311726

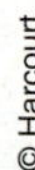

SCHOOL HOME CONNECTION

Dear Family,

Today we started a new chapter, Subtraction. We will learn to subtract objects from a larger group of objects. We will also learn to read and complete subtraction sentences.

Love,

____

take away, are left

There are 3 birds.
1 bird flies away.
Now 2 birds are left.

subtraction sentence

$3 - 1 = 2$

3 minus 1 equals 2.

- Have your child use objects and make up a story in which some of the objects are taken away.

BOOKS TO SHARE

To read about subtraction with your child, look for these books at your local library.

Ten Little Mice, by Joyce Dunbar. Gulliver, 1990.

Elevator Magic, by Stuart J. Murphy. HarperCollins, 1997.

10, 9, 8, by Molly Bang. HarperCollins, 2000.

Visit *The Learning Site* for additional ideas and activities. www.harcourtschool.com

Math Game

START

3 8 5 2 7 1 6 4 9 1 8 3 5 2 7 1 6

END

MATERIALS: game marker for each player, number cube (1–6)
DIRECTIONS: Players take turns tossing the number cube and moving that many spaces. Each player subtracts 1 from the number on which he or she lands. If the player subtracts correctly, the marker stays on that space. If not, the marker goes back to where it was. The first player to reach END wins.

Name ______________________

Problem Solving Strategy
Act It Out

Listen to and act out the story. Count how many are left. Write the number that tells how many are left.

PROBLEM SOLVING

Listen to and act out the story. Count how many are left. Write the number that tells how many are left.

HOME ACTIVITY • Make a stack of 5 books. Have your child count the books. Take 2 books away, and have your child count the books that are left.

Name ______________________________

Model Subtraction

HANDS ON

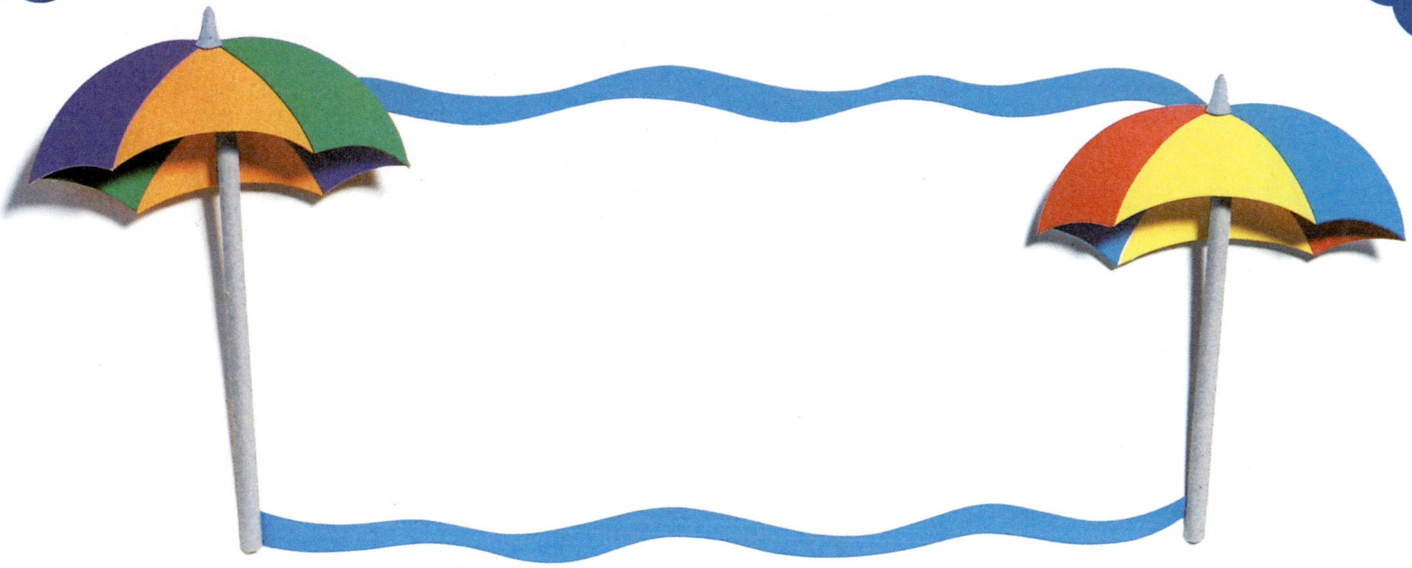

5 3 2

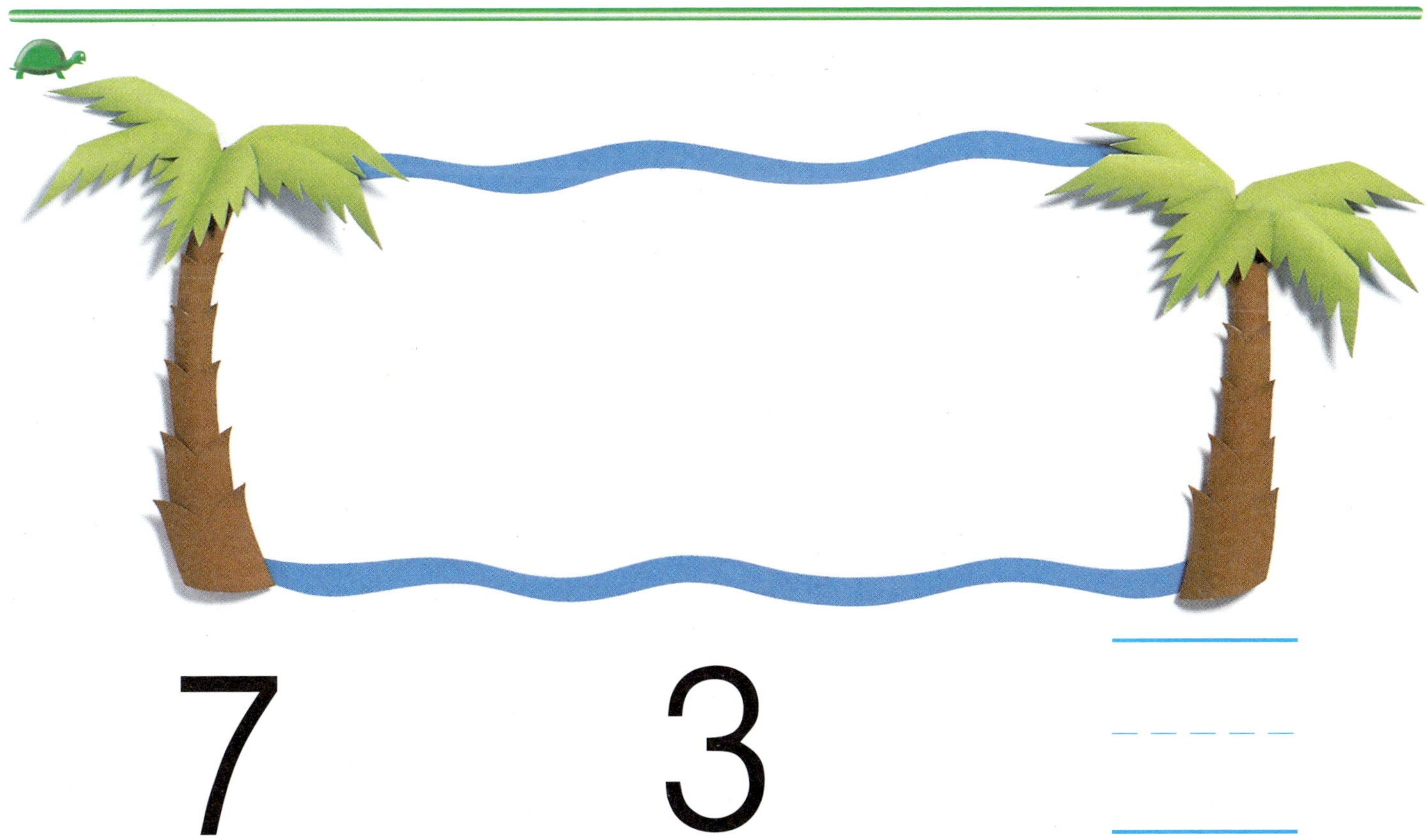

7 3 ___

Listen to the story. Model the story with connecting cubes. Write the number that tells how many are left.

6 3

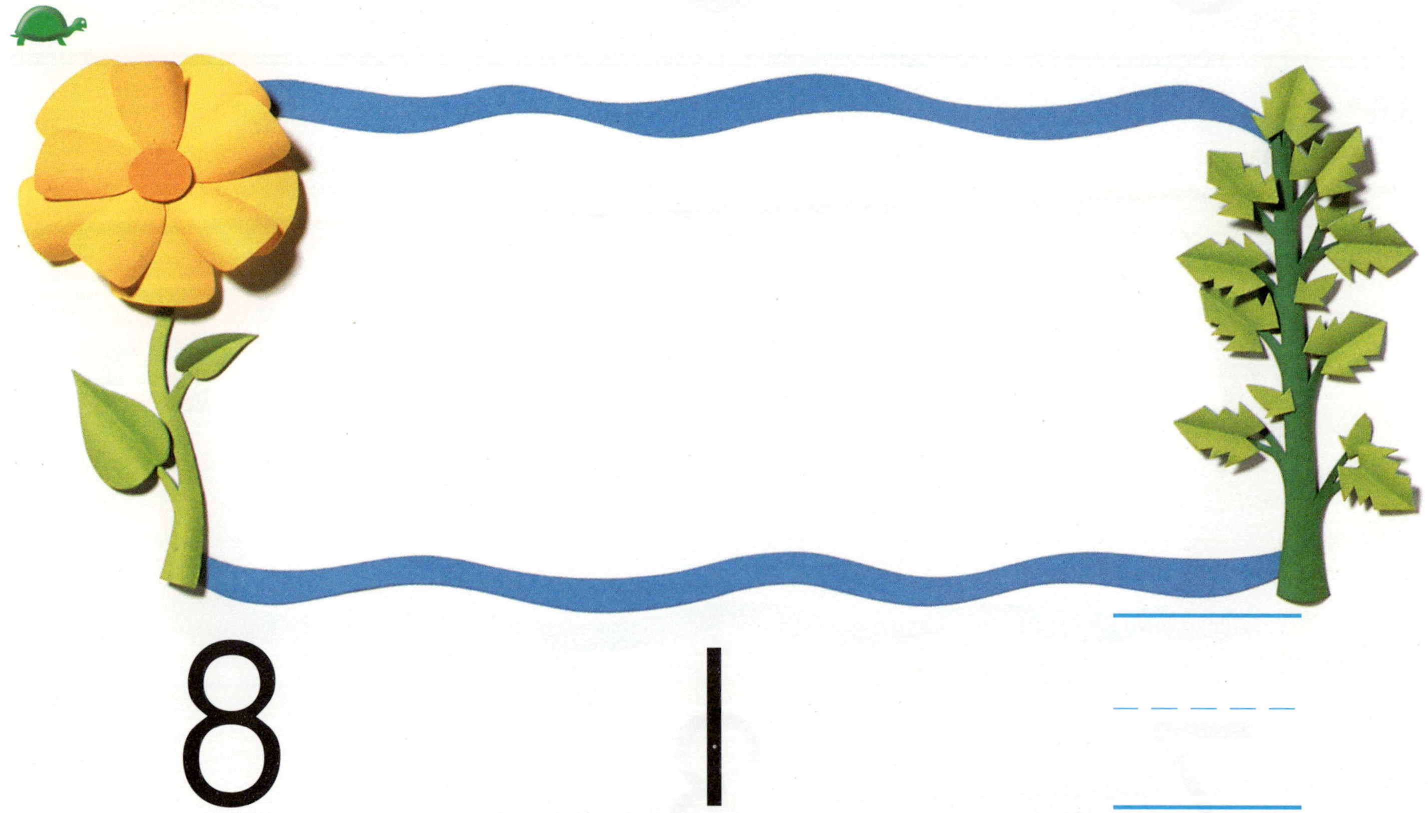

8 1

Listen to the story. Model the story with connecting cubes. Write the number that tells how many are left.

HOME ACTIVITY • Tell your child a subtraction story about having 4 crackers and eating 2 of them. Have your child act out the story, using real crackers, and tell you how many crackers are left.

Name ______________________________

Subtraction Patterns

10 − 1 = 9

9 − 1 = ___

8 − 1 = ___

7 − 1 = ___

Count the pelicans. Mark an X on the pelican that is flying away. Write the number that tells how many pelicans are left.

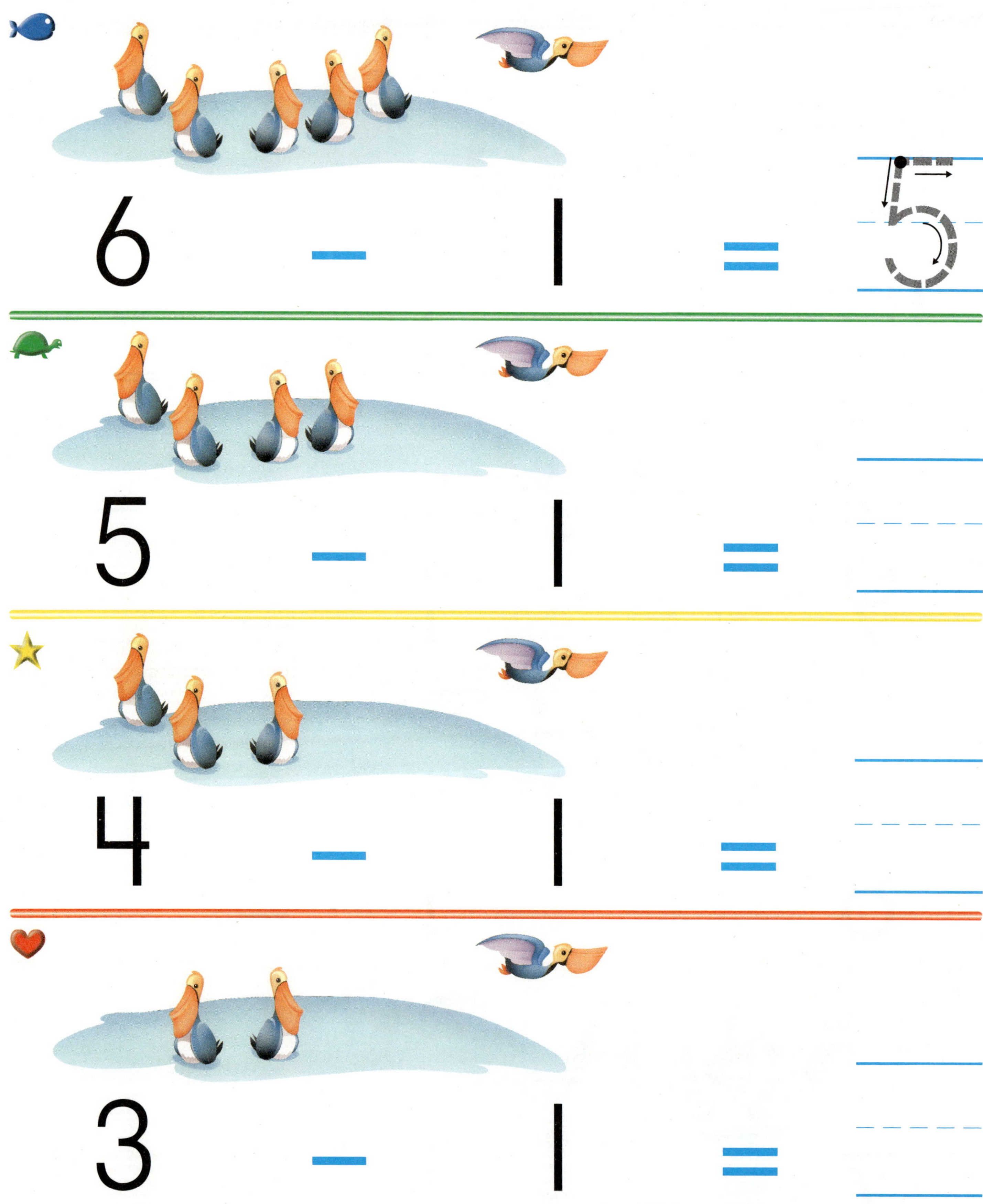

Count the pelicans. Mark an X on the pelican that is flying away. Write the number that tells how many pelicans are left.

HOME ACTIVITY • Have your child tell you about the number pattern on this page.

Name ______________________

Use Pictures to Subtract

4 − 3 = 1

___ − ___ = ___

Tell the subtraction story. Complete the subtraction sentence.

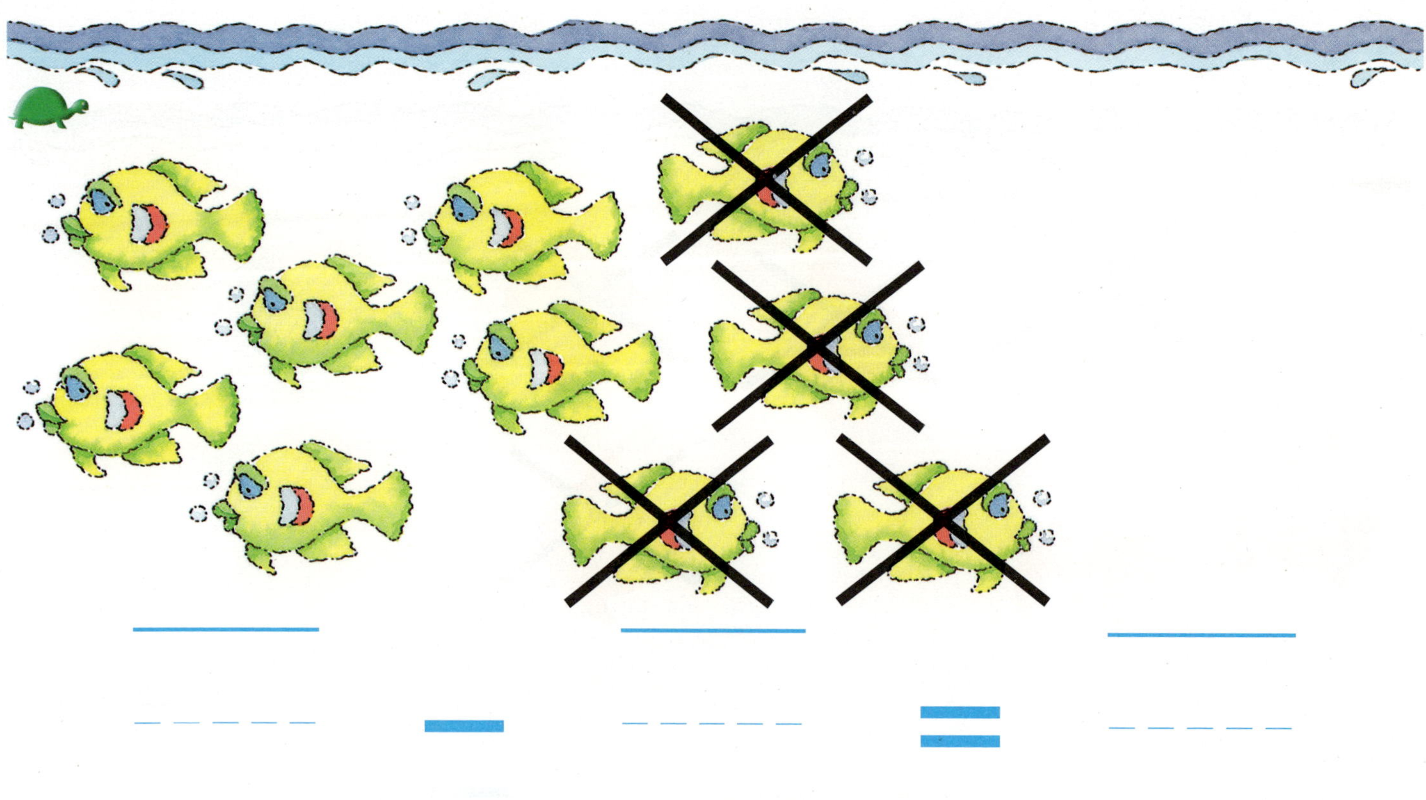

Tell the subtraction story. Complete the subtraction sentence.

HOME ACTIVITY • Encourage your child to tell a subtraction story. You may wish to have your child draw the subtraction story.

Name ______________________________

Review

7 3 ____

10 – 1 = ____

____ – ____ = ____

____ – ____ = ____

Listen to the story. Model the story with connecting cubes. Write the number that tells how many are left.

Count the pelicans. Mark an X on the pelican that is flying away. Write the number that tells how many pelicans are left.

Tell the subtraction story. Complete the subtraction sentence.

Cumulative Review

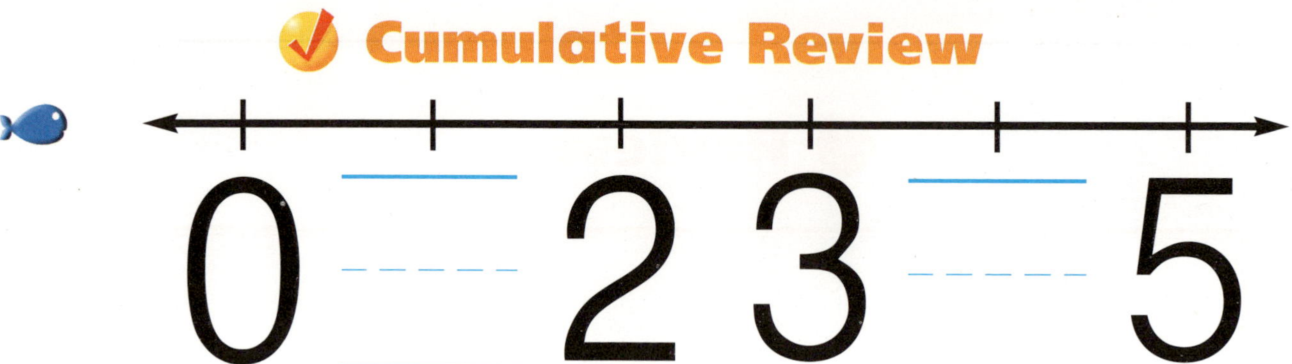

March

Sunday	Monday	Tuesday	Wednesday	Thursday	Friday	Saturday
	1	2	3	4	5	6
7	8	9	10	11	12	13
14	15	16	17	18	19	20
21	22	23	24	25	26	27
28	29	30	31			

Saturdays

Days in March

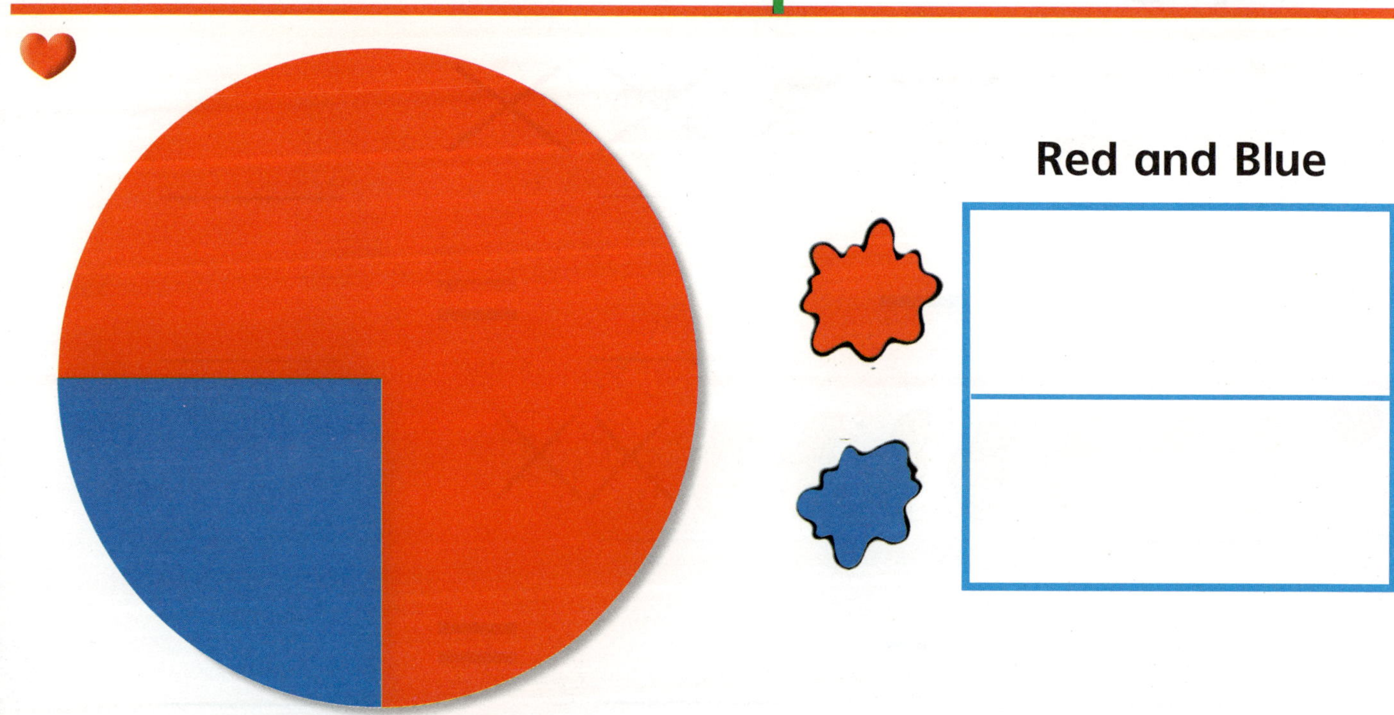

- Write the number that is before two. Write the number that is after three.
- Look at the calendar. Count the Saturdays. Write how many.
- Look at the calendar. Write how many days in March.
- Use a paper clip and a pencil to make a spinner. Spin ten times. Make a tally mark in the table after each spin. Circle the row with more tally marks.

Name ______________________________

Subtract with Money

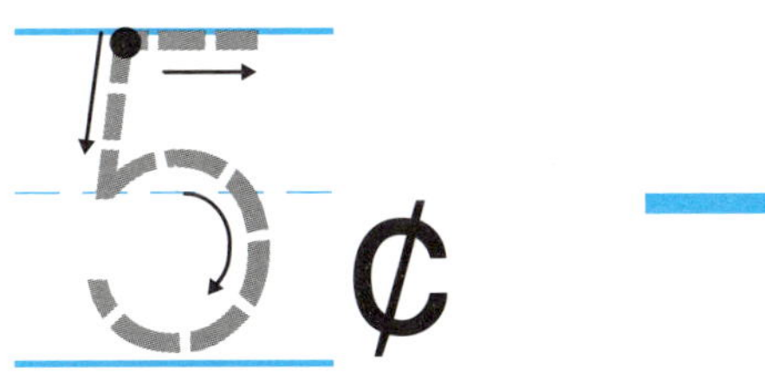

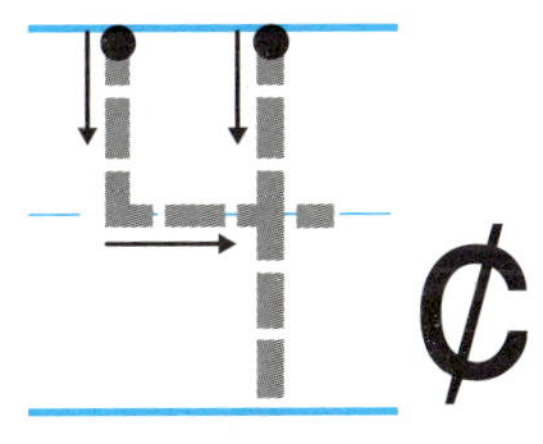

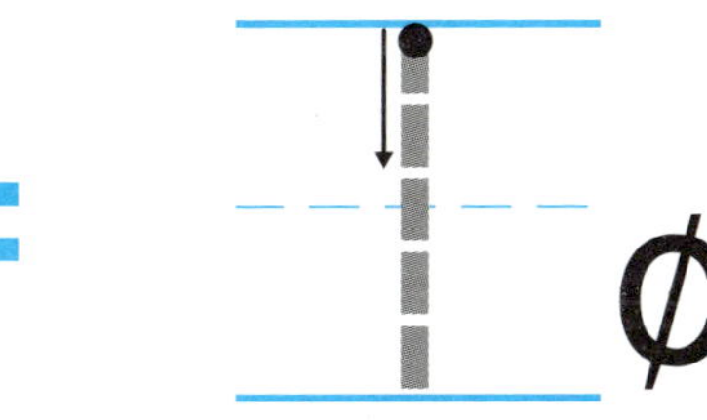

5¢ − 4¢ = 1¢

___¢ − ___¢ = ___¢

Listen to the story. Complete the subtraction sentence to tell how much money is left.

___¢ − ___¢ = ___¢

___¢ − ___¢ = ___¢

Listen to the story. Complete the subtraction sentence to tell how much money is left.

HOME ACTIVITY • Have your child use real pennies to model these subtraction problems.

Name ______________________

Subtraction Problems

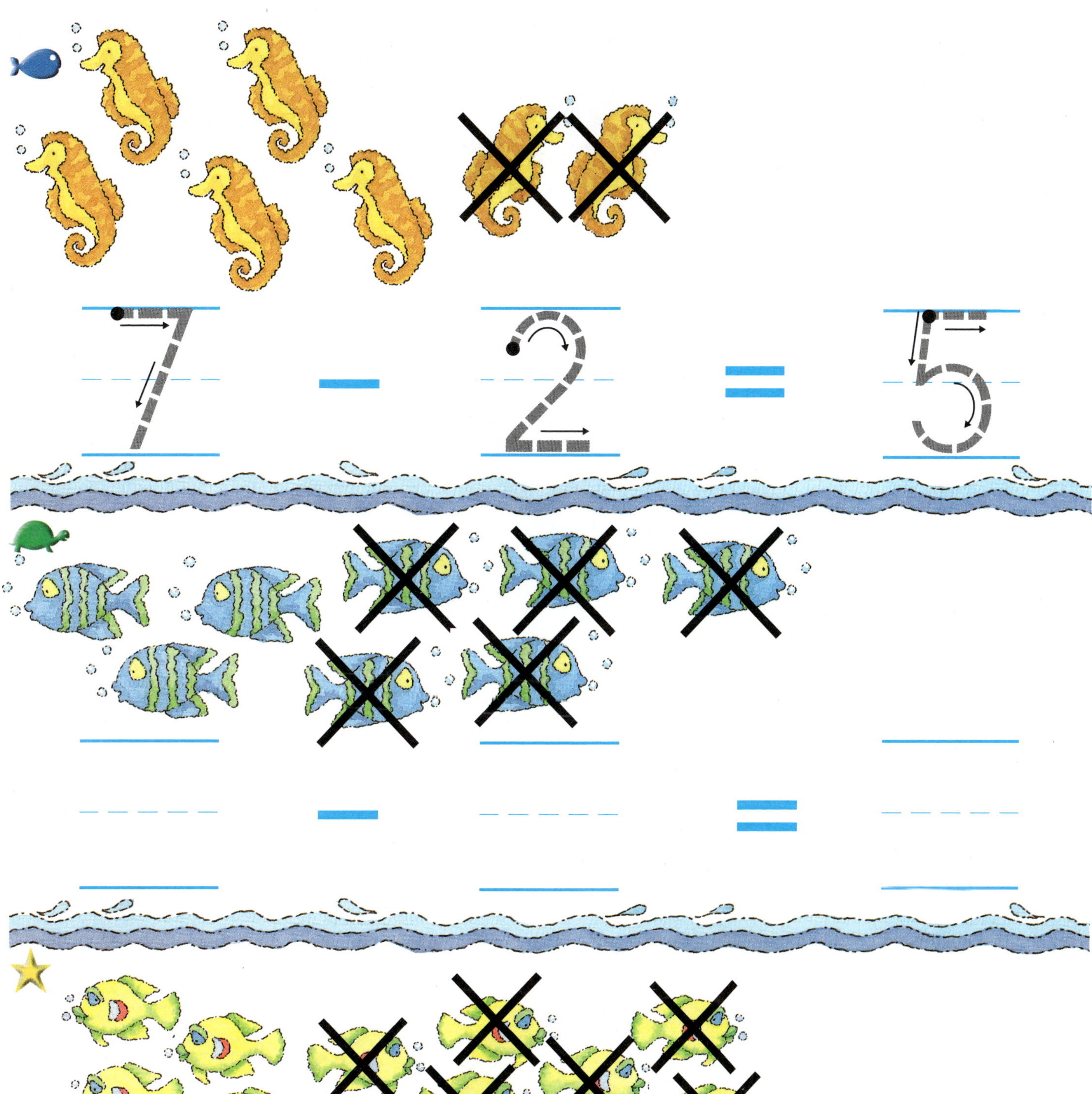

−   =

Tell the subtraction story. Then complete the subtraction sentence.

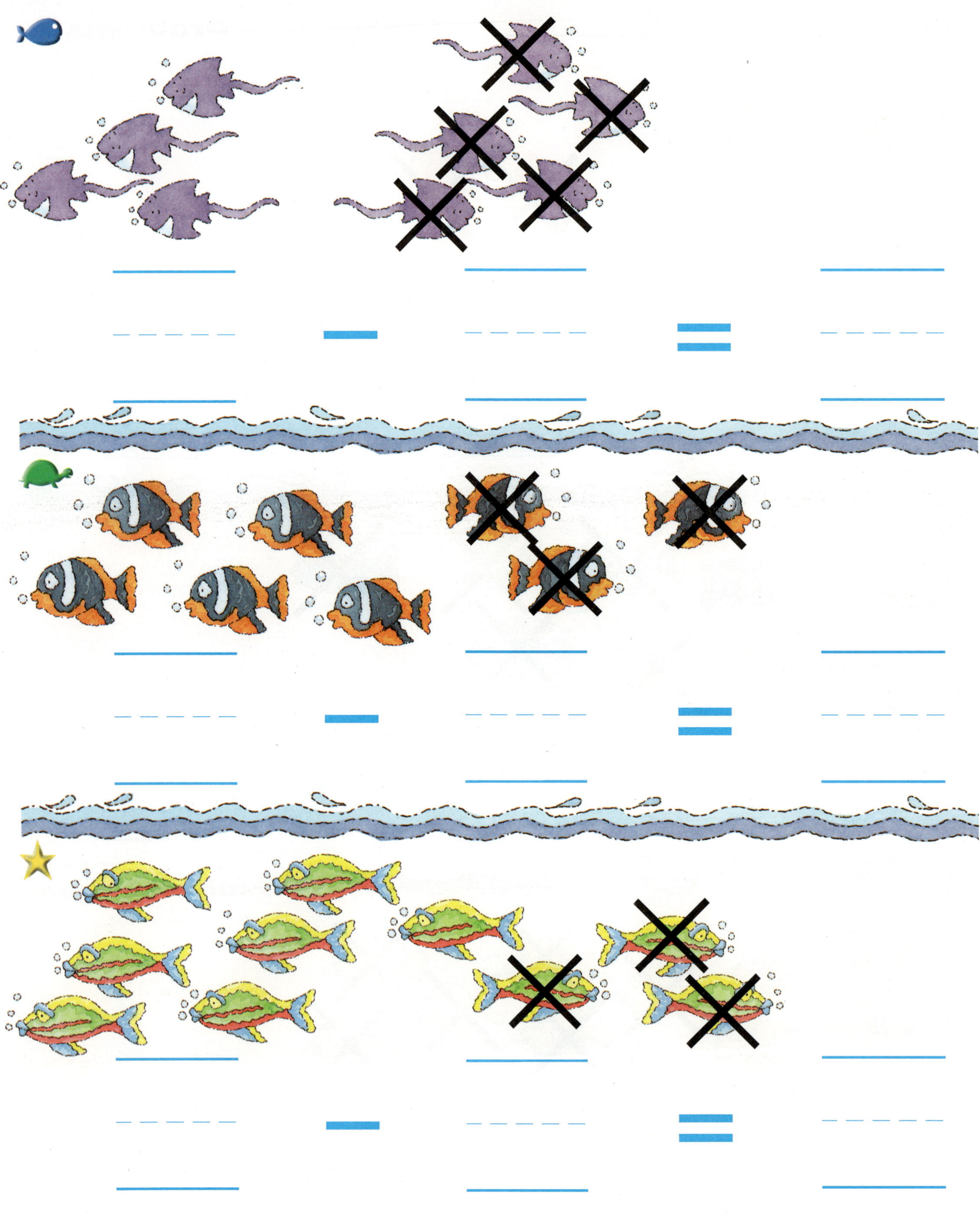

Tell the subtraction story. Then complete the subtraction sentence.

HOME ACTIVITY • Have your child use objects to model the subtraction sentences on this page.

Name ______________________________

Subtraction Stories

Tell a subtraction story. Act out your story with objects. Draw the objects, and mark an X on the ones you subtract. Complete the subtraction sentence.

______ − ______ = ______

______ − ______ = ______

Tell a subtraction story. Act out your story with objects. Draw the objects, and mark an X on the ones you subtract. Complete the subtraction sentence.

HOME ACTIVITY • Tell your child a short subtraction story, and have him or her draw a picture for it.

Name ______________________________

Problem Solving Skill
Choose the Operation

6 + 4 = 10 6 − 4 = 2

3 + 2 = 5 3 − 2 = 1

6 + 2 = 8 6 − 2 = 4

Tell a story about the picture. Circle the number sentence that tells what is happening in the picture.

PROBLEM SOLVING

$5 + 5 = 10$ $5 - 5 = 0$

$9 + 1 = 10$ $9 - 1 = 8$

$7 + 2 = 9$ $7 - 2 = 5$

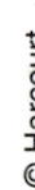

Tell a story about the picture. Circle the number sentence that tells what is happening in the picture.

HOME ACTIVITY • Ask your child to tell you why he or she chose addition or subtraction for each problem.

How Many Are Left?

By ______________________________

HOME ACTIVITY • **This book will help review subtraction. Invite your child to share this book with you.**

How many are left? ______

5 balloons

4 balloons

How many are left? ______

How many are left? ______

3 balloons

2 balloons

How many are left? ______

How many are left? ______

1 balloon

5 bags of popcorn

Name ______________________________

Review

____ ¢  ____ ¢  ____ ¢ 

____ − ____  ____

____ − ____ = ____

7 + 2 = 9   7 − 2 = 5

Listen to the story. Complete the subtraction sentence that tells how much money is left.

Tell the subtraction story. Then complete the subtraction sentence.

Tell a subtraction story. Act out your story with objects. Draw the objects, and mark an X on the ones you subtract. Complete the subtraction sentence.

Tell a story about the picture. Circle the number sentence that tells what is happening in the picture.

Cumulative Review

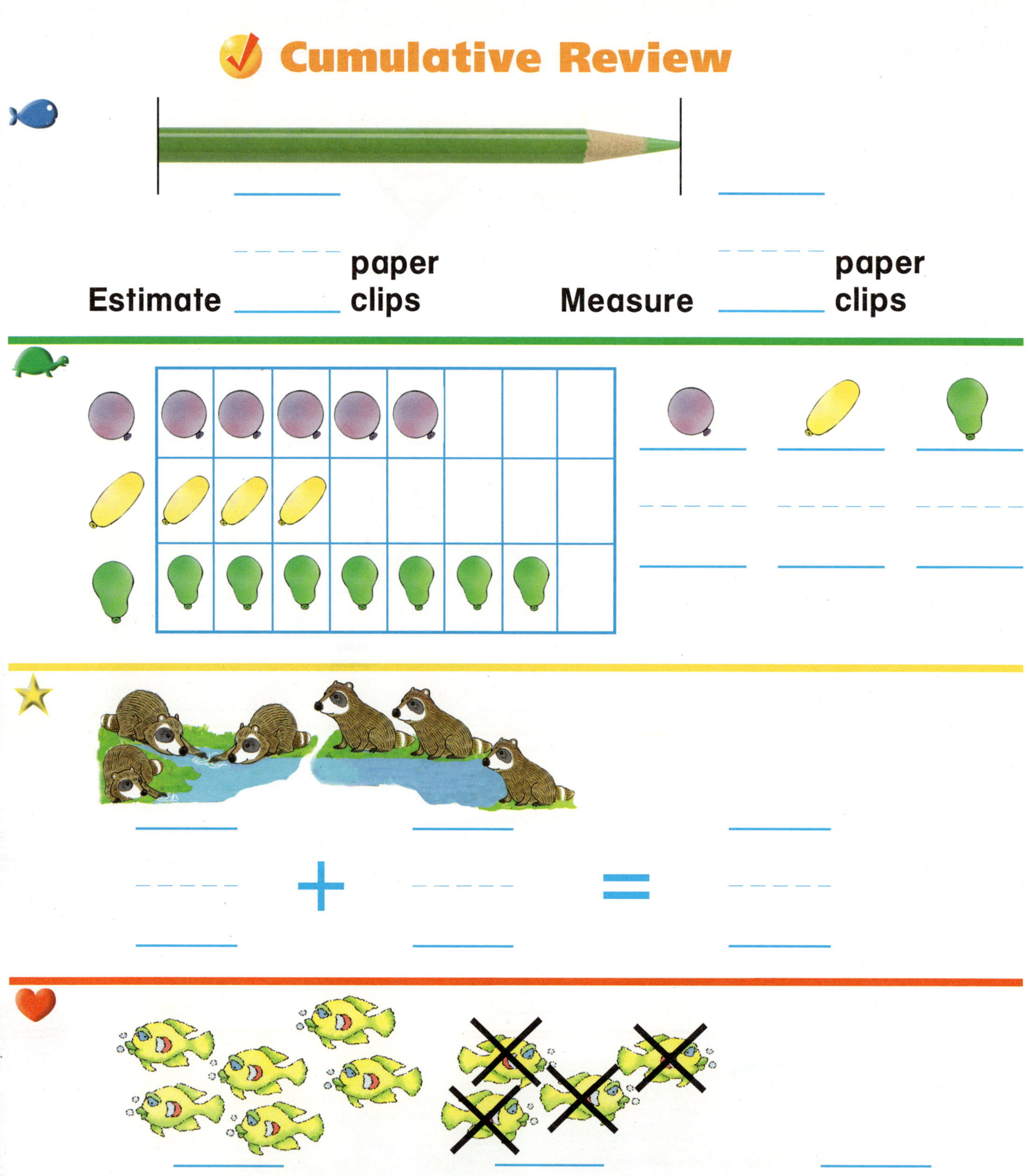

- Estimate how many paper clips long. Then measure the object. Write how many paper clips long.
- Look at the graph. Write how many of each kind of balloon. Circle the number that shows the most balloons. Mark an X on the number that shows the fewest balloons.
- Tell a story about the animals in the picture. Complete the addition sentence.
- Tell the subtraction story. Complete the subtraction sentence.

Name ________________________________

Test

10 − 1 = ____

____ − ____ = ____

____ − ____ = ____

9 + 1 = 10   9 − 1 = 8

Count the pelicans. Mark an X on the pelican that is flying away. Write the number that tells how many pelicans are left.

Tell the subtraction story. Then complete the subtraction sentence.

Tell a subtraction story. Act out your story with objects. Draw the objects, and mark an X on the ones you subtract. Complete the subtraction sentence.

Tell a story about the picture. Circle the number sentence that tells what is happening in the picture.

CHALLENGE

Add and Subtract

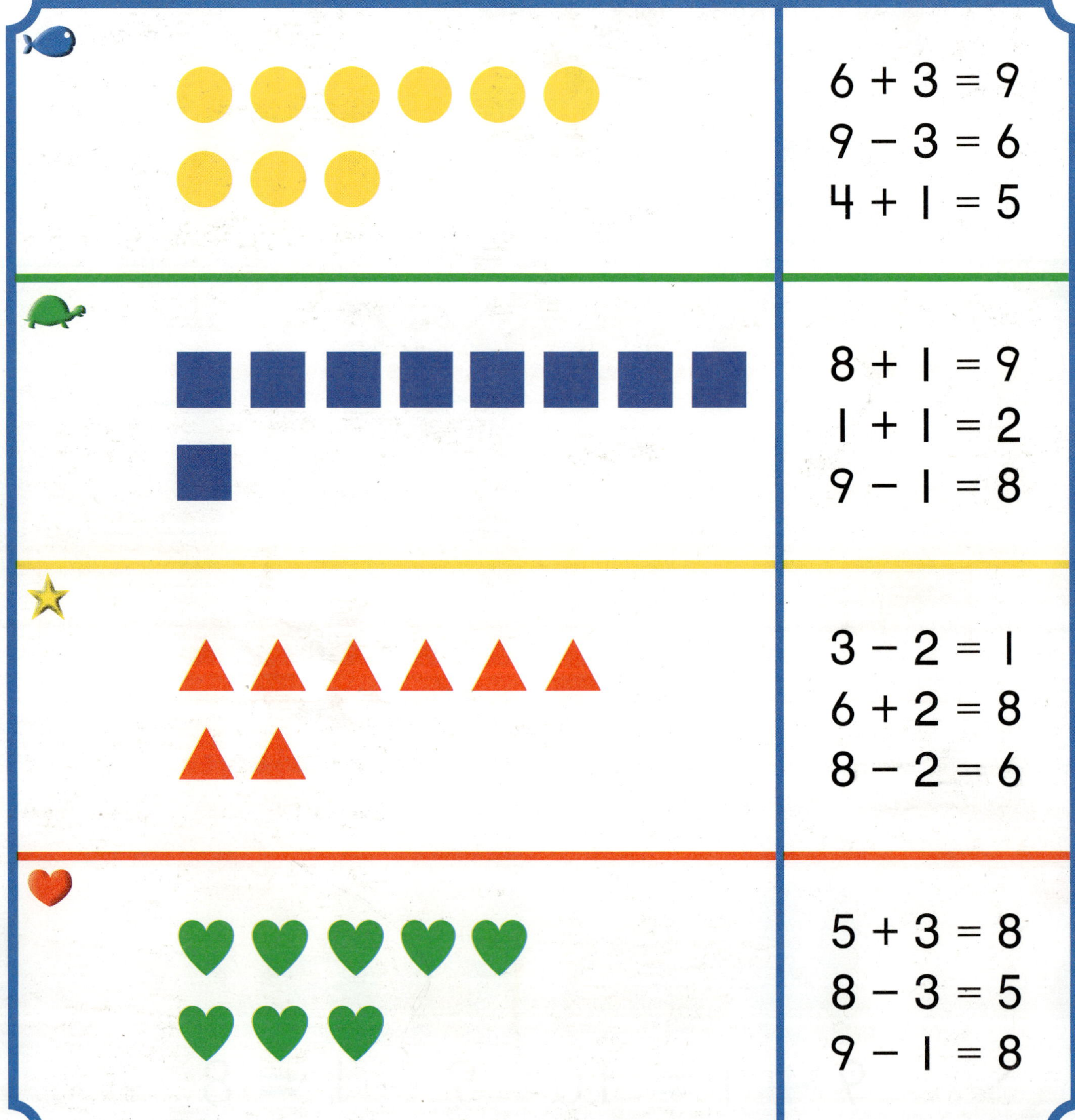

Circle the addition sentence that matches the picture. Circle the subtraction sentence that uses the same numbers.